PRECALCULUS

Fundamentals of Mathematical Analysis

PRECALCULUS
Fundamentals of Mathematical Analysis

E. R. Lorch

COLUMBIA UNIVERSITY

W· W· NORTON & COMPANY · INC · *New York*

Copyright © 1973 by W. W. Norton & Company, Inc.
First Edition

Library of Congress Cataloging in Publication Data

Lorch, Edgar Raymond, 1907-
    Precalculus; fundamentals of mathematical analysis.

    1. Mathematical analysis.   I.   Title.
QA300.L64   515   72–13411
ISBN 0-393-09378-6

Printed in the United States of America

1 2 3 4 5 6 7 8 9 0

CONTENTS

Preface   ix

I. NUMBER SYSTEMS   3

    1. The Natural Numbers   3
    2. The Integers   16
    3. The Rational Numbers   23
    4. The Real Numbers   29
    Appendix: Uniqueness of Factorization into Primes   39

II. REAL FUNCTIONS   43

    1. The Concept of a Function   43
    2. The Addition and Multiplication of Functions   49
    3. Graphs   54
    4. Linear Polynomials   62
    5. Quadratic Polynomials   70
    6. Maximum and Minimum Problems   82
    7. Some Famous Inequalities   85
    8. Functional Equations   93
    9. Periodic Functions   97

10. Some Special Methods in Graphing   100
11. Implicit Functions   103

III. POLYNOMIAL FUNCTIONS   111

1. The Unique Representation Property   111
2. The Definition of Degree   118
3. The Division Algorithm   123
4. The Remainder Theorem and the Factor Theorem   127
5. The Fundamental Theorem of Algebra   132
6. Rational Functions   135
Appendix: The Behavior of Polynomials at Infinity   139

IV. ALGEBRAIC FUNCTIONS   143

1. Square Roots and nth Roots   143
2. The Circle   147
3. The Ellipse   154
4. The Hyperbola   161
5. Algebraic Functions   167
Appendix: On the Existence of Square Roots   171

V. EXPONENTIAL AND LOGARITHMIC FUNCTIONS   173

1. Integral Exponents   173
2. Rational Exponents   177
3. Properties of the Exponential Function   180
4. On the Existence of the Exponential Function   185
5. Applications of the Exponential Function   192
6. The Logarithmic Function   195
7. Applications   201

VI. THE CIRCULAR FUNCTIONS   207

1. The Winding Number   207
2. The Definition of the Circular Functions   213
3. Illustrations   225
4. Elementary Identities and Equations   230
5. The Addition Formulas   234
6. Multiple Angle Formulas   238
7. The Inverse Functions   243

VII. MATHEMATICAL INDUCTION   250

1. The Method of Proof   250

2. The Binomial Theorem   255
3. The Exponential Function   260

VIII. TRIGONOMETRY   263

1. Angles and Triangles   263
2. Right Triangles   267
3. Laws of Sines and Cosines   273

IX. POLYNOMIALS AND APPROXIMATION THEORY   280

1. Approximation by Polynomials   280
2. Expansions About a Point   288
3. Graphs of Polynomial Functions   291
4. Abstract Power Series   297

Tables   305

Answers and Solutions   323

Index   377

PREFACE

Analysis is that branch of mathematics which has as its skeleton the real number system. It encompasses all those subjects whose existence depends on the amazingly unique properties of the "reals." At an elementary level these subjects can be called by a variety of names: elementary functions, polynomials, exponents, and trigonometry, precalculus, algebraic and transcendental functions, analytic geometry. At an intermediate level a substantial study is made of the topology of the reals: limits and continuity are introduced opening the door to the calculus. The present text is concerned with the elementary or precalculus stage. It is written principally for students in their first year of college or in their last year of high school. However, the book should also find an audience among many more advanced readers in the fields of engineering, biology, economics, sociology, and mathematical pedagogy. They should have no difficulty in following the development on their own without formal classroom meetings.

In writing this book, I was guided by two cardinal principles: First, the material had to be within the grasp of the average interested student. Second, it had to be developed in such a way as to be correct. This means that the mathematical development given here—very gently, of course, this first time —is the same as that which is given in fine detail to an advanced student, say in a course in function theory. The reader will never have to go through a future agony of unlearning, nor will he, after further study, seriously have to reassess the relative importance and the interrelations of the concepts here introduced. It was felt that the student has the right to know the truth; or at any rate he has the right to have a chance to know it. The expert will easily detect points at which the development has been strongly influenced by various advanced concepts (behavior of polynomials at infinity and the notion of degree, the exponential power series, functional equations, periodic functions, approximation theory, abstract power series). There is also substantial algebraic theory thrown into bold relief via the structures N, Z, Q, as well as R (the naturals, the integers, the rationals, and the reals). This includes a variety of phenomena, principally those related to rings and fields, which pervade all of analysis. Analysis is, after all, a marriage of algebra and topology. The role of each partner should be perfectly clear. The role of algebra has in the past too often been taken for granted and hence forgotten.

Although the aims described above seem very bold and demanding, the exposition is for the most part easy to follow. There are a few places where the going is uphill. Here the student's progress is carefully watched so that he will not fall behind.

The sections within each chapter contain the discussion of the material. They are followed by a few illustrative examples and some notes or remarks. Then there is a collection of exercises. These start off with very easy tasks of a repetitive nature and move onto more difficult ones and finally to word problems. There are 59 sets of exercises; they furnish the basis for making packaged assignments. All told, there are over 1000 exercises in the book. In preparing these, I have gone far beyond merely setting down the traditional applications. A strong effort has been made to synthesize a whole new class of problems from the materials and experiences available to the student. Although as applications some of these may seem farfetched and without economic importance, they have the very important purpose of mind-stretching, probably the most significant by-product of a good mathematical education. In the course of solving these problems, the reader is reminded at times that serious work thrives best in an atmosphere of enjoyment and good humor. Answers to about one half of the exercises are provided in the back of the book. Some worked-out problems will also be found there.

Historical data were culled from a variety of sources. I owe much to my friend Professor Carl Boyer's distinguished work, *A History of Mathematics*. I have a debt of gratitude to my friend and colleague Professor Leonard Gillman, who suggested this undertaking in the first place and has during the years made innumerable suggestions. During the terminal period of rewriting, Dr. Harriett Wagman gave detailed and valuable criticism concerning the pacing of the material. In addition she substantially expanded the list of exercises so as to offer greater possibilities for drilling. Many younger friends have made contributions to the undertaking: Dr. David Hsieh and Dr. Tsu Chi Wu; also David Te Selle, Howard Kellogg, and Kate March. I am especially grateful to Mary Pell of W. W. Norton & Company for the careful attention she gave to all aspects of the book's production. My affectionate acknowledgement is gladly extended to my editor, Joseph B. Janson, II, who exercised with grace and high flair the mixed duties of taskmaster, stimulator, and warm friend.

EDGAR R. LORCH

Ramatuelle, France
July 4, 1972

PRECALCULUS
Fundamentals of Mathematical Analysis

Chapter I

NUMBER SYSTEMS

1. THE NATURAL NUMBERS

Numbers are at the heart of all mathematical activity. No branch of mathematics can be developed extensively without becoming involved with numbers. This is especially true of the subject matter of this book. Thus it is reasonable that we begin by studying numbers.

Let us make a correction. We are not so much concerned with numbers but rather with *number systems*. A solitary number, such as 20, is not of great interest. But, if along with 20 we consider other numbers such as 2, 3, 4, 5, and we see some of the relations that exist among them—such as $4 \times 5 = 20$ or $2 \times 3 \times 4 > 20$—the door is opened to a very rich world of possibilities.

Since number systems lie at the base of everything that will be studied, let us recall briefly what these systems are. Even though these have been studied in the past it will be noted that many new properties are developed below. Thus the present chapter should be studied with a certain amount of care.

First recall briefly what a set is. A *set* is a collection of objects. For example, the set of letters in the English alphabet is a collection consisting of 26 objects of which a few are a, b, c, d. The objects in the set are called *elements*. Also, it is said that the elements *belong* to the set. Thus, b belongs to the English alphabet. Another example of a set is the U.S. Senate. This set consists of one hundred elements. (Each element is called a senator; there are two senators for each of the 50 states.) Given any set, it is possible to determine whether a given object belongs to it. If this is not the case, the set is not properly defined. Consider, for example, the author of this book. He does *not* belong to the U.S. Senate. Nor for that matter does he belong to the English alphabet. On the other hand, the letter x belongs to the English alphabet, it does not belong to the U.S. Senate. We shall be interested in mathematical sets. For example, we shall discuss later the set of polynomials, we shall investigate the set of trigonometric identities, and we shall study special sets of points in the plane called lines, circles, ellipses, hyperbolas. The words "set" and "collection" will be used interchangeably. They mean the same thing.

Expressions such as "the set of all good men," and "the set of all well-made cars" should not be used since there is no agreement on whether a given man is good or whether a given car is well made. This illustrates what is meant in saying that a set should be well-defined.

Here are further examples of sets:

The set of all people who were born in the United States.
The set of all former presidents of the United States.
The set of all dodos anywhere on earth.

Note that the moon does not belong to any of these sets. Abraham Lincoln belongs to the first two sets. Robert E. Lee belongs to the first set but not to the second. The third set is empty since the dodo disappeared as a species of bird a long time ago. Every element in the second set is also an element in the first set.

In this chapter we shall be interested in sets of numbers. The special sets that interest us are the set of natural numbers, the set of integers, the set of rational numbers, and the set of real numbers. For example, the set of *natural numbers* has as elements the numbers

$$0, 1, 2, 3, 4, 5, \cdots . \tag{1}$$

It is customary to denote sets by using braces: { } and by putting the elements inside. Thus the set of natural numbers is

$$\{0, 1, 2, 3, 4, 5, \cdots \}. \tag{2}$$

The three dots "$\cdots$" are to be read: "and so on." The set of natural numbers is also denoted by the letter **N**. Thus we write

$$\mathbf{N} = \{0, 1, 2, 3, 4, 5, \cdots \}. \tag{3}$$

Remark: The sets $\{0, 1, 2, \cdots \}$ and $\{1, 2, 3, \cdots \}$ are not the same since 0 belongs to the first and does not belong to the second. Many years ago, mathematicians worked with the second set rather than the first and gave to that second set the name "the set of natural numbers." Today, the tendency is to use the name in the way introduced above. This has many advantages.

Note that the set of natural numbers is infinite. In fact, it is the first and the most important infinite set in the history of human culture and civilization. By far the largest part of mathematics deals with infinite sets. Thus it is through this set that one enters into the essence of mathematics.

Another remark: In the development of this and the following chapters, we shall not stress the notion of set. It will be there, underlying all of our discussions. But this notion will be left in the background and set manipulations will be used intuitively. To be specific, we shall talk very little about subsets, unions, intersections, and complements. We may also become a little relaxed in our language. For example, we may say "consider the natural numbers" instead of saying "consider the set of natural numbers." This kind of language shortcut is allowable in mathematics providing it is not abused.

The natural numbers are constructed from the first two of these numbers, 0 and 1, in a very special way. Add 1 to 0 and 1 is obtained. Add 1 to 1 and we get 2. Add 1 to 2 and we get 3. *All* the natural numbers can be obtained by continuing this process. This is a very important fact that will be used in Chapter VII, where proofs by induction will be studied. This fact receives a name: "the principle of mathematical induction." It may be stated formally as follows:

I–1 Principle of Mathematical Induction
Consider a collection of natural numbers that has the properties:
  (a) *0 is in the collection;*
  (b) *whenever a is in the collection, a + 1 is also in the collection.*
Then this collection contains all natural numbers.

A word of advice. We shall in the future give names to some of our results that may not make much sense to the reader at the time. For example, at this moment, we haven't talked about *induction* and it is far from clear why such an obvious statement as I–1 should be labeled as a *principle*. It is advisable to consider these names as mere labels and not to worry for the time being about the reasons for using these labels. The reasons will come to the surface later.

It may be appropriate here to make further remarks about this matter and others that will come up later. As was just said, the above principle does not state anything mysterious. It may be checked in a few steps. (Exercises that come at the end of the section will reveal its meaning better.) There will be other italicized statements and definitions later in the chapter. Some may be new; others will be old and familiar. For example, the theorem on the unique factorization into primes is made use of from the age of eight onwards. The commutative laws of addition and multiplication are inculcated into children at a very early stage. Our purpose in putting these down at this point is to give a complete list of all the basic facts about numbers from which all others can be derived. These *are* the basic materials. It is important to know this. For the present, the thing to do is to read these fundamental facts, solve some exercises on them, and go on. Later on it will become clearer how all the pieces fit together.

Let us continue with our study of the set of natural numbers. In this set, certain operations and certain relations are defined. As has just been noted two natural numbers can be *added* and the result will be a natural number; for example, $2 + 7 = 9$. We can proceed similarly for multiplication; for example, $4 \times 5 = 20$. We can also *compare* two numbers: $2 < 6$ and $19 > 13$.

If it is desired to make statements about arbitrary natural numbers, letters of the alphabet are used to denote them. Thus the statement $a + b = c$ is used to state the fact that the natural numbers a, b, and c are related by the equation $a + b = c$. Similarly, one may wish to consider three natural numbers p, q, and r such that the product of p and q equals r. This is written $p \times q = r$ or $p \cdot q = r$ or even $pq = r$.

Rather than to say merely that we can add, multiply, and compare, we must also state that addition, multiplication, and comparison satisfy certain conditions, frequently called *laws*. The word "law" is used to indicate a general statement that is true either because it can be proved to be true or because it is assumed. The laws for addition and multiplication are the following:

Let a, b, and c be any natural numbers. Then

$$a + b = b + a \quad \text{(commutativity of addition);} \tag{4}$$

$$a \cdot b = b \cdot a \quad \text{(commutativity of multiplication);} \tag{5}$$

$$(a + b) + c = a + (b + c) \quad \text{(associativity of addition);} \tag{6}$$

$$(a \cdot b) \cdot c = a \cdot (b \cdot c) \quad \text{(associativity of multiplication);} \tag{7}$$

$$a \cdot (b + c) = a \cdot b + a \cdot c \quad \text{(distributivity).} \tag{8}$$

Thus if $a = 3$, $b = 4$, and $c = 5$, the above read $3 + 4 = 4 + 3$; $3 \cdot 4 = 4 \cdot 3$; $(3 + 4) + 5 = 3 + (4 + 5)$; $(3 \cdot 4) \cdot 5 = 3 \cdot (4 \cdot 5)$; and $3 \cdot (4 + 5) = 3 \cdot 4 + 3 \cdot 5$. Each of these equations should be checked.

If one prefers, these various conditions may be called the "commutative laws" and the "associative laws." The last one is more properly called the "distributive law for multiplication over addition." Note that (5) and (8) give

$$(b + c)a = ba + ca. \tag{8'}$$

Each natural number is special in its own way. However there are two natural numbers, 0 and 1, that are truly exceptional. If a is any natural number, then

$$a + 0 = a; \tag{9}$$

$$a \cdot 0 = 0; \tag{10}$$

$$a \cdot 1 = a. \tag{11}$$

Thus, in addition, 0 doesn't change things; and in multiplication, 1 doesn't change things. For this reason 0 is sometimes called the *additive identity* and 1 is called the *multiplicative identity*. They can also be referred to as the *neutral elements* for addition and multiplication.

Another important property of the set of natural numbers is that if a and b are natural numbers such that $a \cdot b = 0$, then either $a = 0$ or $b = 0$. In other words,

$$\text{From} \quad ab = 0 \quad \text{follows} \quad a = 0 \quad \text{or} \quad b = 0 \quad \text{(or both).} \tag{12}$$

Let us show by an example how the various laws are used in arithmetic.

PROBLEM: Prove that $(a + b)^2 = a^2 + 2ab + b^2$. (Remember that a^2 means $a \cdot a$.) To do this write c for $a + b$. That is, set $c = a + b$. Then

$$(a + b)(a + b) = c(a + b).$$

By (8), $c(a + b) = c \cdot a + c \cdot b$. Thus, substituting back the value of c, we get

$$(a + b)(a + b) = (a + b)a + (a + b)b.$$

By (8'), $(a + b)a = a^2 + ba$ and $(a + b)b = ab + b^2$. Thus we have (so far)

$$(a + b)^2 = (a^2 + ba) + (ab + b^2).$$

By (5), $ba = ab$; thus, by substitution,

$$(a + b)^2 = (a^2 + ab) + (ab + b^2).$$

By (6),

$$(a^2 + ab) + (ab + b^2) = [(a^2 + ab) + ab] + b^2$$
$$= [a^2 + (ab + ab)] + b^2 = (a^2 + 2ab) + b^2.$$

Here we use the fact that

$$ab + ab = 1 \cdot ab + 1 \cdot ab = (1 + 1)ab = 2ab$$

Thus we have finally

$$(a + b)^2 = a^2 + 2ab + b^2,$$

where the order of addition on the right doesn't matter since addition is associative.

The purpose of the example is to show that the ordinary identities of algebra are based on the use of the commutative, associative, and distributive laws. To carry out all the individual steps is long and tedious. We shall no longer refer to this matter and in the future will write down freely such simple identities as

$$(1 + x)^3 = 1 + 3x + 3x^2 + x^3$$

without more than the briefest justification.

If a, b, c are natural numbers with $c \neq 0$ (this means "c is not equal to 0") and $a = b \cdot c$, one says that c divides a and that c is a divisor of a (also, a is a multiple of c). Thus the divisors of 12 are 1, 2, 3, 4, 6, and 12. If $a > 1$, then 1 and a are divisors of a. If there are no further divisors, then a is said to be a *prime number* (or, a is prime). For example, 2, 3, 5, and 7 are prime numbers. On the other hand, 4, 6, and 9 are not prime numbers; they are *composite* numbers.

If 2 divides a, then a is called an *even* number. If 2 does not divide a, a is called an *odd* number. It is very easy to tell whether a number written in the decimal notation is even or odd. It is also very easy to tell whether a number is divisible by 5. There are quick tests to determine whether a number written decimally is divisible by 3. There are also quick tests (that no one need remember) to tell whether a number is divisible by 11. There is no quick test to determine whether a number is divisible by 641. If someone really wishes to know, he should divide by 641 and watch for the remainder (see the following section). A nice way to do this is to write down a table of multiples of 641 and then check to see if the given number is among them. This is one way that a computer would solve the problem.

A note on the exercises that occur periodically throughout the book. The first exercises at the end of any section, frequently in many parts (a), (b), (c), and so on, are usually meant to test comprehension of the text. If it is not possible to solve these exercises rapidly, it is advisable to return to the text and read it once more. Exercises labeled with higher numbers are frequently a bit more difficult than the others. Some of the exercises may be very easy. This is particularly true in this chapter, which develops a combination of old and new material. On the other hand, some exercises may be a bit difficult. It is important to develop the correct attitude toward problem solving. This activity is not like Greco-Roman wrestling, where one is looking for a quick victory. It is much more like hiking, where some of the going is very smooth and some is a bit thorny; and in the process much ground is covered.

The first set of exercises deals with the natural numbers. One of the branches of mathematics that deals with the natural numbers is called number theory. The first set of exercises contains many problems from number theory. In almost all of these, the role of the prime factorization theorem, which will be discussed later, is apparent. There are also a few problems on the principle of mathematical induction, the associative, commutative, and distributive laws, and finally a few problems on sets that can be solved on the basis of our very brief discussion of sets.

Exercises I.1.a

1. Find all the divisors of 24, 81, 120.

2. Prove that the sum of the divisors of 6 equals 2×6; the sum of the divisors of 28 equals 2×28. Can you find other numbers that have this remarkable property?

3. Find the first 20 primes. Find all primes less than 100.

4. There is a theorem to the effect that if p is a prime, then

$$1 \cdot 2 \cdot 3 \cdots (p - 1) + 1$$

is divisible by p. Check this for the first 5 primes. (For example, for $p = 5$, we have $1 \cdot 2 \cdot 3 \cdot 4 + 1 = 24 + 1 = 25$ and 25 is divisible by 5.) This is known as Wilson's theorem.

5. There is a theorem to the effect that if p is a prime, then for any number a, $a^p - a$ is divisible by p. Check this for $a = 0, 1, 2, 3$ and for $p = 2, 3, 5$. This is known as Fermat's Little Theorem.

6. Find as many sets of natural numbers x, y, z (not 0) such that

$$x^2 + y^2 = z^2.$$

You may be interested in knowing that there are no natural numbers x, y, z (not 0) such that

$$x^n + y^n = z^n$$

for $n = 3, 4, 5, \cdots$ up to $n = 100$ and much beyond.

It is suspected but not known that there are no such x, y, z for *any* $n > 2$.

7. Many numbers are the sum of two cubes. For example, $2 = 1^3 + 1^3$, $9 = 1^3 + 2^3$, $35 = 2^3 + 3^3$. The smallest number that can be expressed as the sum of two cubes in two different ways is 1729. Can you find these two distinct expressions? The above was noted (in a fraction of a second) by the Hindu mathematician Ramanujan. It has been said that he had each natural number as a personal friend.

8. Using the laws for addition and multiplication, prove that for any natural numbers a, b, c, d,

   (a) $(a + b) + c = (c + b) + a$;
   (b) $(a + b) + (c + d) = (a + d) + (c + b)$;
   (c) $(1 + a)^3 = 1 + 3a + 3a^2 + a^3$;
   (d) $a(b + c) + b(c + a) + c(a + b) = 2(ab + bc + ca)$.

9. Given the natural numbers a and b, prove that

   (a) if a and b are even, $a + b$ is even;
   (b) if a is even, $a \cdot b$ is even.

10. List all the solutions in natural numbers a, b, c of the equation $a + b + c = 5$.

11. List all the solutions in natural numbers a, b, c of the equation $a(b + c) = 6$.

12. Give an example of a set containing a former president of the United States, two teachers, a mathematics text, an airline, and three other elements not including any planet.

13. Give four examples of sets distinct from the ones in the text.

14. Give examples of three sets each of which has at least one element in common with the other two and at least one element not in either of the other two.

15. Give examples of four sets of numbers A, B, C, D such that no two are equal and each is a subset of the next. (Two sets A and B are equal if every element in A is also in B and if every element in B is also in A.)

16. What are the elements of the sets $\{3, 4\}$ and $\{3, 7, 10\}$? What are the elements of the set $\{\{3, 4\}, \{3, 7, 10\}\}$? This gives an example of a set whose elements are sets.

17. A student erroneously using the principle of mathematical induction thought he had proved that the set $\{5, 6, 7, 8, \cdots\}$ contained all natural numbers. What probably was his error?

18. State a principle similar to I–1 which defines all even natural numbers; all odd natural numbers.

19. The *union* of two sets A and B, written $A \cup B$, is that set whose elements are precisely the elements in A or in B or in both. Show that for any sets A, B, C

$$A \cup B = B \cup A \quad \text{(commutative law for union)};$$
$$(A \cup B) \cup C = A \cup (B \cup C) \quad \text{(associative law for union)}.$$

This gives an example of an operation satisfying the laws (4) and (6). Remember the definition of equality of sets. The example is continued below.

20. The *intersection* of A and B, written $A \cap B$, is that set whose elements consist precisely of the elements both in A and in B. Show that for any sets A, B, C

$$A \cap B = B \cap A \quad \text{(commutative law for intersection)};$$
$$(A \cap B) \cap C = (A \cap B) \cap C \quad \text{(associative law for intersection)}.$$

21. Show that for any sets A, B, C

$$A \cap (B \cup C) = (A \cap B) \cup (A \cap C);$$
$$A \cup (B \cap C) = (A \cup B) \cap (A \cup C).$$

This shows that the distributive law (8) works in both directions: intersection over union and union over intersection. Remarkable!

Historical Note. Pierre Fermat (1601–1665), educated as a lawyer in Toulouse, France, studied equations with respect to rectangular axes probably before the famous book written on this subject by his contemporary, Descartes, had appeared. However, because of archaic notation this was not known until later. He is considered the founder of the modern theory of numbers. His most famous conjecture, frequently referred to as his "last theorem," has not been solved to this day. Some of his other conjectures have received answers (some "yes" and some "no"). He has been called "the prince of amateurs" in mathematics.

Srinivasa Ramanujan (1887–1920) was one of the exceptional mathematical geniuses of the twentieth century.

We have looked at the operations of addition and multiplication. We shall now look at the relations: "greater than," "greater than or equal to," "less than," and "less than or equal to." These are written ">," "≥," "<," and "≤." Thus we have the following types of statements:

$a > b$ (a is greater than b);
$a \geq b$ (either a is greater than b or a is equal to b);
$a < b$ (a is less than b);
$a \leq b$ (either a is less than b or a is equal to b).

For example, the following statements are correct: $8 > 5$, $8 \geq 5$, $3 < 7$, $3 \leq 7$, $3 \leq 3$.

If a and b are any fixed natural numbers, then some but not all of the above will be true. Specifically, *one and only one of the following three relations holds*:

$$a < b,$$
$$a = b, \tag{13}$$
$$a > b.$$

The three possibilities in (13) lead to a powerful method of proof. Suppose we wish to prove that two numbers a and b are equal. According to (13) it suffices to show that $a < b$ and $a > b$ lead to contradictions. The only remaining alternative is $a = b$. Examples of this method of proof can be found later on.

Relations of the type $a < b$, $a \leq b$, $a > b$, and $a \geq b$ are called *inequalities*. The relations (13) introduce *order* into the natural numbers. We shall put off listing some very important properties of these relations of order until we consider the integers.

There are many ordered systems besides the natural numbers. As will be seen, the integers, the rational numbers, and the real numbers are all ordered systems. However, the natural numbers with the order introduced above have a property not shared by these other systems. This property is given a name: *the well-ordering property*. Now this name may seem a bit bizarre. It does not mean that the natural numbers are ordered and that the job is well done. The phrase "well-ordering" alludes to an additional property that an ordered system may have.

This property of the natural numbers is important in many types of arguments.

I–2 Well-Ordering Property of N

Let **M** *be any collection of natural numbers that contains at least one element. Then* **M** *contains an element a which is smaller than any other element. That is, if b is any other element of* **M**, *then a < b.*

As examples to the above consider the following:

(1) Let **M** be the set of all prime numbers p such that $p > 62$. Then the least element in **M** is 67. Other elements in **M** are 101, 641, 257.

(2) Let **M** be the set of all odd integers that are divisible by 3, 11, and 15. The least number in **M** is 165. Other elements in **M** are 495 and 1155.

A further note on the relations (13). These do not merely introduce order into the natural numbers, they introduce *total order*. There are ordering relations that do not satisfy (13). Consider the following example. Let S be the set of all human beings that ever lived. The relation "is an ancestor of" is an ordering of S. But it is not true for every two humans a and b that one of the following holds: a is an ancestor of b; b is an ancestor of a; a is identical to b. It is almost certain that none is true for two members of your mathematics class.

Let us now examine a process that is probably very familiar: the process for dividing one natural number by another, thus obtaining a quotient and a remainder. Let us divide 23 by 7. We know the answer: the quotient is 3 and the remainder is 2. That is, $23 = 7 \times 3 + 2$. How is it really obtained? The process is as follows:

  (i) Note that $7 < 23$ and hence, 7 goes into 23 at least once.
  (ii) Subtract 7 from 23, leaving 16: that is, $23 = 7 + 16$.
  (iii) Note that $7 < 16$ and hence 7 goes into 16 at least once. Write $16 = 7 + 9$.
  (iv) Note that $7 < 9$ and that $9 = 7 + 2$.
  (v) Write

$$23 = 7 + 16 = 7 + 7 + 9 = 7 + 7 + 7 + 2 = 7 \times 3 + 2.$$

This gives the final result. Note that the remainder 2 satisfies the double inequality: $0 \leq 2 < 7$.

The scheme illustrated above is called the *division algorithm*. The word "algorithm" means method or device. The division algorithm is very important in the theory of factorization. It is also quite simple. When studying polynomials in Chapter III, a division algorithm will be developed that is quite similar to the present one.

I–3 Division Algorithm

Let a and b be natural numbers with $b \neq 0$. Then there exist natural numbers q and r such that

$$a = bq + r \quad with \quad 0 \le r < b. \tag{14}$$

The numbers q and r are unique.

Remarks: The expression $0 \le r < b$ is read: r is greater than or equal to 0 and is less than b. The numbers q and r are called the quotient and remainder after dividing a by b. As has just been said, the word algorithm means method or device. In the present case the algorithm not only shows that q and r exist, but gives a method for finding them.

PROOF: If $a < b$, write $q = 0$ and $r = a$. This gives $a = b \cdot 0 + a$ and the result is proved.

If $a \ge b$, subtract b from a, obtaining $a - b$. If $a - b < b$, write $a - b = r$ and this gives $a = b \cdot 1 + r$.

If $a - b \ge b$, subtract b from $a - b$ and so on. In other words, find that natural number q such that $0 \le a - qb$ and $a - qb < b$. Then write $a - bq = r$, which gives the result $a = bq + r$.

To show uniqueness, suppose that

$$a = bq_1 + r_1 \quad and \quad a = bq_2 + r_2.$$

Then $bq_1 + r_1 = bq_2 + r_2$. If $r_1 = r_2$, then since $bq_1 = bq_2$ one has $q_1 = q_2$ and this shows uniqueness. If $r_1 \neq r_2$, then by (13) one of the two is larger than the other. Suppose that $r_2 > r_1$. In this case, $bq_1 + r_1 = bq_2 + r_2$ gives

$$bq_1 - bq_2 = r_2 - r_1. \tag{15}$$

Since b divides the left side of (15) it divides $r_2 - r_1$. However, $r_2 - r_1 < b$ and (since $r_2 > r_1$) $0 < r_2 - r_1$. Thus $0 < r_2 - r_1 < b$. Since there is no number greater than 0 and less than b which b divides, we have a contradiction. Thus the case $r_1 \neq r_2$ cannot arise.

For an application of the algorithm, see Equation (23) and what follows.

Let us now consider the factorization of natural numbers into primes.

If one considers a specific number, say 24, there are many factorizations possible: $24 = 3 \times 8$; $24 = 4 \times 6$; $24 = 2 \times 12$; $24 = 2 \times 2 \times 2 \times 3$. Of these, only $24 = 2 \times 2 \times 2 \times 3$ is a factorization into primes. There is no other factorization into primes. This property that has been described for 24 is valid for any number $a > 1$. We state it as a theorem.

I–4 Prime Factorization Theorem

Let a be a natural number such that $a > 1$. Then there exist (not necessarily distinct) prime numbers $p_1, p_2, \cdots, p_s$ such that

$$a = p_1 \cdot p_2 \cdots p_s. \tag{16}$$

Furthermore, the factorization above is unique (except for order).

To prove the theorem it is necessary to show that there exists at least one factorization and that there exists at most one factorization. To start with, let us prove the existence of at least one factorization.

Suppose that it is false that every natural number larger than 1 can be expressed as a product of primes. Then there is at least one natural number $d > 1$ such that d cannot be expressed as a product of primes. By the Well-Ordering Property I–2 there is a least natural number $a > 1$ with that property. Now a cannot be prime, because if $a = p$ we have a factorization of the type (16)—there is just one term in the product. Since a is not prime, then $a = b \cdot c$ with $1 < b < a$ and $1 < c < a$. Because $b < a$, b *does* have a factorization into primes, say,

$$b = p_1 \cdot p_2 \cdots p_s. \tag{17}$$

Also, c has such a factorization, say,

$$c = q_1 \cdot q_2 \cdots q_t. \tag{18}$$

Since $a = b \cdot c$, we get

$$a = (p_1 \cdots p_s)(q_1 \cdots q_t) \tag{19}$$

and this is a factorization into primes for a. This contradicts our assumption, made above, that there did exist a number d without factorization. Thus no such number exists; that is, all natural numbers $a > 1$ have a factorization into primes.

The proof of uniqueness is a little longer but is quite elementary. In order not to interrupt the flow of ideas, it is deferred to an appendix at the end of the chapter.

Here is an interesting application of the theorem which will be useful later. *There exist no natural numbers c and d such that $c \neq 0$, $d \neq 0$, and*

$$c^2 = 2d^2. \tag{20}$$

PROOF: We see right away that if such numbers exist, then $c > 1$ and $d > 1$. Write the factorization for d into primes:

$$d = p_1 \cdot p_2 \cdots p_s. \tag{21}$$

If 2 occurs among the primes $p_1, p_2, \cdots, p_s$, it occurs, say, n times. Now

$$d^2 = (p_1 \cdot p_2 \cdots p_s)(p_1 \cdot p_2 \cdots p_s) \tag{22}$$

and in d^2, the prime factor 2 occurs $2n$ times.

The same argument shows that the factor 2 occurs $2m$ times in c^2. Now if $c^2 = 2d^2$, then the factor 2 occurs $2n + 1$ times in $2d^2$.

This leads to the conclusion that the number of times the prime 2 enters into the above factorization is both even and odd. This is obviously impossible and therefore Equation (20) has no solutions.

How do we know that there are no natural numbers that are both even and odd? The following lines will serve as a reminder.

Assume that for some natural numbers m and n,

$$2m = 2n + 1. \tag{23}$$

Use the division algorithm setting $a = 2m$ and $b = 2$. Then $a = bq + r$ gives $q = m$ and $r = 0$. Now set $a = 2n + 1$ and $b = 2$. Then $a = bq + r$ gives $q = n$ and $r = 1$. It is impossible to have both $r = 0$ and $r = 1$.

Exercises I.1.b

1. Find the quotient and remainder for the following pairs of numbers.

   (a) $a = 27$, $b = 4$; (b) $a = 28$, $b = 4$;
   (c) $a = 641$, $b = 32$; (d) $a = 101$, $b = 1$;
   (e) $a = 1$, $b = 101$; (f) $a = 0$, $b = 6$;
   (g) $a = 96$, $b = 24$.

2. Find the factorization into primes of the following numbers.

   (a) 30; (b) 8; (c) 64;
   (d) 324; (e) 101; (f) 641;
   (g) 2077.

3. Show that there exist no nonzero natural numbers a and b such that

   (a) $a^2 = 3b^2$; (b) $a^3 = 2b^3$;
   (c) $a^2 = 6b^2$; (d) $a^{17} = 31b^{17}$.

4. How many natural numbers c are there with $1 < c < 20$ which satisfy the equation $a^2 = cb^2$ where a and b are appropriate nonzero natural numbers?

5. Prove that the sum of 3 consecutive numbers is divisible by 3; the sum of 5 consecutive numbers is divisible by 5. Is this true for the sum of 4 consecutive numbers? of 6 consecutive numbers?

6. Prove that if n is an odd number, then the least remainder after dividing n^2 by 4 is 1.

7. Prove that if n is an odd number, then the least remainder after dividing n^2 by 8 is 1.

8. Let m and n be natural numbers with $m > n$ and let $x = m^2 - n^2$, $y = 2mn$, and $z = m^2 + n^2$. Show that

$$x^2 + y^2 = z^2.$$

9. Make a chart of values for x, y, z in Problem 8 corresponding to $m = 2$, 3, 4 and $n = 1, 2, 3$.

10. Show that the sum of two odd numbers is an even number; the sum of an even number and an odd number is an odd number. Show that the product of two odd numbers is an odd number.

11. In each of the sets of natural numbers given below, determine the least element; calculate at least two other elements in the set.

(a) The set of natural numbers greater than 7 and divisible by 6.
(b) The set of natural numbers which when divided by each of 6 and 21 leave a remainder of 3.
(c) The set of all natural numbers > 1 each of which is the square of a natural number.
(d) The set of all natural numbers > 1 each of which is the cube of a natural number.
(e) The set of all natural numbers > 1 each of which is simultaneously a square of some natural number and the cube of some other natural number.

12. For sets A and B, write $A \subset B$ in case every element of A lies in B. Give examples of two sets such that each of the statements: $A = B$, $A \subset B$, $B \subset A$ is false. Compare with (13).

13. Show that the statement "Every set of natural numbers contains an element which is larger than any other element in the set" is false.

2. THE INTEGERS

The set of integers is the set whose elements are 0, 1, 2, $\cdots$ and also $-1, -2, -3, \cdots$. This set is described by the symbol **Z**. Thus,

$$\mathbf{Z} = \{\cdots, -2, -1, 0, 1, 2, \cdots\}. \tag{1}$$

It is clear that every natural number is an integer. Obviously, there are many integers that are not natural numbers. The necessity for extending the system of natural numbers to the system of integers arises from the following: It is not always possible to subtract in **N**. For example, $5 - 8$ has no answer in **N**. For this reason, **N** is extended to a larger collection, **Z**, in which subtraction can always be performed. We know that in **N** we can add and multiply (obtaining an answer again in **N**). Now in **Z** we can add, subtract, and multiply and the result is in **Z**. Note that neither in **N** nor in **Z** is it always possible to divide. For example, there is no solution in **Z** or in **N** to the equation $8x = 5$; that is, it is impossible to divide 5 by 8 in **Z**.

A system of numbers in which it is possible to perform the three operations of addition, subtraction, and multiplication is sometimes called a *ring*. We add hastily that addition and multiplication should have the properties given in (4), (5), (6), (7), (8) of Section 1 for commutativity, associativity, and distributivity. We add without proof another property of distributivity, namely,

$$a(b - c) = ab - ac. \tag{2}$$

A reminder about the meaning of subtraction. The statement $a - b = c$ means that $a = b + c$. Similarly for division, the statement $a/b = c$ where $b \neq 0$ means that $a = bc$.

The notion of order is transferred from the natural numbers to the integers in such a manner that the following relations hold:

If a is any integer, then one and only one of the following is true:

$$a > 0,$$
$$a = 0, \tag{3}$$
$$-a > 0.$$

The order discussed here has the property that if a is a natural number, $a \neq 0$, then $a > 0$. If, for an integer a, one has $a > 0$, one says "a is positive" as well as "a is greater than 0." If $-a > 0$, one also writes $a < 0$ and says "a is negative." The relation $a \not> 0$ (read: a is not greater than 0) means that either $a = 0$ or $a < 0$.

The relation of positivity has the following properties:

$$\text{If } a > 0 \text{ and } b > 0, \text{ then } a + b > 0. \tag{4}$$

$$\text{If } a > 0 \text{ and } b > 0, \text{ then } a \cdot b > 0. \tag{5}$$

If a and b are arbitrary integers, one writes

$$a > b \quad \text{in case} \quad a - b > 0, \tag{6}$$

and

$$a < b \quad \text{in case} \quad a - b < 0. \tag{7}$$

If a and b are natural numbers, (6) and (7) are precisely the conventions introduced earlier.

We prove now that

$$\text{if } a > b \text{ and } b > c, \text{ then } a > c. \tag{8}$$

Note first that by (6)

$$a > b \text{ is the same as } a - b > 0;$$
$$b > c \text{ is the same as } b - c > 0.$$

By (4),

$$(a - b) + (b - c) > 0, \quad \text{that is,} \quad a - c > 0.$$

This is the same as $a > c$.

Similarly,

$$\text{if } a > b \text{ and } c > 0, \text{ then } ac > bc. \tag{9}$$

This can be seen as follows:

$$a > b \qquad \text{is the same as} \qquad a - b > 0.$$

By (4) one obtains from $a - b > 0$ and $c > 0$,

$$ac - bc = (a - b)c > 0, \qquad \text{that is,} \qquad ac > bc.$$

If $a > b$ and $c > d$ and if $b > 0$ and $d > 0$, then $ac > bd$. That is, inequalities of positive numbers may be multiplied. In particular, the case $a = c$ and $b = d$, gives $a^2 > c^2$.

To prove this, note that since $a > b$ and since $c > 0$, one has $ac > bc$. Next, from $c > d$ and $b > 0$, follows that $bc > bd$. Finally, the inequalities $ac > bc$ and $bc > bd$ yield $ac > bd$. It is important to make sure that all quantities are positive before multiplying inequalities.

EXAMPLE 1:   Prove that for any integer $a \neq 0$, $a^2 > 0$.

PROOF: Since $a \neq 0$ either $a > 0$ or $-a > 0$. In the first case, using (5), multiply $a > 0$ by $a > 0$ obtaining $a^2 > 0$. In the second case multiply $-a > 0$ by $-a > 0$ obtaining $(-a)^2 > 0$ or $a^2 > 0$. That $(-a)^2 = a^2$ can be shown easily with the help of the distributive law given in (2).

EXAMPLE 2:   Find all integers x such that $x^2 \leq 4$.

SOLUTION: Write $x^2 \leq 4$ in the form $4 - x^2 \geq 0$; that is, $(2 + x)(2 - x) \geq 0$. If $(2 + x)(2 - x) = 0$, then either $2 + x = 0$ and $x = -2$ or $2 - x = 0$ and $x = 2$. Assume now that $(2 + x)(2 - x) > 0$. Now, by the laws for multiplying inequalities, we have: Either both $2 + x > 0$ and $2 - x > 0$; or both $2 + x < 0$ and $2 - x < 0$. If $2 + x > 0$ then $x > -2$. If $2 - x > 0$, then $x < 2$. Putting all this together gives $-2 \leq x \leq 2$, that is, $x = -2, -1, 0, 1, 2$.

If both $2 + x < 0$ and $2 - x < 0$, then $x < -2$ and $x > 2$. This is impossible. [To see this add $-2 > x$ to $x > 2$ obtaining $-2 > 2$ or $0 > 4$! This violates (3)]. This example has the virtue of bringing to light the ways in which reasoning with inequalities proceeds. There are other more direct solutions for the problem of finding all integers x, such that $x^2 \leq 4$.

EXAMPLE 3:   Find all pairs of integers (x, y) such that $x^2 + y^2 < 2$.

SOLUTION: If $x^2 + y^2 < 2$, then certainly (since $x^2 \geq 0$ and $y^2 \geq 0$), $x^2 < 2$ and $y^2 < 2$. If $x^2 < 2$ then $x^2 \leq 1$ and as in Example 2, $-1 \leq x \leq 1$ and $-1 \leq y \leq 1$. By actual trial we obtain the pairs that satisfy $x^2 + y^2 < 2$. They are: $(-1, 0)$, $(0, -1)$, $(0, 0)$, $(1, 0)$, and $(0, 1)$.

EXAMPLE 4: Prove that for any natural number n, $2^n > n$.

PROOF: Suppose there are natural numbers n such that $2^n \ngtr n$. Then there exists the smallest such number k. Since $2^0 = 1$, we have $2^0 > 0$; also $2^1 > 1$ and $2^2 > 2$. Thus $k > 2$ and we have $2^k \ngtr k$ but $2^{k-1} > k - 1$. If we multiply both sides of the inequality $2^{k-1} > k - 1$ by 2, we get $2 \cdot 2^{k-1} > 2(k - 1)$; that is, $2^k > 2k - 2$. Adding the inequalities $2^k > 2k - 2$ and $k > 2$ gives $2^k + k > 2k - 2 + 2$, that is, $2^k > k$. This contradicts our assumption about k. Thus no such number exists and $2^n > n$ for all n. The proof just given is logically equivalent to one based on mathematical induction. Mathematical induction will be studied in Chapter VII.

Exercises I.2.a

1. Find all integers x such that

   (a) $x > 2$ and $x^2 \le 25$; (b) $x \ge 2$ and $x^2 < 25$;
   (c) $x^2 \ge 4$ and $x^2 \le 25$; (d) $(x - 1) > 2$ and $(x - 1)^2 \le 25$;
   (e) $(x - 2)^2 \ge 4$ and $(x - 2)^2 \le 25$; (f) $x > n$ and $x^2 \le 4n^2$.

2. Find all pairs of integers (x, y) such that

   (a) $x^2 + y^2 < 10$; (b) $x^2 + y^2 < 1$;
   (c) $x^2 + y^2 \le 1$; (d) $x^2 + y^2 \le 25$ and $x = 2y$;
   (e) $x^2 + y^2 = 25$; (f) $x^2 + 2y^2 \le 5$.

3. Prove the following theorem for integers: Let **M** be a collection of integers with the properties:

   (a) If a and b are in **M**, then $a + b$ is in **M**.
   (b) If a is in **M** and n is an integer, then $n \cdot a$ is in **M**.

   Then there exists an integer b such that **M** is the collection $\{ \cdots, -b, 0, b, 2b, \cdots \}$. This is called the *Principal Ideal Theorem* for **Z**. [*Hint:* Use the Well-Ordering Principle and the Division Algorithm.]

We now introduce the notion of absolute value of a number a, written $|a|$. The definition is

$$|a| = a \qquad \text{if } a > 0;$$
$$|a| = 0 \qquad \text{if } a = 0; \qquad \qquad (10)$$
$$|a| = -a \qquad \text{if } a < 0.$$

Thus, $|5| = 5$; $|-3| = 3$; $|0| = 0$. In all cases, $|a| \ge 0$; and $|a| = 0$ only if $a = 0$. In all cases: $|a^2| = a^2 = |a|^2$; $|a| \ge a$.

The principal relations concerning absolute values are the following: For any two numbers a and b,

$$|ab| = |a| \cdot |b|; \tag{11}$$

$$|a + b| \le |a| + |b|. \tag{12}$$

Before considering these two relations, let us prove: *If c and d are positive numbers (that is, c > 0 and d > 0) and if c² = d², then c = d. If c² > d², then c > d.*

Given two numbers $c > 0$ and $d > 0$, precisely one of the following is true: $c = d$; $c > d$; $c < d$. If $c = d$, then $c^2 = d^2$. Suppose $c > d$. Keeping in mind that all numbers are positive, we may multiply this inequality by itself. This gives $c^2 > d^2$. If $c < d$, we obtain similarly $c^2 < d^2$. This means that for positive numbers c and d, the relations $c^2 = d^2$, $c^2 > d^2$, $c^2 < d^2$ imply $c = d$, $c > d$, $c < d$ in that order. This can be seen as follows. Suppose, for example, that $c^2 > d^2$. Then we have just one of $c = d$, $c > d$, $c < d$. Now $c = d$ and $c < d$ are impossible by the above. Thus $c > d$. Note that this shows that $c^2 \le d^2$ implies $c \le d$.

Now we prove (11). If $a = 0$ or $b = 0$, the proof is trivial. We thus assume that $a \ne 0$ and $b \ne 0$.

$$|ab|^2 = (ab)^2 = a^2 \cdot b^2 = |a|^2 \cdot |b|^2 = (|a| \cdot |b|)^2.$$

Since $ab \ne 0$, $|ab| > 0$. Also $|a| > 0$ and $|b| > 0$, hence $|a| \cdot |b| > 0$. We then apply the result obtained in the previous paragraph with $c = |ab|$ and $d = |a| \cdot |b|$. This finishes the proof of (11).

Turn now to the proof of (12). If $a + b = 0$, the proof is trivial. Assume that $a + b \ne 0$. Hence $|a + b| > 0$. Also $|a| + |b| > 0$, because $|a| + |b| = 0$ implies $|a| = 0$ and $|b| = 0$; this in turn implies $a = 0$ and $b = 0$; this gives $a + b = 0$. Write $c = |a + b|$ and $d = |a| + |b|$. Now

$$\begin{aligned}
c^2 &= |a + b|^2 = (a + b)^2 = a^2 + 2ab + b^2 \\
&= |a|^2 + 2ab + |b|^2 \le |a|^2 + |2ab| + |b|^2 \\
&= |a|^2 + 2|a| \cdot |b| + |b|^2 = (|a| + |b|)^2 = d^2.
\end{aligned} \tag{13}$$

Thus $c^2 \le d^2$ and hence $c \le d$; that is, $|a + b| \le |a| + |b|$. This completes the proof of (12).

Let us verify (11) and (12) in a few cases. Suppose $a = 3$ and $b = -5$. Then $|a| = 3$, $|b| = 5$, $|ab| = |-15| = 15$, $|a + b| = |-2| = 2$. Thus (11) reads $15 = 3 \cdot 5$ (which is true) and (12) reads $2 \le 3 + 5$ (which is true; in fact $2 < 3 + 5$).

Suppose $a = -3$ and $b = -5$. Then $|a| = 3$, $|b| = 5$, $|ab| = 15$, $|a + b| = |-8| = 8$. In this case (11) reads $3 \cdot 5 = 15$ and (12) reads $8 \le 3 + 5$ (which is true; in fact $8 = 3 + 5$).

EXAMPLE 1:   Show that if x is an integer such that $|x| < 5$, then $-5 < x < 5$. Show the converse also. In other words,

$$|x| < 5 \quad \text{if and only if} \quad -5 < x < 5. \tag{14}$$

SOLUTION: If $|x| < 5$, then since $0 \leq |x|$ we can multiply the inequality with itself, obtaining $|x|^2 < 25$. But $|x|^2 = x^2$, so this gives $x^2 < 25$. Finally, if $x^2 < 25$, then $x > -5$ and $x < 5$. This can be seen as follows. If $x > 5$, then squaring, we see that $x^2 > 25$. If $x = 5$, then $x^2 = 25$. Hence if $x^2 < 25$ we have $x < 5$. If $x < -5$, then $-x > 5$ and $x^2 > 25$. If $x = -5$ then $x^2 = 25$. Since $x^2 < 25$, we conclude that $x > -5$. The proof in the other direction is obtained by reversing the above steps. Another type of proof of the above is given in Example 2 preceding Exercises I.2.a. Note that

$$|x| \leq 5 \qquad \text{if and only if} \qquad -5 \leq x \leq 5. \tag{15}$$

EXAMPLE 2: Find all integers x such that $|x + 3| \leq 2$.

SOLUTION: From the preceding example we see that $|x + 3| \leq 2$ is true if and only if $-2 \leq x + 3 \leq 2$. Subtracting $3 = 3$ from this double inequality gives $-2 - 3 \leq x \leq 2 - 3$ or $-5 \leq x \leq -1$. Thus the integers we are looking for are: $-5, -4, -3, -2, -1$.

EXAMPLE 3: Find all pairs of integers (x, y) such that

$$|x^3| + |y^3| \leq 20. \tag{16}$$

SOLUTION: Let us first find all pairs of natural numbers such that

$$x^3 + y^3 \leq 20.$$

If for some natural number x, $x^3 > 20$, then for any natural number y, $x^3 + y^3 > 20$ because $x^3 + y^3 \geq x^3 > 20$. Thus we start by finding those natural numbers x such that $x^3 \leq 20$. These are $x = 0, 1, 2$. For the numbers y such that $y^3 \leq 20$ we also have $y = 0, 1, 2$. Thus the pairs (x, y) for which $x^3 + y^3 < 20$ are among the nine pairs for which $0 \leq x \leq 2$ and $0 \leq y \leq 2$. Each one of these nine pairs does satisfy the inequality (this should be checked).

The pairs of integers (x, y) satisfying (16) are those for which $|x| \leq 2$ and $|y| \leq 2$. Thus there are 25 such pairs.

If a and b are integers then $|a - b|$ can be considered to be the distance from a to b. Thus the distance from 0 to 5 equals that from 3 to 8, $|5 - 0| = |8 - 3| = 5$. Since we have met the notion of distance for pairs of points in the plane and now are meeting it for pairs of numbers, it seems appropriate to speak about the general notion of distance. We say that we have a distance $d(A, B)$ defined for pairs of objects A, B providing the following properties are satisfied:

$$
\begin{aligned}
&d(A, B) = 0 && \text{if } A = B; \\
&d(A, B) > 0 && \text{if } A \neq B; \\
&d(A, B) = d(B, A); \\
&d(A, C) \leq d(A, B) + d(B, C) && \text{for arbitrary } A, B, C.
\end{aligned}
\tag{17}
$$

The symbol $d(A, B)$ is read: "the distance from A to B." If for the integers a, b we write $d(a, b) = |b - a|$ we see immediately that $d(a, b) = 0$ if $a = b$; $d(a, b) > 0$ if $a \neq b$; $d(b, a) = |a - b| = |b - a| = d(a, b)$; and by virtue of (12) we have for any a, b, c

$$d(a, c) = |c - a| = |(b - a) + (c - b)|$$
$$\leq |b - a| + |c - b| = d(a, b) + d(b, c).$$

Thus if we set $d(a, b) = |b - a|$, then $d(a, b)$ is a *distance*. The last relation in (17) is called the *triangle inequality*. It derives its name from the theorem proved in plane geometry: If ABC is any triangle, then the distance from A to C is less than the distance from A to B plus the distance from B to C.

Given the above, an expression $|x - 3| < 5$ can be thought of as: x is an integer whose distance to 3 is less than 5. Similarly, we have seen that for any integer x, if $|x - 3| < 5$ then $-5 < x - 3 < 5$ and conversely. Thus the statement $|x - 3| < 5$ is equivalent to the statement $-2 < x < 8$. The first statement is given in terms of distances; the second in terms of order. Sometimes it is easier to write a statement in terms of distances, sometimes in terms of order.

There are many variations of the inequality (12). Some of the more important variations on (12) are given in Exercises 4 and 5 below. They are very important in the sequel.

EXAMPLE 1:   Find all integers x such that $|x| < 5$ and $|x - 3| < 3$.

SOLUTION: First, $|x| < 5$ is equivalent to $-5 < x < 5$. Next, $|x - 3| < 3$ is equivalent to $-3 < x - 3 < 3$, that is, $0 < x < 6$. Hence the integers x satisfying the problem are $0 < x < 5$.

EXAMPLE 2:   Find all integers x such that $|x| + 5 = |x - 5|$.

SOLUTION: The above is equivalent to $(|x| + 5)^2 = (x - 5)^2$ or $x^2 + 10|x| + 25 = x^2 - 10x + 25$; this gives $-x = |x|$ or $x \leq 0$.

Success here was a matter of luck. It would not take much doing to write down a much more balky problem.

Exercises I.2.b

1. Find all integers x such that

(a) $|x| \leq 3$;

(b) $|x| < 2$;

(c) $|x - 5| \leq 1$;

(d) $|x + 5| < 1$;

(e) $|x - 3| \leq 0$;

(f) $|x + 7| < 0$;

(g) $|x + 7| < 5$ and $|x + 10| < 3$.

2. Find all integers x such that

(a) $|x| = -|x|$;
(c) $|x^2 + x| = 2$;
(e) $|x + 3| = 1$ and $|x - 3| = 2$.

(b) $|x| - 2 = |x + 2|$;
(d) $|x - 3| = 3$ and $|x - 7| = 4$;

3. Prove that if x and y are even integers such that $x < y$ then $x < (x + y)/2 < y$. Show the same for odd integers x and y. Show that

$$\frac{x^2 + y^2}{2} > \left(\frac{x + y}{2}\right)^2.$$

4. Prove that for any integers a, b

(a) $|a - b| = |b - a|$;
(c) $|a + b| \geq |a| - |b|$;
(e) $||a| - |b|| \leq |a + b|$;

(b) $|a - b| \leq |a| + |b|$;
(d) $|a - b| \geq |a| - |b|$;
(f) $||a| - |b|| \leq |a - b|$.

5. Prove that for any integers a, b, c, d

(a) $|a + b + c| \leq |a| + |b| + |c|$;
(b) $|a + b + c + d| \leq |a| + |b| + |c| + |d|$;
(c) $|a + b + c| \geq |a| - |b| - |c|$;
(d) $|a - b - c - d| \geq |a| - |b| - |c| - |d|$.

6. Find all integers s, t such that

$$|s| + |t| = 4.$$

7. Suppose that for two integers a and b, $|a + b| = |a| + |b|$. What can you say about a and b?

8. Solve in integers the equations

(a) $|x - y| = 1$;
(c) $|x^2 - y^2| = 1$;

(b) $|x^2 - y^2| = 0$;
(d) $|xy| = 9$.

3. THE RATIONAL NUMBERS

The system of rational numbers is a familiar one. Examples of rational numbers are $\frac{1}{3}, \frac{2}{7}, -\frac{5}{3}, 0, 5, -16$. The set of rational numbers is denoted by $\mathbf{Q}$. A number x is rational providing it can be expressed as the quotient of two integers p and q: $x = p/q$, where $q \neq 0$. There are many expressions for the same rational number. For example, p/q, $2p/2q$, $3p/3q$, $\cdots$ all represent the same number. If p and q have no common integral factors, we say that the expression p/q is in lowest terms. If a is an integer, we may write $a = a/1$ thus showing that a is rational. Given two expressions p/q and r/s it is easy to determine whether they represent the same rational number. One has

$$\frac{p}{q} = \frac{r}{s} \qquad \text{if and only if} \qquad ps = qr. \tag{1}$$

Now *ps* and *qr* are integers. Thus the question of the equality of rational numbers is pushed back to that of the equality of integers.

The rule for the addition of two rational numbers p/q and r/s is

$$\frac{p}{q} + \frac{r}{s} = \frac{ps + qr}{qs}. \tag{2}$$

Note that because $q \neq 0$ and $s \neq 0$, it follows that $qs \neq 0$. Thus the expression in (2) is well defined. Since $ps + qr$ and qs are integers, the sum of two rational numbers is rational.

The rule for the multiplication of two rational numbers p/q and r/s is

$$\frac{p}{q} \cdot \frac{r}{s} = \frac{pr}{qs}. \tag{3}$$

Thus the product of two rational numbers is rational.

It is not difficult to show that addition and multiplication satisfy the commutative, associative, and distributive laws given in Section 1, Equations (4) through (8). We shall assume that this has been done.

Not only is subtraction possible in **Q** but also division. As usual we only divide by numbers that are not 0. A rational number r/s is zero if $r = 0$. The answer to the problem: divide p/q by r/s is ps/qr. For example, 2/5 divided by 7/3 equals $(2 \times 3)/(5 \times 7) = 6/35$. This means that the system of rational numbers is a *field*. A field is a number system in which addition and multiplication satisfy the laws mentioned above, and in which the inverse operations, subtraction and division, are also possible. The field **Q** contains the ring **Z** (which in turn contains **N**). In fact **Q** is the smallest field containing **Z**.

The field **Q** may be *ordered* as follows:

$$\frac{p}{q} > 0 \qquad \text{in case} \qquad pq > 0. \tag{4}$$

Since pq is an integer, its positiveness is easily tested. Thus the question of determining the positiveness of a rational number is pushed back to that of determining the positiveness of an integer. We can now show that given any rational number p/q, one and only one of the following relations is valid:

$$\frac{p}{q} > 0,$$

$$\frac{p}{q} = 0, \tag{5}$$

$$-\frac{p}{q} > 0.$$

It is now possible to prove the inequalities analogous to (4) and (5) of Section 2:

$$\text{If } \frac{p}{q} > 0 \text{ and } \frac{r}{s} > 0, \text{ then } \frac{p}{q} + \frac{r}{s} > 0. \tag{6}$$

$$\text{If } \frac{p}{q} > 0 \text{ and } \frac{r}{s} > 0, \text{ then } \frac{p}{q} \cdot \frac{r}{s} > 0. \tag{7}$$

Just as for integers, we write

$$\frac{p}{q} > \frac{r}{s} \quad \text{in case} \quad \frac{p}{q} - \frac{r}{s} > 0. \tag{8}$$

Having reached this point we may prove all the properties of inequalities of rationals which were stated in Section 2 for integers. We shall not give the details here.

The notion of absolute value is introduced exactly as in the case of integers. All the relations concerning absolute value that were derived in Section 2 are still valid in the present context. We shall make use of them where needed without further comment.

The rationals have a property of considerable interest; it is called the *Archimedean property*. Let a and b be rational numbers (thus $a = p/q$ and $b = r/s$ for some integers p, q, r, s). Suppose that $a > 0$ and $b > 0$. The Archimedean property states that there exists a natural number n such that $na > b$. To understand the strength of this property, one should think of a as "small" and b as "big." Then, no matter how small a is and how big b is, there is always a natural number n such that $na > b$. To prove that $n(p/q) > r/s$ for a suitable n, try $n = 2qr$ (see Exercise 11); (it is assumed that $p > 0$, $q > 0$, $r > 0$, $s > 0$).

The Archimedean property has this simple consequence. If $a > 0$ is a rational number, then there exists a natural number n such that $1/n < a$. To prove this let $b = 1$ and by the preceding paragraph find n such that $na > b$. This means that between 0 and a there is always a rational number $1/n$ for a suitable n. It is easy to show that between any two rational numbers there is another such number (and hence infinitely many such). See Exercise 12.

The development of the rationals over two thousand years ago marked a big step forward in mathematics and in human civilization. For the first time, man could add, subtract, multiply, and divide in an unrestricted way. However, certain operations still could not be performed. For example, in elementary geometry we learned that the diagonal of a square having side 1 has a length equal to $\sqrt{2}$. Thus with ruler and compass we can construct, starting with a segment of length 1, a new segment of length $\sqrt{2}$. However, this construction is not a "rational construction." This statement means that there is no rational number which equals $\sqrt{2}$. To prove this statement, suppose the contrary. Let

$$\frac{r}{s} = \sqrt{2} \text{ with } r \text{ and } s \text{ integers. Assume that } r > 0 \text{ and } s > 0. \qquad (9)$$

Then, by squaring and clearing fractions,

$$r^2 = 2s^2. \qquad (10)$$

However, as was proved in Section 1, there are no natural numbers r and s satisfying (10). Hence $\sqrt{2}$ is not rational. Referring once more to Section 1, and using the method just outlined for $\sqrt{2}$, one sees that $\sqrt{3}$, $\sqrt{5}$, $\sqrt{6}$, $3\sqrt{2}$, and $3\sqrt{5}$, as well as many other numbers are not in $\mathbf{Q}$. In other words, if we wish to perform operations leading to these numbers (such as solving the quadratic equation $x^2 = 2$ or the cubic $x^3 = 5$) we have to go beyond $\mathbf{Q}$; we have to *extend* $\mathbf{Q}$. This will be discussed in the next section on the real numbers.

A point about notation. If a and b are rational numbers with $b \neq 0$, then a/b is a rational number since $\mathbf{Q}$ is a field. However, the notation a/b should not suggest that a and b are integers. For example, if $a = 2/3$ and $b = 7/5$, then $a/b = 2/3 \cdot 5/7 = 10/21$. In the proof of some of the exercises below it is necessary to write a and b as the ratio of two integers and then to proceed. The proofs concerning rationals all are made to depend on proofs concerning integers. The student should keep in mind that in the future most of the properties of integers (associativity, commutativity, positivity, absolute value) can be established for the rational numbers. In the next section, it will be automatically assumed that this has been done.

Exercises I.3.a

1. Write the expressions below in lowest terms.

(a) $\dfrac{2}{10}$;

(b) $\dfrac{15}{27}$;

(c) $-\dfrac{35}{10}$;

(d) $\dfrac{11}{41}$;

(e) -16;

(f) $\dfrac{2 \times 3^2 \times 5^3}{3 \times 7^3}$;

(g) $\dfrac{2^2 \times 5^3 \times 7}{11^2 \times 13}$;

(h) $\dfrac{84}{55}$;

(i) $\dfrac{533}{391}$.

2. Perform the indicated operations on rational numbers and express the result in lowest terms.

(a) $\dfrac{3}{5} + \dfrac{4}{7}$;

(b) $\dfrac{3}{5} + \dfrac{14}{10}$;

(c) $\dfrac{3}{7} + \dfrac{7}{3}$;

(d) $2 + \dfrac{1}{2} + \dfrac{1}{6} + \dfrac{1}{24}$.

3. Prove the relations given below.

(a) $\dfrac{3}{10} = \dfrac{6}{20}$;

(b) $\dfrac{6}{10} = \dfrac{9}{15}$;

(c) $\dfrac{77}{33} = \dfrac{119}{51}$;

(d) $\dfrac{2^2 \times 3 \times 5^3}{3^2 \times 11^4} = \dfrac{2^2 \times 7 \times 5^4}{3 \times 5 \times 7 \times 11^4}$;

(e) $\dfrac{7}{9} + \dfrac{4}{15} = \dfrac{47}{45}$;

(f) $\dfrac{7}{5} - \dfrac{5}{9} = \dfrac{38}{45}$;

(g) $\dfrac{7}{8} + \dfrac{8}{7} > 2$;

(h) $\dfrac{10}{9} - \dfrac{9}{10} > \dfrac{1}{5}$.

4. Simplify the following expressions in which $a, b, c, r, s, \cdots$ are integers.

(a) $\dfrac{a^2 b}{ab^3}$;

(b) $\dfrac{a^3 b^2 c}{ab^2 c^3}$;

(c) $\dfrac{8rs^2}{2^5 s^3}$;

(d) $\dfrac{2^2 \cdot 3^4 \cdot a^2 b^5}{3^2 \cdot 5^2 \cdot ac^4}$.

5. Perform the indicated operations, writing the answers in simple form (a, b, c, x, y are integers).

(a) $\dfrac{a}{b^2} + \dfrac{2b}{a^2 b}$;

(b) $\dfrac{a+b}{b^2} + \dfrac{a-b}{a^2}$;

(c) $\dfrac{a^2 b^3}{ac^2} \cdot \dfrac{4bc}{a^2}$;

(d) $\dfrac{x^2}{a^2} + \dfrac{y^2}{b^2}$;

(e) $\dfrac{x^2}{a^2} - \dfrac{y^2}{b^2}$;

(f) $\dfrac{a}{b} + \dfrac{b}{a}$;

(g) $\dfrac{1}{a} + \dfrac{1}{b} + \dfrac{1}{c}$;

(h) $\dfrac{x^2}{2} + xy + \dfrac{y^2}{2}$;

(i) $\dfrac{x^3}{6} + \dfrac{x^2 y}{2} + \dfrac{xy^2}{2} + \dfrac{y^3}{6}$;

(j) $x^2 + 2 + \dfrac{1}{x^2}$;

(k) $\dfrac{2}{1/a + 1/b}$.

6. Prove that if a and b are rational and if $0 < a < b$, then $1/b < 1/a$. [*Hint:* Write $a = r/s$, $b = u/v$, where r, s, u, v are integers and proceed.]

7. Prove the equalities given below (a, b, c are integers).

(a) $\dfrac{2a}{3b} = \dfrac{4a^2b}{6ab^2}$;

(b) $\dfrac{6a^2}{3ab} = \dfrac{2a}{b}$;

(c) $3a = \dfrac{6a^3b}{2a^2b}$;

(d) $\dfrac{1/a + 1/b}{1/ab} = a + b$;

(e) $\left(a + \dfrac{1}{a}\right)^2 = \dfrac{a^4 + 2a^2 + 1}{a^2}$;

(f) $\dfrac{a + 1/a}{b + 1/b} = \dfrac{b\,a^2 + 1}{a\,b^2 + 1}$.

8. If $a = \frac{2}{3}$ and $b = \frac{15}{2}$ find a natural number n such that $na > b$. How many answers can you give to this problem? What is the least value of n? Do the same for $a = 1/1000$, $b = 1000$; for $a = 15$, $b = 1$.

9. Prove that if p/q is rational then one and only one statement in (5) holds.

10. Using the definition given in the text that $p/q > 0$ in case that $pq > 0$, prove that if $p/q > 0$ and $r/s > 0$, then

(a) $\dfrac{p}{q} + \dfrac{r}{s} > 0$;

(b) $\dfrac{p}{q} \cdot \dfrac{r}{s} > 0$.

11. Prove that for any two positive rational numbers $a = p/q$ and $b = r/s$, the integer $n = 2qr$ satisfies $na > b$. Why not use $n = qr$? Assume $p > 0, q > 0, r > 0, s > 0$.

12. Prove that between any two rational numbers there is another rational number.

13. Write down 100 rational numbers between 1 and 2.

14. Write down 100 positive rational numbers each of which is larger than its successor.

15. (a) Show that the numbers 0.3, 0.33, 0.333, $\cdots$ are all rational.
   (b) Show that the numbers 3, 3.1, 3.14, 3.141, 3.1415, 3.14159, $\cdots$ are all rational.

Historical Note. Archimedes was born around 287 B.C. He lived in Syracuse (Sicily) and died there in 212 B.C. at the hands of a Roman soldier who belonged to the army besieging the city. Archimedes is commonly regarded as the greatest mathematician of antiquity. In the difficult pastime of choosing the greatest mathematician of all ages, many put him at the top of the list. Archimedes attributed to Eudoxus (approximately 408–355 B.C.) the "axiom of Archimedes" which is essentially the principle we stated in the text.

4. THE REAL NUMBERS

Although the system of rational numbers has a remarkable collection of desirable properties, it is still impossible to perform certain operations within it. We have seen, for example, that there is no rational number whose square is 2. Similarly there is no rational number whose square is 3 or whose cube is 3 or any of whose (integral) powers 4, 5, 6, $\cdots$ is 3. Now this impossibility of solving an equation such as $x^2 = 2$ or $x^n = 3$ where $n = 2, 3, \cdots$ is not by itself disastrous, but it is symptomatic of a serious drawback: The rational number system is like a sieve with extremely fine mesh but with a very large number of holes. There are many problems that cannot be solved in rational terms because the desired solution is precisely over a hole.

Let us try to explain what this means. Suppose we take a line l and choose a unit of length. Suppose we choose some fixed point 0 on l and start measuring distances from 0. It will be recalled that we have briefly mentioned the notion of distance at the end of Section 2 and that we have indicated its principal properties [see Equation (17)]. It is clear that there are two points having distance 3 units from 0. To the one on the right of 0 we attach the number 3; to the one on the left of 0 we attach the number -3. See Figure I.1. What we

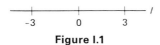

Figure I.1

have done for the number 3 can also be done for any rational number. If p/q is any positive rational number, one can find two points on the line l whose distance from 0 is p/q. The one to the right of 0 is labeled p/q, the one to the left $-p/q$. In this way we find a point on the line for every rational number. The result is suggested in Figure I.2.

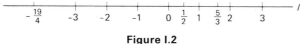

Figure I.2

Note that the points so obtained are "*dense*" on the line. This means that they are so thickly distributed that there is no interval without rational points. That is, if one were to look at a line with a microscope, no matter how powerful, one would always see rational points. However, the points so obtained do not *fill* the line. For example, there are two points on the line whose distance from 0 is $\sqrt{2}$. But there is no rational distance that gives these points. Thus the "rational line" of Figure I.2 has gaps in it. There are points to the right of 0 that one would like to label $\sqrt{2}, 3\sqrt{2}, 4\sqrt{3}$, and so on. And as long as one restricts himself to using rational labels, those points cannot be talked about. It is as if they did not exist.

Now, what is desirable is to have a number system in which each point of the line corresponds to a number and each number corresponds to a point. The rationals have the property that each number corresponds to a point but lack the property that each point corresponds to a number. The *real number system* is that system which has both properties.

To obtain an idea of what a real number is, let us look once more at $\sqrt{2}$. We have learned how to obtain the value of $\sqrt{2}$ to any desired accuracy and we know that decimally, the expression starts off by: $\sqrt{2} = 1.4142139\cdots$. What this means is that $\sqrt{2}$ is describable by a sequence of rational numbers, namely,

$$1,\ 1.4,\ 1.41,\ 1.414,\ 1.4142,\cdots. \tag{1}$$

That these numbers are rational is evident if we write them in the form

$$\frac{1}{1},\ \frac{14}{10},\ \frac{141}{100},\ \frac{1414}{1000},\ \frac{14142}{10000},\ \cdots. \tag{2}$$

We say that $\sqrt{2}$ is the *limit* of the sequence; also that the sequence converges to $\sqrt{2}$. *The real number system consists of the rational numbers and of the limits of sequences of rational numbers.* To see precisely what this means would involve us in a detailed study of limits of sequences, and this will not be undertaken here. However, the intuitive picture, using points on a line as in Figure I.2, should make the ideas clear. In these matters, intuition is an excellent guide. It does not lead to incorrect answers. The system of real numbers is denoted by **R**.

If a real number is not rational, it is called *irrational*. The number $\sqrt{2}$ is irrational. So are the numbers $\sqrt{5}$, $3\sqrt{2}$, and many, many others. Still another irrational number is $\pi = 3.14159\cdots$. It is very difficult to show that π is irrational.

Not only are the irrational numbers described by means of sequences in the way that sequence (1) describes $\sqrt{2}$, but any rational can also be described by a sequence. For example, the rational number 1.35 can be described by the sequence

$$\frac{1}{1},\ \frac{13}{10},\ \frac{135}{100},\ \frac{1350}{1000},\ \cdots. \tag{3}$$

Thus one sees that all the real numbers, whether rational or not, are those that are limits of sequences of rational numbers. Expressions such as $1.4142139\cdots$ and $1.35000\cdots$ are called *infinite decimals*. We have, therefore,

> *Each real number can be represented by an infinite decimal and each infinite decimal represents a real number.*

One fact that may be noted is that some real numbers have two infinite decimal representations. For example, the number 3 has the representation

3.00000 · · · and also the representation 2.99999 · · · . This fact is slightly annoying but is not very important. After all, the infinite decimal representations are only position names for numbers. They don't have many uses beyond this. For example, they cannot be used to add or multiply.

Let us move forward to a more important fact: many sequences of rational numbers have the same limit; that is, many sequences *represent* the same real number. For example, $\sqrt{2}$ is represented by (1) and it is also represented by

$$2, 1.5, 1.42, 1.415, 1.14143, \cdots . \tag{4}$$

We can write down several other sequences representing $\sqrt{2}$. For example,

$$1, 2, 1.4, 1.5, 1.41, 1.42, \cdots . \tag{5}$$

This discussion leads to the conclusion that:

> *Each real number can be represented as the limit of a sequence of rationals in many ways. Each converging sequence of rationals represents a real number.*

The sequences (1), (4), and (5) all converge to $\sqrt{2}$. The sequence (1) is said to converge from below; the sequence (4) is said to converge from above.

With this in mind, it is easy to add, subtract, multiply, and divide real numbers. It is conceptually easy. It may take a little time. Suppose that x and y are two real numbers. Choose any sequence of rationals that represent x, say,

$$x: \quad a_1, a_2, a_3, a_4, \cdots , \tag{6}$$

and choose any sequence of rationals that represent y, say,

$$y: \quad b_1, b_2, b_3, b_4, \cdots . \tag{7}$$

Then we can obtain sequences for $x + y$ and $x \cdot y$ (also for $x - y$ and x/y if $y \neq 0$) simply by adding and multiplying the corresponding rational numbers. Thus,

$$x + y: \quad a_1 + b_1, \; a_2 + b_2, \; a_3 + b_3, \cdots ; \tag{8}$$

$$x \cdot y: \quad a_1 \cdot b_1, \; a_2 \cdot b_2, \; a_3 \cdot b_3, \cdots . \tag{9}$$

For example, let us obtain sequences for $\sqrt{2} + \sqrt{3}$ and for $\sqrt{2} \cdot \sqrt{3}$ ($= \sqrt{6} = 2.44956 \cdots$). Use the sequence (1) for $\sqrt{2}$ and since $\sqrt{3} = 1.732 \cdots$, use the sequence $1, 1.7, 1.73, 1.732, \cdots$ for $\sqrt{3}$. This gives

$$\sqrt{2} + \sqrt{3}: \quad 1 + 1, \; 1.4 + 1.7, \; 1.41 + 1.73, \; 1.414 + 1.732, \cdots .$$

If we perform the indicated rational operations, we get

$$\sqrt{2} + \sqrt{3}: \quad 2, 3.1, 3.14, 3.146, \cdots .$$

For the product, we obtain

$$\sqrt{2} \cdot \sqrt{3}: \quad 1 \times 1, \ 1.4 \times 1.7, \ 1.41 \times 1.73, \ 1.414 \times 1.732, \cdots.$$

Carrying out the indicated multiplications gives

$$\sqrt{2} \cdot \sqrt{3}: \quad 1, \ 2.38, \ 2.4393, \ 2.449048, \cdots.$$

Compare this with the answer given above: $\sqrt{6} = 2.44956 \cdots$.

We have just stated how real numbers are to be added and multiplied. This is not meant to indicate that there are no serious problems to be looked at. Far from it. Suppose for example that someone calculating $\sqrt{2} \cdot \sqrt{3}$ started with the expression (4) for $\sqrt{2}$ instead of (1). Then he would obtain for $\sqrt{6}$ a sequence other than the one we just obtained. How do we know that this is a sequence that represents $\sqrt{6}$? This is a delicate question, and there are many others like it. To begin to develop answers to these questions requires delicate machinery. We are not going to develop this machinery here. However, a well-made diagram with the points of the sequence on a line suggest strongly that the sequences we have written down really seem to converge.

Exercises I.4.a

1. Draw a line l, choose a point 0, and a unit of length. Mark down the points whose distance from 0 is 4, $5/2$, $\sqrt{5}$, π, $\pi/2$. ($\pi = 3.14159 \cdots$).

2. Write down a sequence of rational numbers representing the following real numbers [see Equations (1), (2), and (3)].

   (a) $\frac{1}{2} \sqrt{2}$;   (b) $\sqrt{\dfrac{3}{4}}$;

   (c) $\pi \ (= 3.14159 \cdots)$;   (d) $\dfrac{\pi}{6}$;

   (e) 4;   (f) $\dfrac{1}{3}$;

   (g) $\dfrac{2}{7}$;   (h) $2^5 \cdot 5^3$.

3. Write down a second sequence of rational numbers representing each of the above real numbers.

4. Write down a third sequence of rational numbers representing each of the above real numbers.

5. Write down a sequence of rational numbers representing

(a) $\frac{1}{2}\sqrt{2} + \frac{1}{2}\sqrt{3}$;

(b) $\sqrt{3} - \sqrt{2}$;

(c) $\dfrac{1}{\sqrt{3} - \sqrt{2}}$;

(d) $\sqrt{6} + \sqrt{3}$.

6. (a) Write down a sequence for $\sqrt{2}$ and square it.

(b) Write down a sequence representing 2. Write a second sequence representing $\sqrt{2}$. Obtain by division a sequence representing $2/\sqrt{2} = \sqrt{2}$.

7. Write down a sequence for π. Square it. This may suggest that $\pi^2 = 10$. Hundreds of years ago, Hindu mathematicians thought so. Actually $\sqrt{10} = 3.1623$.

8. Write the following rational numbers as infinite decimals.

(a) $\dfrac{1}{2}$;

(b) $-\dfrac{1}{9}$;

(c) $\dfrac{20}{3}$;

(d) $\dfrac{2}{14}$;

(e) 5;

(f) $\dfrac{1}{13}$.

9. Express the following rational numbers as the quotient of two integers.

(a) $0.333 \cdots$;

(b) $0.2700 \cdots$;

(c) $0.555 \cdots$;

(d) $2.333 \cdots$;

(e) $0.999 \cdots$.

10. Prove that

(a) $\dfrac{2}{3} = 0.666 \cdots$;

(b) $\dfrac{1}{11} = 0.0909 \cdots$;

(c) $\dfrac{12}{99} = 0.121212 \cdots$;

(d) $\dfrac{1}{13} = 0.07692307 \cdots$.

11. Write down five numbers that have two distinct infinite decimal representations. Can you describe all numbers with this property?

12. Prove that if a is a rational number, its infinite decimal representation repeats from a certain point on. For example, $\frac{2}{7} = 0.285714285714 \cdots$. [*Hint:* If $a = r/s$ where r and s are integers, then in dividing r by s, since the remainder is always less than s, the quotient must repeat from a certain position. Note that the first few decimals in r/s need not participate in the repetition. Why?]

The question of ordering the real numbers may also be examined. It is possible to introduce a relation of positivity, $x > 0$, which has the properties: If x is a real number, then one and only one of the following holds:

$$x > 0,$$
$$x = 0, \qquad \text{(10)}$$
$$-x > 0.$$

Furthermore, for real numbers x and y,

$$\text{if} \quad x > 0 \quad \text{and} \quad y > 0, \quad \text{then} \quad x + y > 0; \qquad \text{(11)}$$

$$\text{if} \quad x > 0 \quad \text{and} \quad y > 0, \quad \text{then} \quad x \cdot y > 0. \qquad \text{(12)}$$

Next, one writes,

$$x > y \qquad \text{in case} \qquad x - y > 0. \qquad \text{(13)}$$

If it is assumed that these facts have been established, it is possible to derive all the properties of inequalities established for integers and rational numbers [see Section 2, (8), (9), and the discussion following].

The absolute value may be introduced into the real numbers by means of the definition: For any real number x,

$$|x| = x \qquad \text{if} \qquad x > 0;$$
$$|x| = 0 \qquad \text{if} \qquad x = 0; \qquad \text{(14)}$$
$$|x| = -x \qquad \text{if} \qquad x < 0.$$

It is now possible to prove the relations: For any real numbers x and y,

$$|x \cdot y| = |x| \cdot |y|; \qquad \text{(15)}$$

$$|x + y| \leq |x| + |y|. \qquad \text{(16)}$$

We shall not discuss the proofs of these facts. Obviously, the proofs depend on how the relation $x > 0$ is defined, something we have not gone into. An intuitively correct idea of the meaning of the statement "$x > 0$" is that on the line l in Figure I.2, x lies to the right of 0.

We may state an intuitively apparent fact concerning addition and multiplication of real numbers. If x and x' are "close" to each other and y and y' are also close to each other, then $x + y$ and $x' + y'$ are close to each other and so are $x \cdot y$ and $x' \cdot y'$. This property is called "the continuity of addition and multiplication." The phrase "x is close to x'," means that the distance from x to x' is small; that is, $|x - x'|$ is small.

It has been noted above that for every rational number there are sequences of rationals which represent it as a real number [see, for example, (3)]. That is, every rational number is also a real number. We already know that every integer is a rational number and every natural number is an integer. Thus every natural number, integer, or rational number is also a real number. Thus, **R** contains **Q**; **Q** contains **Z**; **Z** contains **N**.

The real numbers have the Archimedean property: If x and y are positive real numbers, there exists a natural number n such that $nx > y$. The proof of this fact is not given.

We have seen so far that the operations of addition, subraction, multiplication, and division can be performed on the real numbers. We have seen that two real numbers can be compared in magnitude (greater than and less than) and we have been able to introduce the notion of absolute value in the real numbers. Also, the Archimedean property holds for real numbers. Now all the above operations, relations, and properties are valid also for rational numbers. A valid question is: What property, if any, distinguishes the reals from the rationals?

There is a most important property possessed by the real numbers and not possessed by the rational numbers. This property can be discussed from several points of view and can be introduced under various names: Completeness, least upper bound property, connectedness. In terms of the number line that was introduced earlier (see Figure I.2), it means that if all the real numbers are represented on the line, there are no gaps or holes. Every point of the line is covered by some real number. The use of the words "completeness" and "connectedness" does indeed convey the absence of gaps. This property is discussed below. The discussion is in terms of *least upper bound* of a set of numbers.

Suppose we are given a set of numbers. For example, we may consider

The set of natural numbers **N**.   (17)

The set of integers **Z**.   (18)

The set of rational numbers x such that $0 < x < 63$.   (19)

We shall call this set A.

The set of rational numbers x such that $x^2 < 2$.   (20)

We shall call this set B.

Notice that the set A has the property that there exists a number k which is at least as large as any number in A. For example, the number $k = 100$ has this property. This is true because if a number is less than 63, it is less than 100. Notice that there are other numbers besides 100 that could play the role of k. For example, 110, 1000, 89, and also 63. We say that the set A is *bounded on the right*. We say also that the numbers 100, 110, 1000, 89, and 63 are *upper bounds* of A.

It will be noted that A is also *bounded on the left*. This means that there exist numbers that are as small as any number in A. The number -5 is one such; so is the number 0.

The set B is also bounded on the right and on the left. For example, the number 4 is such that if x is a rational number whose square is less than 2, then $x < 4$. Other *real* numbers that are bounds for the set B are 3, 2, π, and $\sqrt{2}$.

The set $\mathbf{Z}$ is not bounded either on the right or on the left. There is no number that is greater than every integer and there is no number that is less than every integer. Notice that the set $\mathbf{N}$ of natural numbers is bounded on the left, but not bounded on the right.

If we have a set C of numbers that has the property that k bounds it on the right, we call k an *upper bound* for C. Thus, if x is a number in C, then $x \leq k$. We have seen that if k is an upper bound, there are many others; for example, $k + 1$ is also an upper bound. This raises the question: Is there a *least upper bound*? One says that l is a least upper bound of C providing that

(a) l is an upper bound of C;
(b) no number smaller than l is an upper bound of C.

We see rather easily that the sets A and B introduced above do indeed have a least upper bound. The least upper bound of A is 63 and the least upper bound of B is $\sqrt{2}$. Let us look at the matter a little more closely. It is a fact that both A and B have least upper bounds but this is true because we are considering sets of real numbers. Suppose that we were discussing rational numbers only. Then the set A would have a least upper bound, namely 63. The set B would not have a (rational) least upper bound. That is, given any rational upper bound for B, it can be shown that there is a smaller rational upper bound!

The question that can now be asked is this: Given a set of real numbers that has an upper bound, does it always have a least upper bound? The answer is "yes" and we formulate it as a very important principle.

I–5 Least Upper Bound Principle

If $\mathbf{M}$ *is a set of real numbers that has an upper bound, then it has a least upper bound.*

Here then is a property of the real number system that does not hold for the rational number system. It is this property which represents the essential difference between the two systems. And it is this property which makes it possible to construct all of mathematical analysis, including the material discussed in this book.

We state explicitly that we have not proved the principle. We have merely explained its meaning. We shall not at this point give applications of the principle. Some applications are suggested in the exercises that follow. We shall invoke the principle on some occasions in future chapters. The alert reader may note that the principle is used in some arguments without being appealed to by name. The reason for this situation can be explained as follows: Our point of view is that the real numbers can be represented as the points of a line in the way that was explained at the beginning of this section (see Figures I.1 and I.2). Thus the model of the line may safely be used and all the properties of the real numbers that are needed can be derived from it. The role of the least upper bound principle is to establish once and for all the relation between the real numbers and the points of the line so that one can proceed intuitively without fear of making mistakes.

A companion to I–5 is a *Greatest Lower Bound Principle* for a set that has a lower bound. It is left as an exercise to define the notion of greatest lower bound and to state the principle concerning its existence (see Exercise 2).

In this section, we have tried to give an introduction to the theory of real numbers. Our aim has been to present the material in such a way that if one were later to study the real number system rigorously, one could come back to this section and see the general lines of such study here. At the same time we wish to stress once more that the real numbers may be geometrically realized as the points of the ordinary geometric line of our intuition. Thus we should be ready to allow ourselves to be guided freely by our intuition. The intuition does not lead us astray as far as reasoning on the line is concerned (the situation for the plane is more complicated). Finally a word may be in order as to what the mathematical subject of *analysis* is. It is always difficult to define mathematical subjects (algebra, geometry, and so on). However, the "taste" of the subject can be described. From that point of view analysis is that branch of mathematics which is based on the concept of the real number system. This includes analytic geometry, trigonometry, calculus, and all the subjects these lead to. None of these subjects is conceivable unless the real numbers are available to deal with. In that sense, the present book develops a background to analysis.

Exercises I.4.b

1. Prove, using the Archimedean principle, that if $x > 0$ is a real number, there exists a natural number n such that $1/n < x$.

2. Give a precise definition of the concept of greatest lower bound. State the greatest lower bound principle for a set of numbers **M**. Prove it. [*Hint:* Replace each x in **M** by $-x$ and apply the l.u.b. principle.]

3. Determine whether each of the sets of real numbers below is bounded from above, from below. Find three bounds from above and from below in each case where it applies and find the least upper bound and the greatest lower bound.

   (a) The set of numbers x such that $0 \le x \le 1$;
   (b) The set of numbers x such that $0 \le x < 1$;
   (c) The set of numbers x such that $x < 1$;
   (d) The set of numbers x that are rational;
   (e) The set of rational numbers x such that $x^2 < 5$;

(f) The set of real numbers x such that $x^2 < 5$;

(g) The set of irrational numbers x such that $x^2 < 5$.

4. Find the least upper bounds and greatest lower bounds (if any) of the sets below. Do these bounds belong to the set?

(a) The set of numbers x such that $|x - 1| < 2$;

(b) The set of numbers x such that $|2x - 3| < 5$;

(c) The set of numbers x such that $|x - 1| \leq 2$;

(d) The set of numbers x such that $-3 \leq 4x - 2 < 3$;

(e) The set of numbers x such that $|x^2 - 5| \leq 1$;

(f) The set of all numbers x such that $|x| > 1$;

(g) The set of all numbers x such that $|x| \geq 0$.

5. Prove that if a and b are rational numbers with $a < b$, then $(a + b)/2$ is a rational number and $a < (a + b)/2 < b$. Thus between any two rational numbers there is another rational number. Give another formula for a rational number between a and b.

6. Prove that if a and b are rational numbers with $a < b$, then $c = a + (b - a)(\sqrt{2}/2)$ is an irrational number such that $a < c < b$. Thus between any two rational numbers there is an irrational number.

7. Show that if a is irrational and r is rational then $a + r$ is irrational. Show that if a is irrational, $1/a$ is irrational. Show that if $m > 0$ is a natural number, there exists an irrational number a such that $a > m$. Show that if $m > 0$ is a natural number there exists a positive irrational number b such that $b < 1/m$.

8. Consider the sequence of rational numbers $3, 3.1, 3.14, 3.141, \cdots$ which converges to the number π. What is the least upper bound of this sequence?

The above problem suggests that if x is any real number, there is an increasing sequence of rational numbers whose least upper bound is x.

Historical Note. The real number system was only put on a firm logical foundation during the nineteenth century. This program was called the "arithmetization of analysis." Up to this point in history, mathematicians had invoked geometrical arguments to make their conclusions tenable. There are several ways of rigorizing the development of the real number system. It can be done by Cantor sequences, Dedekind cuts, and other devices. The list of distinguished men who contributed to the program is extensive. It would include Bernhard Bolzano (1781–1848), A. L. Cauchy (1789–1857), Karl Weierstrass (1815–1897), H. E. Heine (1821–1881), J. W. R. Dedekind (1831–1916), and Georg Cantor (1845–1918). The first was a Czechoslovak, the second a Frenchman, all the others were Germans.

UNIQUENESS OF FACTORIZATION INTO PRIMES

We prove below that the factorization into primes of a natural number $a > 1$ is unique. This will complete the proof of Theorem I-4. The proof is not difficult and it is not short.

We first show:

I-6 Theorem

Let a and b be natural numbers that are greater than 1. There exists a unique natural number c such that

(a) *c divides a and c divides b;*

(b) *if d divides a and d divides b, then d divides c.*

The number c is called the greatest common divisor of a and b. We write $c = gcd\{a, b\}$.

PROOF: If $a = b$ then $c = a$. Suppose now that $a > b$. From the division algorithm one obtains

$$a = bq_1 + r_1, \qquad 0 \le r_1 < b. \tag{1}$$

If $r_1 = 0$, then obviously, $gcd\{a, b\} = b$. Suppose $r_1 \neq 0$. Then applying the division algorithm to b and r_1 one obtains

$$b = r_1 q_2 + r_2, \qquad 0 \le r_2 < r_1. \tag{2}$$

We continue this procedure if $r_2 \neq 0$ obtaining

$$r_1 = r_2 q_3 + r_3, \tag{3}$$

and so on. This gives a collection of natural numbers $r_1, r_2, r_3, \cdots$ with $b > r_1 > r_2 > r_3 > \cdots$. Such a chain must terminate after some number of steps, say n steps. That is, we get

$$r_{n-2} = r_{n-1}q_n + r_n, \qquad 0 < r_n < r_{n-1}, \tag{4}$$

$$r_{n-1} = r_n q_{n+1} + 0. \tag{5}$$

We claim that $r_n = gcd\{a, b\}$. To see this, note that r_n divides r_{n-1} [see Equation (5)]. Equation (4) shows that r_n divides r_{n-2}. Going back up the chain of equations, we see that r_n divides $r_{n-3}, \cdots, r_2, r_1$, then b and also a. This proves property (a) in the theorem.

To prove property (b), note that if d divides a and b then d divides r_1 by Equation (1). Going to Equation (2) we see that since d divides b and r_1, d divides r_2. Going on in this way we finally see that d divides r_n. The question of the uniqueness of gcd$\{a, b\}$ is left as an exercise.

A most important property of the greatest common divisor follows:

I–7 Theorem

If c is the greatest common divisor of a and b, there exist integers x and y such that

$$ax + by = c. \tag{6}$$

For the sake of simplicity we are stating and proving this theorem in terms of integers. A slightly more cumbersome statement and proof can be established using only natural numbers.

PROOF: Using (4), we obtain

$$r_n = -q_n r_{n-1} + r_{n-2}. \tag{7}$$

Since

$$r_{n-3} = r_{n-2} q_{n-1} + r_{n-1}, \tag{8}$$

we obtain by substitution in (7) that

$$r_n = -q_n(r_{n-3} - r_{n-2} q_{n-1}) + r_{n-2}. \tag{9}$$

This gives r_n in terms of r_{n-2} and r_{n-3}. We substitute here an expression for r_{n-2} similar to (8) and we obtain r_n in terms of r_{n-3} and r_{n-4}. If this is kept up, we finally make substitutions with the help of (1) and (2) and obtain an expression of the form

$$r_n = ax + by. \tag{10}$$

This proves (6).

We are now ready to prove the uniqueness of factorization into primes. This means that if for a natural number $a > 1$ we have two factorizations

$$a = p_1 \cdot p_2 \cdots p_s = q_1 \cdot q_2 \cdots q_t, \tag{11}$$

then $s = t$ and the second factorization is nothing but a rearrangement of the first.

Now if there is a natural number $a > 1$ which has two essentially distinct factorizations, then by the Well-Ordering Property of **N**, I–2, there is a smallest such natural number. We shall assume that the number a in (11) is the smallest natural number having two distinct factorizations.

We know that p_1 and q_1 are primes and that they are distinct, for otherwise we could cancel p_1 and q_1 in (11) and obtain a number smaller than a with distinct factorizations. Thus the gcd of p_1 and q_1 is 1 and integers x and y can be found such that

$$p_1 x + q_1 y = 1. \tag{12}$$

Multiply all terms in (12) by $p_2 \cdots p_s$; then using (11) we see that the first term becomes ax, hence we write

$$ax + q_1 p_2 \cdots p_s y = p_2 \cdots p_s. \tag{13}$$

Now q_1 divides a and it divides $q_1 p_2 \cdots p_s y$; hence q_1 divides $p_2 \cdots p_s$.

It is clear that $q_1 \neq p_2$ since otherwise, we could have cancelled them in (11) thus obtaining a smaller number than a with two distinct factorizations. Thus the gcd of q_1 and p_2 is 1. We repeat the previous argument and show that q_1 divides $p_3 \cdots p_s$. Repeating sufficiently often we see that q_1 divides p_s, which means $q_1 = p_s$ since p_s is a prime. This is a contradiction.

Our contradiction implies that no number a having distinct factorizations into primes exists.

The above proof concerns natural numbers. There exist number systems, more precisely, there are rings, in which factorization into primes is not unique. An example does not lie directly under the surface; one has to probe deep for it. See Exercise 5 for further information. If we give up the operation of addition and are content to restrict ourselves to multiplication, it is easy to give examples with nonunique factorization. Consider the "system" $\{1, 4, 7, 10, \cdots\}$ formed in a rather obvious way. Then we note that $4 \times 25 = 10 \times 10$ and that each of 4, 10, 25 is a "prime" in our "system." Check that the product of two numbers in the set is again in the set.

Another multiplicative system without unique factorization is the following: $\{1, 4, 6, 9, 11, 14, 16, \cdots\}$. Here $4 \times 9 = 6 \times 6$, yet 4, 6, and 9 have no factors within the system except the trivial ones. Once more the product of two numbers in the system is in the system. This is so because the numbers in the system are the natural numbers of the form $5n \pm 1$ where n is a natural number.

Exercises I-Appendix

1. Consider the set of all real numbers of the form $a + b\sqrt{2}$ where a and b are integers. Show that the sum of two such numbers is again such a number; do the same for products. Thus these numbers form a ring. Note that 2 is not a prime in the ring since $2 = \sqrt{2} \times \sqrt{2}$. It can be shown that factorization into primes is unique in this ring.

2. Consider the multiplicative system of odd natural numbers: $\{1, 3, 5, 7, \cdots\}$. Show that factorization into primes is unique.

3. Consider the multiplicative system $\{1, 6, 11, 16, \cdots\}$. Obtain distinct prime factorizations for 1296. What is the number of primes occurring in each factorization?

4. Assuming elementary acquaintance with complex numbers, show that the set of numbers of the form $a + b\sqrt{-1}$ where a and b are integers, form a ring. It may be shown that unique factorization holds in this ring.

5. Assuming elementary acquaintance with complex numbers, show that the numbers of the form $a + b\sqrt{-5}$, where a and b are integers, form a ring. It can be shown that unique factorization into primes does not hold in this ring.

6. In the proof of Theorem I-6, it is not shown that $\gcd\{a, b\}$ is unique. Prove this.

Historical Note. It was taken for granted during a great part of the last century that the factorization into primes in any ring of the type indicated above in Problems 1, 4, and 5 is unique. It came as quite a shock that this was not the case. In order to restore the property of uniqueness the notion of ideal was introduced into algebra. The notion of ideal is given in Exercise 3 of I.2.a.

Chapter II

REAL FUNCTIONS

1. THE CONCEPT OF A FUNCTION

In this chapter we shall introduce and discuss real functions. These functions are but a special type of functions that is studied in considerable detail in more advanced mathematics. At this stage, some experience with real functions has already been accumulated. Suppose, for example, that we are asked to consider an equation such as

$$y = x^2 + 3x - 2. \tag{1}$$

The intention here is usually the following: We are to choose a number x, say $x = 2$. Then the equation above is used to calculate a corresponding number y; in this case, $y = 2^2 + 3 \times 2 - 2 = 4 + 6 - 2 = 8$. If we had started with $x = 3$, the corresponding value of y obtained would have been $y = 16$. The value $x = -1$ gives $y = -4$. We are interested here in assigning real values to x. This gives corresponding real values to y.

The fact that x is allowed to take on many values, one at a time, of course, is indicated by calling it a *variable*. Since x takes on real values, it is called a *real variable*. In our example above and throughout most of this book, the corresponding values of y are also real. Thus what we are proposing to study are *real functions of a real variable*. In the title of this chapter, these have been called *real functions*, for short. From now on, we shall frequently refer to them simply as functions.

Let us give further examples of functions before setting down a formal definition. Consider the equation

$$y = \sqrt{x}. \qquad (2)$$

Note: By definition, $\sqrt{x}$ is a unique positive number. Thus $\sqrt{4} = 2$. The statement $\sqrt{4} = \pm 2$ is false. Here, if $x = 9$, $y = 3$. If $x = 0$, then $y = 0$. If we set $x = 2$, we obtain for y a real number, $y = \sqrt{2}$; if we are interested in having the decimal value of $\sqrt{2}$, it is approximately 1.414. The important fact is that $\sqrt{2}$ is a real number.

What happens if x is negative? Since the square root of a negative number is not real, we decide to exclude such numbers from consideration. Thus for this function, it is required that $x \geq 0$.

If we were to consider the function defined by $y = \sqrt{x - 3}$, then clearly we would restrict the values of x to satisfy $x \geq 3$. Similarly, if the function is defined by

$$y = \frac{1}{x}, \qquad (3)$$

then clearly $x = 0$ is to be excluded.

These examples suggest that when using formulas to define functions, a proper determination must be made at the beginning as to what values of x are permissible.

So far, we have considered functions defined by equations. Such functions will hold the major part of our attention. However, it is important to understand that functions need not be given by formulas. They may be given by a rule, as the following illustration shows:

The postage of first class mail in the United States (1972) is calculated as follows: The first ounce or less costs 8 cents. A letter weighing more than 1 ounce and at most 2 ounces requires 16 cents $= 2 \times 8$ cents of postage. A letter weighing more than 2 ounces and at most 3 ounces requires 24 cents $= 3 \times 8$ cents postage. And so on.

If x represents the number of ounces of a letter and y represents the postage in cents required by the letter, then we have a precise rule for computing the value of y for any value of x. In this case x is restricted to be positive, that is, $x > 0$.

The student will also note that the function defined by $y = x^2 + 3x - 2$ or the function defined by $y = \sqrt{x}$ can be given by a verbal rule. For example, the rule for the latter is: Choose a number x which is positive or zero. Take its square root. This gives the value of y. Actually, the only advantage that formulas have over rules is that they are briefer. Formulas are the shorthand of the mathematician.

We are now ready to set down precisely the notion of function (that is, of a real function of a real variable). We start with a set of real numbers. Call this set **M**. Let x represent any number in **M**. We have a formula or a rule that allows us to calculate for each such number x a corresponding real number y. This then is the notion of function. Note that two things are given here: The set of real numbers **M** called the *domain* of the function and the rule for calculating the real number y which corresponds to each number x in **M**. Note that for each x in **M** there is one y and there is only one y.

To represent arbitrary functions letters of the Roman or Greek alphabet are used. Thus the letters f, g, h, φ are frequently used. The function above is written in symbols as follows:

$$f: \mathbf{M} \to \mathbf{R}. \tag{4}$$

This means that the rule f is defined on **M**, and that it takes on values in **R**; that is, it takes on real values. If x is a number in **M** and y is the number associated with x, one writes

$$y = f(x) \qquad \text{(read: } y \text{ equals } f \text{ of } x\text{).}\tag{5}$$

Thus in our first example we had

$$f(x) = x^2 + 3x - 2. \tag{6}$$

For that same example we have

$$f(2) = 2^2 + 3 \times 2 - 2 = 8. \tag{7}$$

Similarly, $f(3) = 16, f(-1) = -4$. If a and b are unspecified numbers, then

$$f(a) = a^2 + 3a - 2, \tag{8}$$

and

$$f(a + b) = (a + b)^2 + 3(a + b) - 2. \tag{9}$$

As has been indicated earlier, the numbers x and y are called *variables*. One says that x is the *independent variable* and that y is the *dependent variable*.

Note the manner in which a specific function is introduced. For example, we say: Consider the function f defined by $f(x) = x^2 + 3x - 2$. Sometimes for short we are tempted to say: Consider the function $f(x) = x^2 + 3x - 2$; or even: Consider the function $y = x^2 + 3x - 2$. In the remainder of the book we shall refer to functions in several ways. This is standard practice and is recommended. For the most part, the correct and somewhat roundabout way of speaking of functions is used. At times, however, the more relaxed shorter form has advantages.

Let us consider now a few special functions. First of all, consider the function f which associates to each real number x the number x. Here $\mathbf{M} = \mathbf{R}$. In symbols

$$f(x) = x. \tag{10}$$

This is called the *identity function*. It is very important in algebra and analysis. It is also a very simple function. Note that for the identity function f, $f(0) = 0$, $f(-2) = -2, f(a) = a, f(a + b) = a + b$.

Now let c represent a fixed number (for example, $c = 5$). Consider the function f which associates to each real number x (once more, $\mathbf{M} = \mathbf{R}$) the number c. In symbols,

$$f(x) = c. \tag{11}$$

For example, if $c = 5$, then $f(3) = 5, f(0) = 5, f(5) = 5$, and so on. This function is called a *constant function*. (Note that there is a constant function for each value of c.) If in particular $c = 0$, we obtain the *zero function* and write also $f = 0$. Thus, if $f = 0$, then $f(x) = 0$ for each x. We may say in this case that f is identically zero. Similarly, if $g(x) = 5$ for each x, we may write $g = 5$, and say that g is identically equal to 5.

Suppose f and g are two functions and that f and g are both defined for the same set of real numbers $\mathbf{M}$. Suppose further that if x is any number in $\mathbf{M}$ then $f(x) = g(x)$. In that case we shall say that f and g are equal and we shall write

$$f = g. \tag{12}$$

Thus, if $f = g$ we have $f(x) = g(x)$ for every x; and, as we have just said, if $f(x) = g(x)$ for every x, we have $f = g$.

As an example of equal functions consider the following: Let f be defined for positive x by $f(x) = (x^2 - 4)/(x + 2)$. Let g be defined for positive x by $g(x) = x - 2$. Then $f = g$.

Let us introduce a diagram that will make clear the notion of function. We do this with the function defined by $f(x) = 2x + 7$. We can represent the fact that $f(1) = 9, f(2) = 11, f(-3) = 1$, by connecting with an arrow the associated numbers on left and right. See Figure II.1. We shall say

Figure II.1

that the function *maps* x into $2x + 7$; or we can write

$$x \mapsto 2x + 7. \tag{13}$$

The diagram for the constant function defined by $f(x) = 5$ is shown in Figure II.2.

There are other diagrammatic representations of functions. One of them, by *graphs*, will receive our attention later.

We add an important remark concerning the role played by the set $\mathbf{M}$ in the definition of function. The functions treated in this book are real functions of a real variable. Thus every function f is defined on a set of real

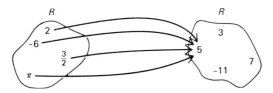

Figure II.2

numbers and takes on real values. In most cases it will be apparent what the set **M** is. For that reason it will not be formally written down. For example, the identity function f defined by $f(x) = x$ is assumed to be defined for all real numbers x. The function g defined by $g(x) = \sqrt{x}$ is assumed to be defined for all $x \geq 0$. The general rule for determining **M** is that it consists of the largest collection of real numbers for which the function makes sense. In case this general rule does not hold, it is necessary to state explicitly what the domain **M** is.

A hint concerning notation. So far, the letters used for the variables have been x and y. Other frequently used letters are u and v, r and s, and even letters from the Greek alphabet λ and μ, ξ and η. For functions, letters such as f, g, h, φ, ψ, and so on are used. Thus one meets expressions such as $s = g(t)$, $v = \varphi(u)$, $\eta = \psi(\xi)$, and so on. Be sure to cultivate flexibility with regard to functional notation. See also the Greek alphabet in the back of this book.

Here follows an example of functions f and g for which $f \neq g$. Suppose f and g are defined for all x and suppose they are given by the formulas $f(x) = 6x - 5$ and $g(x) = x^2$. Then to show that $f \neq g$ it suffices to select one special x such that $f(x) \neq g(x)$. Try $x = 0$. This gives $f(0) = -5$ and $g(0) = 0$. Thus $f \neq g$. [Note that the fact that $f(1) = g(1)$ proves nothing in this connection.]

Another way in which $f \neq g$ can arise is much more delicate. It is possible that $f(x) = g(x)$ for all x for which *both* functions are defined but that $f \neq g$ simply because they are not defined on the same sets. For example, if $f(x) = (x^2 - 4)/(x - 2)$ and $g(x) = x + 2$ where it is understood that the domains of definition are as large as possible, then g is defined for all real x and f is defined for all real x except $x = 2$ [because according to the instructions, $f(2)$ gives 0/0 and we don't handle such symbols]. Thus $f \neq g$. Such types of distinct functions will be avoided wherever possible.

Exercises II.1.a

1. Given the function defined by the following equation, determine the largest permissible domain **M** for that function.

   (a) $f(x) = -x$; (b) $f(x) = \sqrt[3]{x}$;

(c) $g(s) = s^5 + 3s - 2$;   (d) $h(x) = \dfrac{1}{x^2 - 4}$;

(e) $f(x) = \dfrac{1}{x + 2}$;   (f) $v(t) = 27$;

(g) $f(x) = \sqrt{x} + \dfrac{1}{x - 2}$;   (h) $f(x) = \dfrac{\sqrt{x^2 - 4}}{x}$;

(i) $g(x) = \dfrac{1}{x} + \dfrac{1}{x + 1}$;   (j) $s(t) = \sqrt{t} + \sqrt{t - 3}$;

(k) $s(t) = \sqrt{t}\sqrt{t - 3}$;   (l) $s(t) = \sqrt{t(t - 3)}$.

2. (a) If a function f is defined by $f(x) = x^3 - 2x + 1$, calculate $f(0), f(1)$, $f(\tfrac{5}{2}), f(3)$.
 (b) The same for $f(x) = (3x^2 + 3)^3$.
 (c) The same for $f(x) = \sqrt{x} + 1$.

 (d) The same for $f(x) = \dfrac{1}{x + 2}$.

 (e) The same for $f(x) = x$.
 (f) The same for $f(x) = 3$.
 (g) The same for $f(x) = c$.

3. If f is defined by $f(x) = x^2 + 3$, calculate $f(a), f(2a), f(\sqrt{a})$ $(a > 0)$; $f(a + b), f(a) + f(b)$. Show that $f(0) + f(1) = f(2)$. Show that $f(2) + f(3) \neq f(2 + 3)$.

4. Show that for the function $f(x) = \sqrt{x}$ there exist no distinct values a and b such that $f(a) = f(b)$.

5. On a certain railroad line, passenger fares from the terminal are determined according to the following table:

ZONE	DISTANCE FROM TERMINAL (MILES)	FARE (DOLLARS)
1	1–10	1.25
2	10.1–25	1.75
3	25.1–50	2.50
4	50.1–100	3.50

Calculate the fare to a station 8.3 miles from the terminal; 53 miles; 89.5 miles.

6. Give an example of a function for which there is no simple formula.

7. If a function f is defined by $f(x) = x^2 - 4x + 7$, calculate the values of x, if any, for which $f(x) = 7, f(x) = 3, f(x) = 2, f(x) = a$. Do the same for the function $f(x) = 2$. Do the same for the function $f(x) = x$.

8. Write down four functions f for which $f(0) = 0, f(2) = 8, f(-2) = -8$.

9. Suppose someone has defined a certain number of functions (say, 5 or 31). Give a method for defining a function distinct from all these. Use this method to define a function distinct from any function appearing in Exercises 1 through 8.

10. Prove that if $f(x) = cx$ where c is a constant, then for any numbers a and b, $f(a + b) = f(a) + f(b)$.
    A student thought that for the function $g(x) = x^2$, it was true that $g(a + b) = g(a) + g(b)$. What formula in algebra should he review?

2. THE ADDITION AND MULTIPLICATION OF FUNCTIONS

Functions have many properties in common with numbers. In particular, two functions may be added or they may be multiplied. They may also be subtracted, divided (a little extra care is needed here), and functions may be multiplied by constants. Let us illustrate by considering an example.

Let f be the function defined for all x by

$$f(x) = x^3, \tag{1}$$

and let g be the function defined for all x by

$$g(x) = 2x^2 - 4. \tag{2}$$

What shall we mean by $f + g$ and $f \cdot g$? Clearly the only reasonable definition for $f + g$ is the function which associates to x the number $x^3 + (2x^2 - 4)$. Similarly the function $f \cdot g$ associates to x the number $x^3(2x^2 - 4)$.

The definitions for the addition and the multiplication of the functions f and g may be written in the form

$$(f + g)(x) = f(x) + g(x); \tag{3}$$

$$(f \cdot g)(x) = f(x) \cdot g(x). \tag{4}$$

Another way of writing this is the following: If f and g are arbitrary functions, then

$$\text{for} \quad f + g, \quad \text{one has} \quad x \mapsto f(x) + g(x) \tag{5}$$

and

$$\text{for} \quad f \cdot g, \quad \text{one has} \quad x \mapsto f(x) \cdot g(x). \tag{6}$$

A word should be said about the values x for which $f + g$ and $f \cdot g$ are defined. Clearly, the domain of the sum and product cannot include any points for which f and g are not defined. Thus both $f + g$ and $f \cdot g$ are defined precisely for those numbers x for which both f and g are defined.

The definition of $f - g$ is straightforward.

$$\text{For } f - g, \quad \text{one has} \quad x \mapsto f(x) - g(x). \tag{7}$$

Also, if c represents a constant, that is, if c represents some fixed number, then

$$\text{for } cf, \quad \text{one has} \quad x \mapsto cf(x). \tag{8}$$

For two functions f and g the quotient f/g is defined as follows: For the number x, the function f/g has the value $f(x)/g(x)$. This requires that $g(x) \neq 0$ since the operation of division is possible only if the denominator is not zero. Thus the quotient of two functions is defined for those numbers x for which (i) both f and g are defined; (ii) $g(x) \neq 0$. We repeat:

$$\text{for } \frac{f}{g} \quad \text{one has} \quad x \mapsto \frac{f(x)}{g(x)} \qquad [g(x) \neq 0]. \tag{9}$$

EXAMPLE 1: Suppose f and g are defined by

$$f(x) = x^3, \qquad g(x) = x^2 + 1. \tag{10}$$

Then for $x = 2$ we have

$$(f + g)(2) = 2^3 + (2^2 + 1) = 13;$$
$$(f - g)(2) = 8 - (2^2 + 1) = 3;$$
$$(f \cdot g)(2) = 8 \cdot 5 = 40; \tag{11}$$

$$\frac{f}{g}(2) = \frac{8}{5}.$$

For $x = a$ (where a is some number),

$$(f + g)(a) = a^3 + (a^2 + 1);$$
$$(f - g)(a) = a^3 - (a^2 + 1);$$
$$(f \cdot g)(a) = a^3(a^2 + 1); \tag{12}$$

$$\frac{f}{g}(a) = \frac{a^3}{a^2 + 1}.$$

Note that for any number a, $a^2 + 1 \neq 0$. Thus, f/g is defined for all x.

EXAMPLE 2: Suppose that f and g are defined by

$$f(x) = \sqrt{x} + 1 \quad \text{and} \quad g(x) = x - 1. \tag{13}$$

Then one obtains

$$(f + g)(x) = (\sqrt{x} + 1) + (x - 1) = \sqrt{x} + x;$$
$$(f - g)(x) = \sqrt{x} - x + 2;$$
$$(f \cdot g)(x) = (\sqrt{x} + 1)(x - 1); \tag{14}$$

$$\frac{f}{g}(x) = \frac{\sqrt{x} - 1}{x - 1}.$$

Note that $f + g$, $f - g$, and $f \cdot g$ are defined for $x \geq 0$; f/g is defined for $x \geq 0$, $x \neq 1$.

We see that except for the complications concerning domains of definition, functions behave much like numbers. That is, they may be added, subtracted, multiplied, and divided. Note that we are now talking of addition, subtraction, multiplication, and division of the functions f and g. We knew a long time ago how to perform the operations on the numbers $f(x)$ and $g(x)$!

There is another operation on functions which is important, namely that of *composition*. We introduce it by means of an example. Suppose f and g are given by

$$f(x) = 2x^2 + 1, \qquad g(x) = x^3. \tag{15}$$

Then by the composition of f and g in that order is meant the function whose value at x is $(2x^2 + 1)^3$. We write $g \circ f$ and read "f followed by g;" also "g of f." Thus,

$$(g \circ f)(x) = (2x^2 + 1)^3. \tag{16}$$

Composition is also written as: $x \mapsto g(f(x))$. Thus

$$(g \circ f)(x) = g(f(x)). \tag{17}$$

The latter way of writing explains why we read f followed by g: For a given number x, we first form $f(x)$ and then $g(f(x))$.

The operation of composition can be made clearer if we write our functions using different symbols. Suppose we write $v = 2u^2 + 1$ and $w = v^3$. Then right away we get $w = (2u^2 + 1)^3$. That is, composition can be explained as a type of substitution:

$$v = f(u) \qquad \text{and} \qquad w = g(v) \tag{18}$$

gives

$$w = g(f(u)) = (g \circ f)(u). \tag{19}$$

Notice that in general $f \circ g \neq g \circ f$. For example, for the two functions given in Equation (15), $(f \circ g)(x) = 2(x^3)^2 + 1 = 2x^6 + 1$. Now for $x = 1$, $2x^6 + 1 \neq (2x^2 + 1)^3$. Hence $f \circ g \neq g \circ f$ by the definition of equality of two functions. The operation of composition is highly important.

For still another example of the composition of functions, consider the functions defined in Equation (13). We have $g(f(x)) = (\sqrt{x} + 1) - 1 = \sqrt{x}$. On the other hand, $f(g(x)) = \sqrt{x - 1} + 1$.

Suppose that we start with the constant functions and with the identity function f defined by $f(x) = x$. What functions can be obtained from these by applying the operations of addition, subtraction, and multiplication of functions? Among the functions obtained in this way will be such as carry x into: (1) c, where c is any constant; (2) $cx + d$, where c and d are any constants; (3) $cx^2 + dx + e$, where c, d, and e are any constants, and so on. It may be seen that the most general function f obtained in this way is given by

$$f(x) = a_0 + a_1 x + a_2 x^2 + \cdots + a_n x^n. \qquad (20)$$

Here the numbers $a_0, a_1, \cdots, a_n$ represent constants; n is some integer equal to or greater than zero; that is, $n \geq 0$. Such functions are called *polynomial* functions. Note that polynomial functions are defined for all real numbers. Note also that the composition of two polynomial functions gives a polynomial. See Exercise 7 below, where the proof is hinted at.

In general, the quotient of two polynomials is not a polynomial. The situation here is similar to that with the integers; here also, the quotient of two integers is not always an integer. Since addition, subtraction, and multiplication of polynomials lead again to polynomials, the family of polynomials is a ring (see Chapter I, Section 2).

The quotient of two polynomial functions is called a *rational* function. It may be seen that the sum, difference, product, and quotient of two rational functions are rational functions. (See Exercises 11 and 12 below.) Thus the rational functions constitute a field (see Chapter I, Section 3). Note that the denominator in the expression of a rational function is a polynomial (not identically zero). Thus a rational function is defined for all values of the variable with the exception of those values which make the denominator equal to zero. We shall see in the next chapter that if f is a polynomial, there are only a finite number of values x such that $f(x) = 0$. Thus, a rational function is defined for all except a finite number of values.

In this book, we shall frequently refer to polynomial functions simply as *polynomials*. From many points of view, polynomials are the simplest functions to consider. It is proved in the calculus that many of the functions that are met can be approximated by polynomials. For these and other reasons, polynomials are important in mathematics. The next chapter is dedicated entirely to the study of polynomials. The material briefly touched upon in the preceding paragraphs will be dealt with at length in that chapter. For that reason, it may be desirable to put off until later questions concerning polynomials and rational functions that may come to mind. In particular, some of the questions taken up in the exercises below are treated in detail in the next chapter.

Exercises II.2.a

1. Given the functions f and g defined by the following equations, find defining equations and domains for $f + g, f \cdot g$, and f/g. Assume in each case that the domains are the largest possible.

   (a) $f(x) = \sqrt{x}$; $g(x) = x^2 - 1$.
   (b) $f(x) = x$; $g(x) = a$, $a \neq 0$.
   (c) $f(x) = x^2 - 4x + 4$; $g(x) = x^2 + 4$.
   (d) $f(x) = x$ if $x \geq 0$; $f(x) = -x$ if $x < 0$; $g(x) = f(x)$.   *Note:*
   In the notation of the preceding chapter, we write $f(x) = |x|$.

   (e) $f(x) = \dfrac{x - 1}{x - 2}$; $g(x) = \dfrac{1}{x}$.

   (f) $f(x) = x^3$; $g(x) = \sqrt[3]{x}$.
   (g) $f(x) = a_0 + a_1 x$; $g(x) = b_0 + b_1 x + b_2 x^2$.
   (h) $f(x) = (x + 1)^3$; $g(x) = x^2 - 4$.

2. For the same functions as in Problem 1, determine $f \circ g$ and $g \circ f$ and find their domains of definition.

3. For the functions in Exercise 1, calculate directly and without using the results of Exercise 1, the numbers: $(f + g)(3)$; $(f \cdot g)(3)$; $(f/g)(3)$; $(3f + 2g)(1)$; $(2f \cdot g)(1)$; $[(f + g)/g](3)$.

4. For the functions f given below calculate $f(2x)$, $f(x + 2)$, $f(2/x)$, $f(x^2)$, $2f(x)$, $2f(3x^2 + 4)$, $[f(x)]^2$, $[f(x^2)]^3$, $(f \circ f)(x)$.

   (a) $f(x) = 3x$;   (b) $f(x) = (3x + 7)$;
   (c) $f(x) = 5$;   (d) $f(x) = 0$;
   (e) $f(x) = x^2 - 1$;   (f) $f(x) = |x|$ [see 1(d)];
   (g) $f(x) = \sqrt{x}$.

5. Give an example of a function f such that for any real numbers a and b,

$$f(a + b) = f(a) + f(b).$$

   Give three functions for which this is not so.

6. Show by direct calculation that if $f(x) = x^2 + 2$ and $g(x) = x^3 - 2x + 1$, then both $f \circ g$ and $g \circ f$ are polynomials.

7. Show that for $f(x) = x$, x^2, x^3, and so on, and for polynomials $g(x)$, $f \circ g$ is a polynomial. Thus show that if f and g are arbitrary polynomials, $f \circ g$ is a polynomial.

8. If $f(x) = (2x + 1)/(3x^2 - 2)$ and $g(x) = x^2/(x - 1)$ indicate as rational functions the functions $f + g$, $f - g$, $f \cdot g$, and f/g.

9. If

$$f(x) = a_0 + a_1 x + a_2 x^2 + \cdots + a_n x^n$$

and

$$g(x) = b_0 + b_1 x + b_2 x^2 + \cdots + b_m x^m,$$

show that

$$f(x) \cdot g(x) = a_0 b_0 + (a_0 b_1 + a_1 b_0)x + (a_0 b_2 + a_1 b_1 + a_2 b_0)x^2 + \cdots$$
$$+ a_n b_m x^{n+m}.$$

Thus the product of two polynomials is a polynomial. This will be taken up in Chapter III.

10. Show that the sum of two polynomials is a polynomial. This along with the result of Exercise 9 shows that the polynomials form a ring (for definition, see Chapter I).

11. Show that the product and quotient of two rational functions are rational functions (in the case of the quotient we exclude division by the zero function).

12. Show that the sum and difference of rational functions are rational functions. (Write down two rational functions in "general form," obtain a common denominator, and add them using Exercise 9.) Exercises 9, 10, 11, and 12 show that the rational functions form a field (Chapter I). These exercises may be solved easily after reading Chapter III.

3. GRAPHS

The notion of the *graph* of a function f is undoubtedly familiar. To illustrate this notion, we begin by explaining how to introduce coordinates in the plane.

Consider a plane. We shall designate it by the letter P. A good representation of a plane is a sheet of paper or a blackboard. We take two lines in the plane intersecting at a point which will be designated by O. Although it is not necessary, we shall assume that these two lines are perpendicular to each other. The usual representation for these lines is given in Figure II.3. The lines will be designated l_x and l_y, as indicated. These lines are called axes: l_x is the x-axis and l_y is the y-axis.

Let us choose on each of these lines two directions which will be held fixed throughout the discussion. It is customary, although not necessary, to choose on l_x the direction to the right from O and on l_y the direction up from O.

Finally, let us choose a unit of measurement for each of the axes. It is not necessary that these two units be the same, but we shall so choose them in most cases for reasons of convenience.

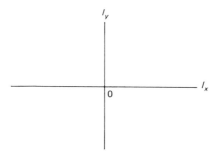

Figure II.3

Referring to the line l_x, we have seen (Chapter I, Section 4) that every real number corresponds to a point of l_x and also that every point on l_x can have its position described by means of a real number. For example, the number 5 corresponds to the point on l_x which is 5 units from O and on the positive side of O. The number -3 corresponds to the point which is 3 units from O and on the negative side of O, that is, on the side of O which is not positive.

Similarly, if A is any point on l_x, then we may measure the distance d which A lies from O. If A lies on the positive side of O, then A's position is described by d. If A lies on the negative side of O, then its position is described by $-d$. We refer to Figure II.4 to make these statements clear.

Figure II.4

We see then that every point on l_x is described by a number called its coordinate; in fact, we shall call this number its x-coordinate. And every number is the x-coordinate of some point on l_x. For example, in Figure II.4, the point A has x-coordinate 8; the point A' has x-coordinate -4. If a point is chosen arbitrarily, its coordinate will be called x.

We proceed in a similar manner with the line l_y. Every point on this line will be described by its y-coordinate.

Now suppose C represents a point in the plane P. We draw from C two lines, parallel to l_x and to l_y (see Figure II.5). Suppose the line parallel to l_y intersects l_x in A; and the line parallel to l_x intersects the line l_y in B. Let x be the coordinate of A (on the l_x-axis) and let y be the coordinate of B (on the l_y-axis). Then the pair of numbers (x, y) describes the position of the point C completely. These will be called the coordinates of the point C. Thus we may refer to C as the point whose coordinates are (x, y). We shall frequently say for short that C *is* the point (x, y).

Note that by the scheme described above, each point has associated with it a unique pair of real numbers; and each pair of real numbers corresponds

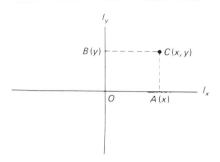

Figure II.5

to a unique point. Note in passing that the two numbers which are coordinates form an ordered pair. For example, (3, 5) and (5, 3) do not represent the same point. If (*a*, *b*) are the coordinates of a point, *a* is called the *abscissa* and *b* is called the *ordinate* of the point. The process that has been described above is called the coordinatization of the plane; or the introduction of coordinates in the plane. The plane *P* with its system of coordinates is called the Cartesian plane. The name is chosen to honor René Descartes, the French mathematician and philosopher, who is considered the founder of analytic geometry.

Now that coordinates have been introduced in the plane, it is easy to define the graph of any function *f*. Let us start with the special case where $f(x) = x^2 - 1$. We write this in the form

$$y = x^2 - 1. \tag{1}$$

If for example $x = 0$, then $y = -1$. The point whose coordinates are $(0, -1)$ is then said to be part of the graph of $y = x^2 - 1$. We also say that $(0, -1)$ is on the graph. Suppose we *plot* the point $(0, -1)$ as indicated in Figure II.6. (Note that for reasons of convenience we label our axes with "*x*"

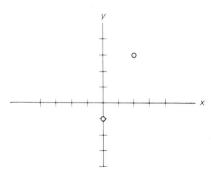

Figure II.6

and "y" instead of "l_x" and "l_y.") Now choose another value of x, say $x = 2$. The corresponding value of y is $y = 3$. We plot the point $(2, 3)$.

The graph of $y = x^2 - 1$ consists of all points (x, y) so obtained. In other words, we are to give to x all possible values and plot the point $(x, x^2 - 1)$.

This is quite a task. However, let us proceed. To start with, we shall give to x a few integral values. (It is easier to compute $x^2 - 1$ if $x = 3$ than if $x = 3.1416$!) We arrange the values found for y in Table II.1 and we plot them

Table II.1

x	-3	-2	-1	0	1	2	3	4	5
y	8	3	0	-1	0	3	8	15	24

(see the little crosses in Figure II.7). We shall leave aside the points $(4, 15)$ and $(5, 24)$ because they are obviously going to be off the paper. Let us now continue our work by plotting some more points shown in Table II.2. We plot

Table II.2

x		$-\frac{5}{2}$	$-\frac{3}{2}$	$-\frac{1}{2}$	$\frac{1}{2}$	$\frac{3}{2}$	$\frac{5}{2}$	
y		$\frac{21}{4}$	$\frac{5}{4}$	$-\frac{3}{4}$	$-\frac{3}{4}$	$\frac{5}{4}$	$\frac{21}{4}$	

these also (see the little circles in Figure II.7). At this stage we note that it will take an enormous amount of time to plot the points (x, y) of the graph for which x lies between -3 and 3. In fact, it will take an infinite amount of time

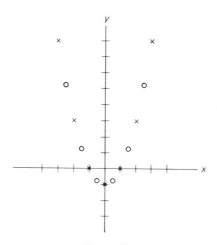

Figure II.7

since there is an infinite number of such points. However, just as we are about to be somewhat discouraged, we note that the information we have on Figure II.7 not only is more complete than that on Figure II.6, but actually induces us to make an intelligent guess as to what the entire graph is. A reasonable guess would be what is represented in Figure II.8.

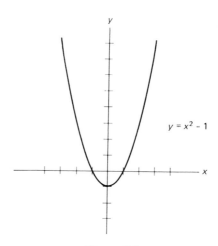

Figure II.8

Let us add a word of caution. The graph consists of a lot of points. These are to be peppered onto the graph paper in the manner that a television tube sprays points on the glass screen to reproduce the contour of a face. Because of the limitations of our energy we have decided to obtain the graph by plotting a few points and then passing a "smooth curve" through them. This we do at our risk. Suppose the graph is not a smooth curve! Fortunately, nice simple functions have nice smooth graphs. However, an example will be given later of a nonsmooth graph (see Exercise 6).

We are now ready to define the graph of a function f.

The graph of the function f consists of all points $(x, f(x))$ in the Cartesian plane. Or, put another way:

The graph of the function defined by $x \mapsto f(x)$ consists of all points (x, y) in the Cartesian plane for which $y = f(x)$. In other words, it consists of all points $(x, f(x))$, where x is any number in the set **M** for which the function is defined.

EXAMPLE 1:   Find the graph of the function defined by $x \mapsto \sqrt{x}$.

SOLUTION: Write $y = \sqrt{x}$ and note that necessarily $x \geq 0$. A table of values of a few points on the graph is shown in Table II.3. We plot these in

Table II.3

x	0	1	2	3	4		9	
y	0	1	1.41	1.73	2		3	

Figure II.9. The estimate as to what the graph looks like is given in Figure II.10. We notice that the graph "goes on" to the right.

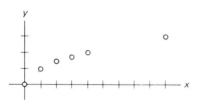

Figure II.9

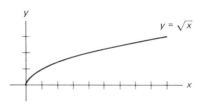

Figure II.10

EXAMPLE 2: Find the graph of the function defined by $x \mapsto 1/x$.

SOLUTION: Write $y = 1/x$. Note that all values of x are admissible except $x = 0$. This should be a warning signal. Note also that when x is very small, y is very large. We first make a chart of a few preliminary values; Table II.4.

Table II.4

x	1	2	3	4		-1	-2	-3	
y	1	$\frac{1}{2}$	$\frac{1}{3}$	$\frac{1}{4}$		-1	$-\frac{1}{2}$	$-\frac{1}{3}$	

Plotting these points, we obtain Figure II.11. Let us now include points close to 0 (the one excluded value of x). See Table II.5.

Table II.5

x	$\frac{1}{2}$	$\frac{1}{3}$	$\frac{1}{4}$		$-\frac{1}{2}$	$-\frac{1}{3}$	$-\frac{1}{4}$	
y	2	3	4		-2	-3	-4	

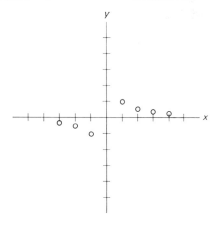

Figure II.11

These are plotted in Figure II.12. We have also indicated our guess as to what the entire graph should look like.

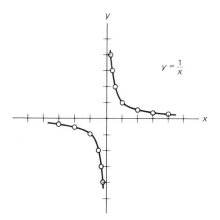

Figure II.12

EXAMPLE 3:   Find the graph of the function f defined as follows: If x is an integer, $f(x) = 1$; if x is not an integer, $f(x) = 2$.

SOLUTION: Without preparing a chart, it is clear that the graph consists partly of a collection of isolated points at height 1 above the x-axis and lying over the integral points on the x-axis, and partly of open line segments of length 1 lying at height 2 above the x-axis. The graph is shown in Figure II.13. Note that the method of drawing a smooth curve through a few points would be quite disastrous here.

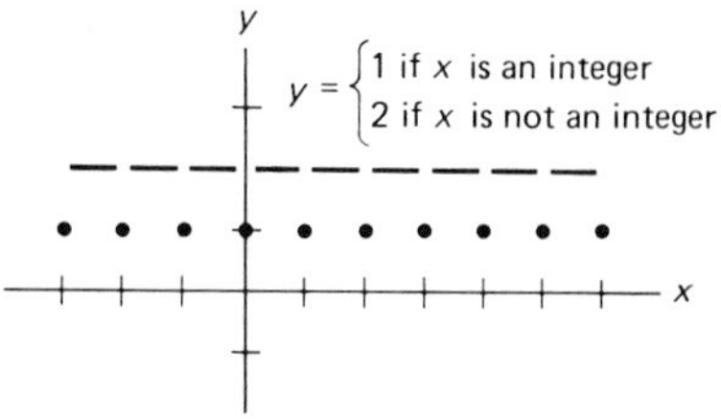

$$y = \begin{cases} 1 \text{ if } x \text{ is an integer} \\ 2 \text{ if } x \text{ is not an integer} \end{cases}$$

Figure II.13

Exercises II.3.a

1. Graph the following functions.

(a) $f(x) = x$;

(b) $f(x) = \dfrac{1}{2} x^2 + 1$;

(c) $f(x) = \dfrac{1}{x + 1}$;

(d) $f(x) = \dfrac{2}{x}$;

(e) $f(x) = \dfrac{1}{x} + 1$;

(f) $f(x) = \sqrt{x} - 1$;

(g) $f(x) = |x|$; that is $f(x) = x$ if $x \geq 0$, $f(x) = -x$ if $x < 0$;
(h) $f(x) = |x| + x$;
(i) $f(x) = |x| - x$;
(j) $f(x) = [x]$. This function is called the *greatest integer function* and is defined by: $[x]$ is the largest integer $\leq x$. Thus $[\sqrt{2}] = 1$ and $[5] = 5$.

2. Graph the functions.

(a) $h(x) = x^2 - 4$;

(b) $r(x) = \sqrt{x^2 - 4}$;

(c) $h(u) = \dfrac{1}{u^2 - 4}$ [graph on (u, v) axes];

(d) $s(x) = (x - 4)^2$;

(e) $g(u) = \sqrt{u^2 - 4}$;

(f) $s(t) = \dfrac{1}{t^2} - 4$.

3. Graph the functions.

(a) $f(x) = \sqrt{4 - x^2}$;

(b) $f(x) = -\sqrt{4 - x^2}$;

(c) $f(x) = \dfrac{2}{3}\sqrt{4 - x^2}$;

(d) $f(x) = \dfrac{3}{2}\sqrt{4 - x^2}$.

4. Graph the functions.

(a) $f(x) = x^3$;

(b) $f(x) = \dfrac{1}{x^3}$;

(c) $f(x) = \sqrt[3]{x}$;

(d) $f(x) = x^3 + 2$;

(e) $f(x) = \dfrac{1}{8} x^3$;

(f) $f(x) = x^4$.

5. Graph the function $\varphi(x) = 1/(1 + x^2)$.

6. A famous function in mathematics is the following: $f(x) = 1$ if x is a rational number; $f(x) = 0$ if x is an irrational number. Can you describe its graph in one or two sentences? *Note:* Drawing a smooth curve through a few points is fatal. Incidentally, this function can be expressed by a formula. This formula is of little value and is never used. The point here is that any "queerness" that the function possesses is not due to the fact that there is no formula for it. What makes the function different from the others so far is that it is *discontinuous* at every point. Example 3 concerns a function which is discontinuous at some points (the integral points).

7. The stopwatch function $f(t)$ is defined by $f(t) = 0$ if $t < 0$; $f(t) = t$ if t satisfies $0 \le t \le t_0$, where t_0 is some fixed constant; $f(t) = t_0$ for $t > t_0$. (That is, the stopwatch is turned on at $t = 0$ and turned off at $t = t_0$. Here t stands for "time.") Graph the function. [In a boxing match $t_0 = 3$ minutes (for one round) and $t_0 - f(t)$ represents the number of minutes left in the round at any time t.] Graph the function given by $t \mapsto t_0 - f(t)$.

8. A function of great usefulness is the following: $g(t) = 0$ if $t < 0$; $g(t) = 1$ if $0 \le t \le t_0$; $g(t) = 0$ if $t > t_0$. This function could be used to measure the flow of electricity in a wire if the current is turned on at $t = 0$ and turned off at $t = t_0$. Graph the function. Note that the stopwatch function above, multiplied by a suitable constant, would give an estimate of the electric expense incurred at any time t.

Historical Note. René Descartes (1596–1650), French philosopher, scientist, and mathematician, published his treatise "Geometry" as an appendix of a famous philosophical work "Discourse on Method ..." in 1637. It is common scientific lore that modern analytic geometry finds its birth in that book. However, none of the devices now present in all texts, such as rectangular axes and equations for simple loci, can be found in Descartes' treatise.

4. LINEAR POLYNOMIALS

We have met polynomial functions in the preceding section. We shall study the simplest type of such functions in this section and the next. The general theory of polynomials will be developed in the next chapter. What is of particular interest now is the graph of these functions. In the present section we shall consider functions defined by equations

$$y = c \qquad (c \text{ a constant}), \tag{1}$$

and

$$y = mx + b \qquad (m \text{ and } b \text{ constants}). \tag{2}$$

In the next section, we consider *quadratic* polynomials given by

$$y = ax^2 + bx + c. \tag{3}$$

The polynomial function f defined by $f(x) = ax^2 + bx + c$ where $a \neq 0$ is called a polynomial function of degree 2. The function f defined by $f(x) = mx + b$ where $m \neq 0$ is called a polynomial function of degree 1. The function f defined by $f(x) = c$ where $c \neq 0$ is called a polynomial function of degree 0. The question of assigning a degree to an arbitrary polynomial is a delicate one; it will be discussed fully in the next chapter. Meanwhile we shall use the language of degree for these three simple cases. Thus we are considering polynomials of degree 0, 1, and 2. In Equation (3) the constant a is called the *coefficient* of x^2. The constant b is the coefficient of x; and the constant c is called the *constant term*. Similar statements can be made relative to the constants m and b in (2).

Consider now a polynomial function f of degree 0. Thus there is a constant $c \neq 0$ such that for all $x, f(x) = c$. Write $y = c$. For the case $c = 3, y = 3$. The graph for this function is given in Figure II.14.

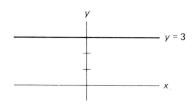

Figure II.14

In Figure II.15 the graph of $y = c$ is given for various values of c. The values of c are indicated near the graph in each case. A *family* of lines parallel to the x-axis is obtained. Note that the graph of $y = 0$ ($c = 0$) is the x-axis. Therefore, we see that:

The graph of a polynomial function of degree 0 is a line parallel to the x-axis. Every line parallel to the x-axis is the graph of a constant function.

This disposes completely of Equation (1).

Consider now Equation (2). We are given a function f such that $f(x) = mx + b$. Here m and b are constants. For example, if $m = 2$ and $b = -3$,

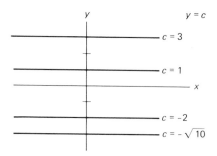

Figure II.15

Equation (2) becomes $y = 2x - 3$. Another special case is $m = 2$ and $b = 0$. This gives

$$y = 2x. \qquad (4)$$

We quickly make a chart of pairs (x, y) satisfying this equation. The graph is given in Figure II.16. The graph of $y = 2x$ is a line through the origin.

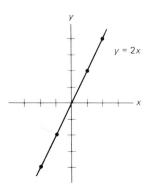

Figure II.16

Now consider the general equation

$$y = mx. \qquad (5)$$

It is not difficult to see that for each value of m, the graph of $y = mx$ is a line through the origin. The coefficient of x, namely m, is called the *slope* of the line. (For an explanation of the use of the word "slope," see the paragraph at the end of this section.) Thus the various values of m yield a family of lines through the origin. We indicate the graph of this family for a few values of m. See Figure II.17.

This shows that:

The graph of the polynomial function f given by $f(x) = mx$ is a line through the origin of slope m. Every line through the origin except the y-axis is the graph of such a function.

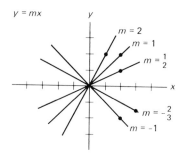

Figure II.17

This gives complete information on the graph of the function $y = mx + b$ for the case $b = 0$.

Suppose now that m has a fixed value, say $m = 2$. Let us allow b to assume several values and see what kind of family is obtained. For example, let $b = -3$. We start with the graph of $y = 2x$ which is given in Figure II.16. To find the graph of $y = 2x - 3$, we take the graph of $y = 2x$ and lower it 3 units. Thus, the points $(0, 0)$, $(1, 2)$, $(2, 4)$ are on the graph of $y = 2x$; the points $(0, -3)$, $(1, -1)$, $(2, 1)$ are on the graph of $y = 2x - 3$. This is easy to check in the equations. The result is shown in Figure II.18. Note that whereas the graph of $y = 2x$ crosses the y-axis at $(0, 0)$, the graph of $y = 2x - 3$ crosses the y-axis at $(0, -3)$.

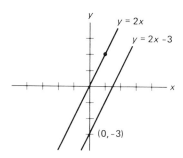

Figure II.18

Now we can consider the graph of the family $y = 2x + b$. This is shown in Figure II.19 for various values of b. This family is a family of parallel lines having slope 2. The line $y = 2x + b$ crosses the y-axis at the point $(0, b)$. That point is called the y-intercept of the line.

Suppose now that one considers the value b to be fixed, say $b = 2$, and let m vary. This gives a family of lines all passing through the point $(0, 2)$. The graph is shown in Figure II.20. Note that each line passing through $(0, 2)$ is the graph of $y = mx + 2$ for some value of m, with the exception of the y-axis.

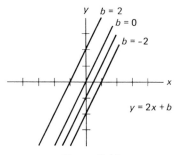

Figure II.19

We are now ready to recapitulate our information concerning the equation $y = mx + b$, that is, concerning a polynomial function of degree 1.

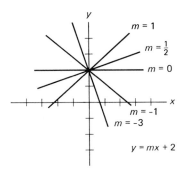

Figure II.20

II–1 Theorem
The graph of the equation

$$y = mx + b, \tag{6}$$

or equivalently, the graph of the polynomial function f for which $f(x) = mx + b$, is a line of slope m passing through the point $(0, b)$. Each line except the y-axis which passes through the points $(0, b)$ is the graph of such an equation.

Because of the properties just enunciated, Equation (6) is called a *linear equation* and a polynomial function f for which $f(x) = mx + b$ is called a *linear polynomial*. Note that a line which is not parallel to the y-axis crosses the y-axis at some point which may be denoted by $(0, b)$. Thus all lines not parallel to the y-axis have an equation of the form (6).

On the other hand, the lines parallel to the y-axis are not the graphs of any function. This can be seen as follows. Take a line parallel to the y-axis, say the line passing through $(4, 0)$. If this line were the graph of a function f, then for $x = 4$, we would have exactly one point $(4, f(4))$ on the graph. However, all the points $(4, 0)$, $(4, 1)$, $(4, 2)$, and so on, are on the graph. This gives a contradiction. The lines parallel to the y-axis can be described by equations. For example, the line parallel to the y-axis passing through $(4, 0)$ is described by the equation $x = 4$. If a represents a constant, then the equation $x = a$ is the equation of a line parallel to the y-axis passing through the point $(a, 0)$. The family of these lines is shown in Figure II.21.

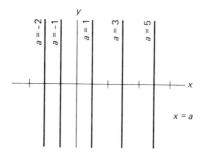

Figure II.21

Note that the equation of the y-axis is $x = 0$.

A general problem concerning lines is the following: Suppose certain information is given concerning a line which determines it. Let it be required to find the equation of the line. The information may be of various kinds. We treat below some cases of this problem. The technique is to assume that the equation is of type (6) and then to compute the value of m and b.

(a) Let the given line have slope 3 and pass through the point $(2, -1)$. Note that $m = 3$. Thus the equation is

$$y = 3x + b \tag{7}$$

for some value of b. To find b, substitute $(2, -1)$ in (7). This gives $-1 = 3 \times 2 + b$; hence $b = -7$. The desired equation is therefore

$$y = 3x - 7. \tag{8}$$

(b) Let the given line pass through the points $(1, 4)$ and $(6, -1)$. Substituting $(1, 4)$ in Equation (6) yields

$$4 = m + b. \tag{9}$$

Next substituting $(6, -1)$ in (6) yields

$$-1 = 6m + b. \tag{10}$$

Equations (9) and (10) may be solved for m and b. This gives $m = -1$, $b = 5$. Thus the desired equation is

$$y = -x + 5. \tag{11}$$

(c) Let the given line have intercepts a and b. This means that the points $(a, 0)$ and $(0, b)$ are on the line. Thus this problem can be solved by the method of the preceding example. However, the problem is more complicated since the given information is given in general form; it does not specify the values of a and b. The answer may be written in the form

$$\frac{x}{a} + \frac{y}{b} = 1. \tag{12}$$

Note that (12) is a linear equation (solve for y) and that $(a, 0)$ and $(0, b)$ satisfy it. Thus (12) is the desired equation. Note that it has been assumed that $a \neq 0$ and $b \neq 0$.

A comment about the reason for calling m in $y = mx$ the slope of the line. The exact reason for using this word will be clear later when we take up elementary trigonometry. However, the reasonableness of the use of the word can be seen from the following. Consider the equation $y = mx$ for the values $m = \frac{1}{2}, m = 1, m = 2$ (see Figure II.17). If $y = \frac{1}{2}x$, then as "x moves to the right," "y moves up" one half as fast. If $y = 2x$, as "x moves to the right," "y moves up" twice as fast. Thus the line $y = 2x$ is steeper than the line $y = \frac{1}{2}x$. In fact, its slope is much larger. The above explanation uses language of suggestive imagery. In fact x doesn't move, nor does y.

Exercises II.4.a

1. Graph the following pairs of points and the line they determine. Find an equation for each line.

(a) $(0, 0), (2, 3)$; (b) $(0, 0), (-2, 0)$;
(c) $(0, 0), (-7, 2)$; (d) $(0, 0), (c, d), \quad c \neq 0$;
(e) $(0, 0), (-3, -4)$; (f) $(0, 0), (c, 3c), \quad c \neq 0$;
(g) $(0, 0), (x_0, y_0), \quad x_0 \neq 0$.

2. Do the same as Exercise 1 for the pairs of points below.

(a) $(-1, -1), (2, -1)$; (b) $(3, 0), (0, 6)$;
(c) $(-1, -1), (2, 2)$; (d) $(-1, 1), (1, -1)$;
(e) $(0, 1), (2, 0)$; (f) $(c, 2c), (2c, c), \quad c \neq 0$;
(g) $(c, d), (-c, -d), \quad c \neq 0$; (h) $(c, d), (d, c), \quad c \neq 0$.

3. Sketch the graphs of the first degree polynomial functions defined below.

(a) $f(x) = 2x + 3$; (b) $h(x) = 2x - 3$;
(c) $f(x) = -2x + 3$; (d) $\varphi(x) = \frac{1}{2}x - 3$;
(e) $f(x) = 4x$; (f) $g(x) = -3x$;
(g) $f(x) + x = 0$.

4. The rate of exchange of French francs into U.S. dollars (in 1968) was 4.9 francs to the dollar. If d is the number of dollars and f is the equivalent number of francs in a given sum, find an expression for f in terms of d; for d in terms of f. Graph the two functions thus found. In the first half of 1971, the rate of exchange was 5.1 francs to the dollar. Find expressions for f in terms of d and d in terms of f.

5. There are two famous temperature scales, Fahrenheit and Centigrade. If F and C represent the number of degrees in each scale, the relation between them is

$$F = 32 + \tfrac{9}{5} C.$$

Graph this curve on the C–F axes. Solve the above for C in terms of F. Graph the result on the F–C axes.

   If $C = 100$, what is F? Same for $C = 0$. At what temperature do we have $C = F$? $C = -F$? A traveler in Europe caught cold. His temperature was $C = 40$. Was he really ill?

6. The gravity on the moon is about $\tfrac{1}{6}$ of what it is on earth. If w_E represents the weight of a man on earth as determined by a spring balance, and w_M represents his weight on the moon, what is the relation between w_M and w_E? Assuming that a 50-lb pack is the maximum pack a given man should carry on the earth, how heavy a pack might he carry on the moon?

7. In the text a proof is given that a line parallel to the y-axis is not the graph of any function. Give a second proof of this fact.

8. On certain airplane flights, the baggage charge is as follows: The first 44 pounds are free. The excess weight beyond 44 pounds costs $2.00 a pound. Obtain a formula for the cost c in terms of the weight w which is valid for $w \geq 44$. Obtain a second formula for the cost c which is valid for $0 \leq w \leq 44$.

9. The following gives examples of the function $y = mx$.

   (1) If $1.00 is put into a savings bank giving 5 percent per year (not compounded), then the interest after t years is $I = 0.05t$. Here $m = 0.05$ and is called the rate of interest.
   (2) If a mountain climber in the Swiss Alps climbs vertically 300 feet an hour, then the height h climbed in t hours is $h = 300t$. Here $m = 300$ and is called the rate of climb.
   (3) In a supermarket the price of a certain cut of meat is $1.25 per pound. The price p is therefore given by $p = 1.25x$ where x is the weight in pounds. Here $m = 1.25$ and is called the unit price.

   Give three further examples leading to the equation $y = mx$ and indicate the name applied to m in each case.

10. The following gives an example of a *piecewise linear function*. In a certain state, income taxes are levied on taxable income as indicated below:

> From $0 to $1000 taxed at 1 percent.
> From $1000 to $3000, $10 plus 3 percent of the excess over $1000.
> From $3000 to $5000, $70 plus 5 percent of the excess over $3000.
> Above $5000, $170 plus 7 percent of the excess over $5000.

Graph the tax against income curve (use appropriate scales). Find the equation of the line giving the tax in each of the intervals given above.

5. QUADRATIC POLYNOMIALS

Having studied polynomials of degree 0 and 1 in the preceding section, we turn to polynomials of degree 2, also called *quadratic polynomials*. A polynomial function f of degree 2 is defined by

$$f(x) = ax^2 + bx + c, \qquad a \neq 0. \tag{1}$$

We may write the function in the form

$$y = ax^2 + bx + c. \tag{2}$$

We are interested in determining the graph corresponding to Equations (1) or (2).

Just as in the preceding section, the study is begun by considering special cases. Suppose to begin with that $b = 0$ and $c = 0$. This gives $y = ax^2$. The case $a = 1$ gives $y = x^2$. This curve is easily graphed. The graph is given in Figure II.22.

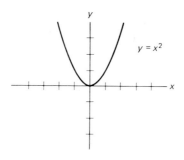

Figure II.22

Next, proceed with the equation

$$y = ax^2. \tag{3}$$

Giving a the values 1, 2, $\frac{1}{2}$, $\frac{1}{4}$, -1, -2, and so on, one obtains a family of curves shown in Figure II.23. These curves are called parabolas. Note that if

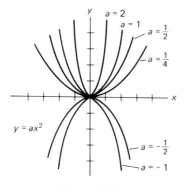

Figure II.23

$a > 0$ the parabolas open upward. In this case each curve has a *minimum* at $x = 0$. If $a < 0$ the parabolas open downward. In this case, the curves have a *maximum* at $x = 0$.

Parabolas not only have simple equations but also arise in many situations in nature in physical phenomena. Notice that all these parabolas are *symmetric* with respect to the y-axis. This means that if the point (x, y) is on the parabola, so is the point $(-x, y)$. For example, in the case of the curve $y = 3x^2$ the points $(1, 3)$ and $(-1, 3)$ are both on the curve. The same is true of $(2, 12)$ and $(-2, 12)$. The graph of the parabola may be obtained by first considering points (x, y) on the curve for which $x > 0$; then by taking the mirror image in the y-axis of the points so obtained.

Next consider Equation (2) for the case $b = 0$. This gives

$$y = ax^2 + c. \tag{4}$$

Suppose first that $a = \frac{1}{4}$ and $c = -3$. This gives $y = \frac{1}{4}x^2 - 3$. The graph of $y = \frac{1}{4}x^2$ is indicated in Figure II.23. To obtain the graph of $y = \frac{1}{4}x^2 - 3$ it is simply necessary to lower the graph of $y = \frac{1}{4}x^2$ by 3 units. The result is shown in Figure II.24.

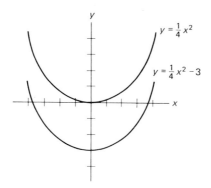

Figure II.24

As further special cases of (3) consider

$$y = \tfrac{1}{4}x^2 + c, \tag{5}$$

$$y = ax^2 - 3. \tag{6}$$

The graphs in these cases for various values of c and a are obtained as follows. In the case (5), we take the graph of $y = \tfrac{1}{4}x^2$ and raise or lower it so as to pass through the point $(0, c)$. The result is shown in Figure II.25.

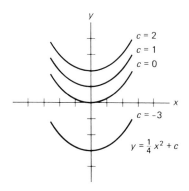

Figure II.25

The graph of (6) is obtained by lowering the entire family of curves $y = ax^2$ given in Figure II.23 by 3 units. The result is shown in Figure II.26.

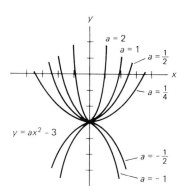

Figure II.26

Note that each parabola in Figure II.25 has a minimum at $x = 0$. The value of y at this point is c. In Figure II.26, the parabolas for which $a > 0$ have a minimum at $x = 0$; those for which $a < 0$ have a maximum at $x = 0$.

Consideration of the special cases just discussed leads to the following conclusions concerning the graph of Equation (4), namely, $y = ax^2 + c$.

The graph of Equation (3) *is symmetric with respect to the y-axis. If a* > 0
the graph has a minimum at x $= 0$; *the minimum value is y* $= c$. *If a* < 0, *the
graph has a maximum at x* $= 0$; *the maximum value is y* $= c$.

Exercises II.5.a

1. Sketch the graph of the following quadratic functions. Indicate maximum
   and minimum points.

   (a) $f(x) = 4x^2$;   (b) $g(t) = -9t^2$;
   (c) $h(x) = x^2 - 4$;   (d) $f(x) = 2x^2 + 4$;
   (e) $k(u) = -2u^2 - 3$ [use (u, v) axes];   (f) $k(u) = -\sqrt{2}u^2 + 3$.

2. A tourist drops a stone from the top of the Leaning Tower of Pisa and
   times its fall to the ground: 3.3 seconds. His friend, who is a physicist, tells
   him that the distance in feet fallen by a given object equals 16.1 times the
   square of the time of fall in seconds. The tourist correctly computes the
   height of the famous tower. What is it?

3. The same physicist remarks that the period of a pendulum (time in
   seconds required for a full swing back and forth) is given by

$$T = 2\pi \sqrt{\frac{l}{32.2}},$$

   where l is the length of the pendulum in feet. Find the length in feet and in
   inches of the pendulum of a grandfather clock (such a clock beats seconds
   and hence has a period of 2 seconds). While the tourist in Problem 2 was
   inside the Pisa Cathedral, he noted that a workman fixing a chandelier
   hanging from the dome gave it a slight oscillating motion. The period of
   the chandelier was 11.2 seconds. The tourist calculates the length of the
   chain suspending it from the dome and finds it is 100 feet. Is this correct?
   Why was this exercise inserted into this section?

   The chandelier is very famous as a work of art. Tradition has it that
   Galileo (1564–1642) discovered the physical law given in the equation
   above by watching its oscillations. It is thought now that the discovery of
   the law predates the making of the lamp in 1587.

4. It is shown in geometry that if a slide is projected on a screen the area of
   the picture on the screen is proportional to the square of the distance of
   the screen to the source of light. A teacher showing slides starts with his
   projector at a distance of 15 feet from the screen. He wants to triple the
   size of his image. At what distance from the screen should he place his
   projector?

5. Let k and m represent positive constants. Find the positive number x_0 such that $kx_0^2 = mx_0$. Show that if $x > x_0$, then $kx^2 > mx$. If $x < x_0$ (and $x > 0$) then $kx^2 < mx$. Draw on one set of axes the graph of $f(x) = kx^2$ and $g(x) = mx$. What are the coordinates of the point of intersection of the two graphs?

6. A driver training agency, in trying to impress on its students the hazards of fast driving, asserts that the stopping distance (when you slam on the brakes) of a car going 60 miles per hour is 4 times the stopping distance for that car going 30 miles per hour. If v represents the speed of the car and s represents the stopping distance, what is the expression for s in terms of v that the agency probably has in mind? From this expression compare stopping distances between 50 miles an hour and 20 miles an hour.

Before considering the general polynomial function of degree 2, we wish to study one more special family. Suppose that in the equation $y = x^2$ we make a slight variation and consider $y = (x - 1)^2$. What happens to the graph? Then again, further variations give $y = (x - 2)^2$, $y = (x - 3)^2$, $y = (x + 1)^2$, and so on. Notice that all these equations arise from polynomial functions of degree 2. For example, $y = (x + 1)^2$ is the same as $y = x^2 + 2x + 1$. In general, we wish to consider the family

$$y = (x - h)^2, \tag{7}$$

where h is some constant. For $h = 2$ the curve is given in Figure II.27. Notice that the curve obtained is the same as that for $y = x^2$ except that the latter has been moved over 2 units to the right. Thus the points $(-1, 1), (0, 0), (1, 1)$ which satisfy $y = x^2$ give rise to the points $(1, 1), (2, 0), (3, 1)$ which satisfy $y = (x - 2)^2$.

The graph of (7) is given in Figure II.28 for several values of h.

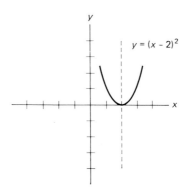

$y = (x - 2)^2$

Figure II.27

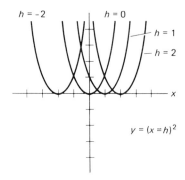

$h = -2$ $h = 0$

$h = 1$

$h = 2$

x

$y = (x = h)^2$

Figure II.28

The situation can be described in words as follows: The graph of $y = (x - h)^2$ can be obtained from that of $y = x^2$ by shifting the y-axis. If $h > 0$ it is shifted to the left by h units. If $h < 0$, it is shifted to the right by $|h|$ units.

We are ready now to consider the graph of the general polynomial function of the second degree. That is, we have to treat the equation

$$y = ax^2 + bx + c, \qquad a \neq 0. \tag{8}$$

We have already seen above that the graph of $y = ax^2 + c$ can be obtained from the graph of $y = ax^2$ by "moving the x-axis" up or down a suitable distance. We shall see below that we can "eliminate" the term bx in (6) by "moving the y-axis" left or right a suitable distance.

To begin with, consider the example

$$y = 2x^2 - 4x - 1. \tag{9}$$

We write below some equations that should be checked.

$$2x^2 - 4x - 1 = 2(x^2 - 2x) - 1; \tag{10}$$

$$2(x^2 - 2x) - 1 = 2(x^2 - 2x + 1) - 3; \tag{11}$$

$$2(x^2 - 2x + 1) - 3 = 2(x - 1)^2 - 3. \tag{12}$$

Thus (10), (11), and (12) lead to

$$2x^2 - 4x - 1 = 2(x - 1)^2 - 3. \tag{13}$$

Hence one may write (9) in the form

$$y = 2(x - 1)^2 - 3. \tag{14}$$

The operations occurring in (10) to (12) are called *completing the square*. They are very important in the study of quadratic expressions.

We make a slight digression. Experience in completing squares is first obtained in a course in intermediate algebra. The method is probably met in a slightly different context, that of solving a quadratic equation. In order to tie our present problem and the quadratic equation problem together, we present the latter.

Let it be required to find all x such that

$$2x^2 - 4x - 1 = 0.$$

Write

$$2x^2 - 4x = 1.$$

Then

$$2(x^2 - 2x) = 1.$$

Hence

$$2(x^2 - 2x + 1) = 1 + 2 = 3.$$

Thus

$$2(x - 1)^2 = 3.$$

This gives

$$(x - 1)^2 = \frac{3}{2},$$

or

$$x - 1 = \pm\sqrt{\frac{3}{2}} = \pm\frac{1}{2}\sqrt{6}.$$

Thus

$$x = 1 \pm \frac{1}{2}\sqrt{6} = \frac{2 \pm \sqrt{6}}{2}.$$

From this it is apparent that the steps in completing the square are the same in both problems. From this discussion it results that the function given in (9) is nothing but the function $y = 2(x - 1)^2 - 3$ in disguise. We know how to graph the function $y = 2x^2 - 3$. Its graph is given in Figure II.29(a).

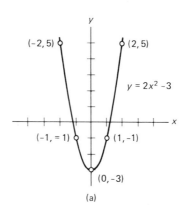

(a)

Figure II.29(a)

How is our original function in (9) related to this one? Clearly, by having the role of x in the latter replaced by $x - 1$ in the former. This may be stated in another way: We obtain the graph of $y = 2(x - 1)^2 - 3$ from that of $y = 2x^2 - 3$ by shifting the y-axis to the left by 1 unit. This gives Figure II.29(b).

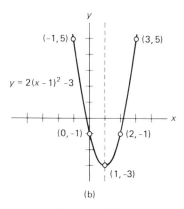

(b)

Figure II.29(b)

The situation in Figure II.29 can be seen as follows. Suppose one writes

$$u = x - 1. \tag{15}$$

Then the equation $y = 2(x - 1)^2 - 3$ becomes $y = 2u^2 - 3$. The first equation is graphed with the help of x, y-axes; the second is graphed with the help of u, y-axes. The sets of axes are shown in Figure II.30.

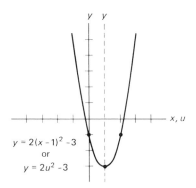

Figure II.30

Let us try one more example. Graph the curve

$$y = -2x^2 + 6x - 5. \tag{16}$$

Completing the square as above gives

$$-2x^2 + 6x - 5 = -2(x^2 - 3x) - 5$$

$$= -2\left(x^2 - 3x + \frac{9}{4}\right) - 5 + \frac{9}{2} \tag{17}$$

$$= -2\left(x - \frac{3}{2}\right)^2 - \frac{1}{2}.$$

Now, the graph of $y = -2x^2 - \frac{1}{2}$ is found easily [Figure II.31(a)]. Thus we obtain the graph of (16) by appropriately shifting the y-axis. The result is given in Figure II.31(b).

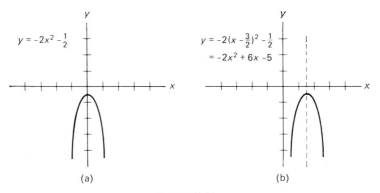

(a)   (b)

Figure II.31

Consider now the general polynomial function of the second degree. It is given by

$$y = ax^2 + bx + c \qquad \text{with} \qquad a \neq 0. \tag{18}$$

Let us complete the square:

$$ax^2 + bx + c = a\left(x^2 + \frac{b}{a}x\right) + c$$

$$= a\left(x^2 + \frac{b}{a}x + \frac{b^2}{4a^2}\right) + c - \frac{b^2}{4a} \tag{19}$$

$$= a\left(x + \frac{b}{2a}\right)^2 + \frac{4ac - b^2}{4a}.$$

We write this in the form

$$y = a\left[x - \left(-\frac{b}{2a}\right)\right]^2 + \frac{4ac - b^2}{4a}. \tag{20}$$

Now, the graph of this function is not difficult to find. In the first place, it is a parabola since its equation reads

$$y = a(x - h)^2 + k, \tag{21}$$

where

$$h \quad \text{stands for} \quad -\frac{b}{2a} \quad \text{and} \quad k \quad \text{stands for} \quad \frac{4ac - b^2}{4a}.$$

To find the graph of this function, we first graph $y = ax^2 + k$ and then shift the y-axis to the left by the quantity $h = -b/2a$ [*Note:* We are assuming that $h > 0$. If $h < 0$, we shift to the right by the quantity $-h$.] Thus the x-coordinate of the vertex of the parabola is given by $x = -b/2a$.

For reasons that will shortly be apparent, the quantity

$$b^2 - 4ac \tag{22}$$

is very important in the theory of quadratic functions. Since it discriminates among many types of behavior, it is called the *discriminant* of the function. It is represented by the symbol Δ, which is the Greek capital D. Thus by definition,

$$\Delta = b^2 - 4ac. \tag{23}$$

In any given case, there are three possibilities for Δ:

$$(1) \ \Delta = 0,$$
$$(2) \ \Delta < 0,$$
$$(3) \ \Delta > 0.$$

As for a, we have two possibilities, namely, $a > 0$ and $a < 0$. Thus there seem to be 2×3, that is, 6 types of quadratic functions. We shall see that this is so and we shall obtain complete information about these 6 types. Remember that if $a > 0$ the parabola opens upward; if $a < 0$ the parabola opens downward (see Figures II.23 and II.26).

Consider first case (1): $\Delta = 0$. Since $y = a(x - h)^2 - \Delta/4a$ and since $\Delta = 0$,

$$y = a(x - h)^2, \tag{24}$$

where, of course, $h = -b/2a$. If $a > 0$ the graph of this is a parabola opening upward with a minimum at $x = h$. The point $(h, 0)$ is the lowest point of the parabola.

If $a < 0$, our parabola opens downward and has the point $(h, 0)$ as its highest point. These two cases are graphed in Figure II.32.

Now consider case (2): $\Delta < 0$. As before,

$$y = a(x - h)^2 - \frac{\Delta}{4a}. \tag{25}$$

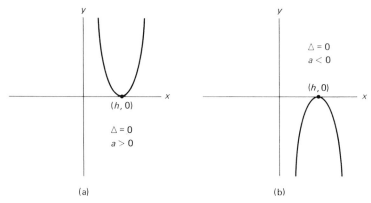

Figure II.32

This gives

$$\frac{y}{a} = (x - h)^2 - \frac{\Delta}{4a^2}.$$ (26)

Now, for all x, one has $(x - h)^2 \geq 0$. Since $\Delta < 0$, we also have $-\Delta/4a^2 > 0$. Thus for all x, we have $y/a > 0$.

If $a > 0$, then $y > 0$ for all x and the parabola lies strictly above the x-axis. If $a < 0$, the parabola lies strictly below the x-axis. These two cases are graphed in Figure II.33.

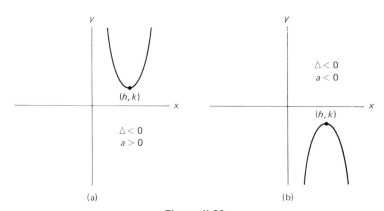

Figure II.33

Consider finally case (3): $\Delta > 0$. Suppose $a > 0$. As before,

$$y = a(x - h)^2 - \frac{\Delta}{4a}.$$ (27)

Since $a > 0$, the parabola opens upward. For $x = h$, we have $y < 0$. This implies that the parabola crosses the x-axis at two distinct points. If $a < 0$

we have a similar result except that the parabola opens downward. These two cases are graphed in Figure II.34.

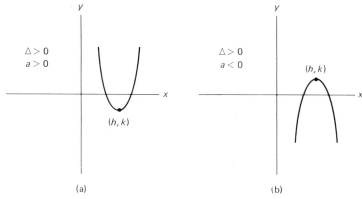

(a)　　　　　　　　　　　　　　　　(b)

Figure II.34

It should be noted that the six cases discussed have different graphs. Thus, if we know the graph, we can determine under which of the six cases it falls. For example, if we note that the graph of the given function looks like that in Figure II.34(b), then $\Delta > 0$ and $a < 0$.

In drawing the graphs in Figures II.32, II.33, and II.34, we have assumed $h > 0$. Naturally, if $h < 0$ the vertex of the parabola appears to the left of the y-axis. See also Table II.6.

Exercises II.5.b

1. Calculate the value of Δ for Problems 1(a), (b), (c), (d), (e), (f) of Exercises II.5.a.

2. Calculate the value of Δ in each of the following cases. Complete the square as was done in the text. Sketch the graphs in each case. Indicate maxima and minima.

   (a) $f(x) = x^2 - 4x + 4$;　　　　(b) $g(x) = -4x^2 - 12x - 9$;
   (c) $\psi(x) = 2x^2 + 2x + 1$;　　　(d) $s(t) = -3t^2 + t - 3$;
   (e) $f(x) = x^2 + x - 1$;　　　　(f) $h(u) = -2u^2 + 4u - 2$;
   (g) $f(x) = x^2 + 4$;　　　　　　(h) $\varphi(t) = t^2 + \sqrt{2}t - 3$;
   (i) $f(x) = -\sqrt{3}x^2 + 3x - 2$;　(j) $g(x) = 2(x - 4)^2 + 3$.

3. If $f(x) = x^2 - 2cx + 1$, determine for what values of c we have $\Delta = 0$, $\Delta > 0$, $\Delta < 0$. Graph the curve for the values: $c = -2, -1, 0, 1, 2$.

4. A scientist knows that one of his experimental curves comes from a function $f(x) = ax^2 + bx + c$. He has three points on the curve: $(0, 3.2)$,

(1, 3.7), (−2, 6.4). Find the values of a, b, c. [*Hint:* Substitute the three points in the equation, obtaining three equations in three unknowns.]

5. Suppose that it is known for a function f that it is of the form $f(x) = c(x - h)^2$ and that it passes through two points (5, 8) and (2, 2). Find c and h.

6. Graph on the same set of axes several members of the family of curves $y = a(x - a)^2$.

Table II.6   Table of Quadratic Functions

$$y = ax^2 + bx + c, \qquad a \neq 0,$$

$$\Delta = b^2 - 4ac, \qquad h = -\frac{b}{2a}, \qquad k = -\frac{\Delta}{4a}.$$

6. MAXIMUM AND MINIMUM PROBLEMS

We shall apply some of the ideas explained above to the solving of a certain class of problems called maximum-minimum problems. In these problems some data is given leading to a function f. It is required to find the value of x which renders $f(x)$ a maximum or a minimum, depending on the problem at hand. If, for example, $f(x) = ax^2 + bx + c$, and $a > 0$, then $x = -b/2a$ gives a minimum. This minimum is positive, zero, or negative depending on whether Δ is negative, zero, or positive.

Let us consider two examples:

EXAMPLE 1: A boy throws a stone vertically into the air. A physicist who watches him says that the distance of the stone in feet above the ground is given by

$$s = 48t - 16t^2, \tag{1}$$

where t is given in seconds measured from the time the stone is thrown. How high does the stone rise in the air?

SOLUTION: We are confronted with a polynomial function of the second degree, $s = at^2 + bt + c$ with $a = -16$, $b = 48$, and $c = 0$. The graph comes under the case of Figure II.34, $a < 0$, $\Delta = 48^2 - 4 \cdot 0 \cdot (-16) = 48^2 > 0$. Thus the maximum height is obtained at $t = -b/2a = 48/32 = 3/2$. This height is (in feet)

$$s_{max} = 48 \times \frac{3}{2} - 16 \times \frac{9}{4} = 72 - 36 = 36 \tag{2}$$

(not a bad throw!). The graph is given in Figure II.35. Note that for reasons of convenience we choose different units on the s- and t-axes.

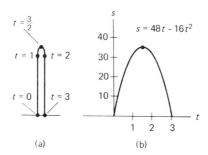

(a) (b)

Figure II.35

EXAMPLE 2: A piece of wood is in the form of a right triangle of sides 16 and 32 inches. A rectangular piece is to be cut out of this, one corner of the rectangle being at the right angle of the piece of wood. Find the area of the maximum rectangle that can be so cut.

SOLUTION: Figure II.36 indicates the situation. The hypotenuse of the triangle is represented by a line passing through the points (0, 16) and (32, 0).

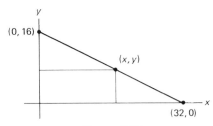

Figure II.36

A point (x, y) on this line represents a possible point for cutting the rectangle. If the area of the rectangle in square inches is A, then

$$A = x \cdot y. \tag{3}$$

We now find the equation of the line. We know that it is the graph of a polynomial function of the first degree. Let the function be given by

$$y = mx + b. \tag{4}$$

Then our previous discussion of these functions (see Section 4) indicates that $b = 16$. Thus $y = mx + 16$. To find m, substitute $(32, 0)$ in this equation. This gives $0 = 32m + 16$ or $m = -\frac{1}{2}$. Hence the equation of the line is

$$y = 16 - \frac{1}{2} x. \tag{5}$$

This gives

$$A = xy = x\left(16 - \frac{1}{2} x\right) = 16x - \frac{1}{2} x^2. \tag{6}$$

A is therefore represented by a polynomial function of the second degree with the coefficient of x^2 negative. Calculation of the discriminant Δ gives $\Delta = 16^2 > 0$. Thus we are dealing with the case given in Figure II.34(b). The value of x giving a maximum is $x = -16/2(-\frac{1}{2}) = 16$, so the maximum area is given by

$$A_{max} = 16 \times 16 - \frac{1}{2} 16^2 = 16 \times 8 = 128.$$

The graph is shown in Figure II.37. Again, we choose different scales on the two axes.

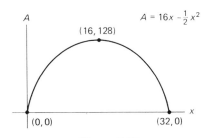

Figure II.37

Exercises II.6.a

1. A ball is thrown vertically upward, leaving the thrower's hand with a velocity of 64 feet per second. The distance traveled in feet is described by

$$s = 64t - 16t^2,$$

where t is the time in seconds. What is the maximum height the ball reaches and at what time does it reach this height? How many seconds elapse before the ball reaches the ground again?

2. If a rectangle has a perimeter of 32 feet what should its dimensions be in order that its area be a maximum? What is the maximum area?
   Solve the same problem if the perimeter is p.

3. A rectangular playground is to be laid out with one side along a river. The other three sides are to be fenced in with 1000 feet of fence. Find the dimensions of the playground if its area is to be a maximum.

4. A little boy discovers that although eating ice cream is pleasant, nevertheless the total amount of pleasure derived during a given eating session does not increase linearly with the quantity. In fact, maximum pleasure arises from a quantity just one half of that quantity n which begins to produce nausea. Show how a quadratic function $p(x) = ax^2 + bx + c$ can adequately represent the quantity of pleasure in terms of the quantity of ice cream x and obtain the value of c and the ratio b/a from the point of nausea. Show that in this problem $\Delta > 0$ and $a < 0$ (naturally $b > 0$ for little boys).

5. A budding rock singer was convinced by his press agent and his astrologer that the average number n of fan letters received daily by him could be given by a quadratic expression $n = at^2 + bt$, where t denotes the time in years after the start of his career (thus $t = 0$ gives $n = 0$). Suppose that at the end of the first year ($t = 1$) he receives 70 letters daily and that at the end of the second year he receives 120 letters daily. Find out when he will be at the maximum of his career as measured by fan mail. Find out in which year he will once more be a forgotten man.

7. SOME FAMOUS INEQUALITIES

In this section we shall use results developed in the preceding two sections to establish some famous inequalities. The first of these is known as the Cauchy Inequality. Other mathematicians who contributed essentially to its early development were Schwarz and Buniakowsky.

   A mathematician would claim that the Cauchy Inequality is very innocent looking and that its proof is very simple. Yet it is one of the most important inequalities in mathematics. It is the nerve center of Euclidean geometry because of its intimate relation to the Pythagorean Theorem. It furnishes the mathematical background for important branches of physics and statistics.

To get into the subject matter, let us state the inequality for a simple case: Consider two pairs of real numbers:

$$c_1, c_2 \quad \text{and} \quad d_1, d_2. \tag{1}$$

Then the inequality asserts that

$$(c_1 d_1 + c_2 d_2)^2 \le (c_1^2 + c_2^2)(d_1^2 + d_2^2). \tag{2}$$

This is the Cauchy Inequality in the simplest case. Note carefully the interplay of the four numbers in (2). We could also indicate under what conditions we have "$=$" instead of "$\le$" in (2). We shall look at this in a moment.

As an example, consider the two pairs of real numbers 1, 2 and 5, 6. Then as may be easily verified, it is true that

$$(1 \times 5 + 2 \times 6)^2 \le (1^2 + 2^2)(5^2 + 6^2). \tag{3}$$

The inequality in general form concerns n-tuples of numbers. Pairs, triples, quadruples, quintuples, and so on are all special cases of n-tuples; namely, they are the cases $n = 2, n = 3, n = 4, n = 5$, and so on. A general n-tuple is written:

$$c_1, c_2, \cdots, c_n. \tag{4}$$

[*Read:* c one, c two, and so on up to c n. Or, if you prefer: c sub one, c sub two, and so on up to c sub n.] We now state:

II–2 Cauchy Inequality
Let

$$c_1, c_2, \cdots, c_n \quad \text{and} \quad d_1, d_2, \cdots, d_n \tag{5}$$

be any two n-tuples of real numbers. Then

$$(c_1 d_1 + c_2 d_2 + \cdots + c_n d_n)^2 \le (c_1^2 + c_2^2 + \cdots + c_n^2)(d_1^2 + d_2^2 + \cdots + d_n^2). \tag{6}$$

To simplify the notation, we shall give the proof for the case $n = 3$. We are given two triples of numbers c_1, c_2, c_3, and d_1, d_2, d_3. If the numbers d_1, d_2, d_3 are all 0, the inequality is trivial. It will be assumed that they are not all 0.

Let x be a real variable and consider the expression

$$y = (c_1 - d_1 x)^2 + (c_2 - d_2 x)^2 + (c_3 - d_3 x)^2. \tag{7}$$

Note first that for all x each of the three parentheses in (7) represents a positive number or 0; thus $y \ge 0$ because y is the sum of three numbers which are positive or zero. Note also that if $y = 0$ for some number x, then each of the parentheses in the expression for y is zero. Thus $c_1 - d_1 x = 0$ with two similar expressions. That is,

$$\text{if } y = 0, \text{ then } c_1 = d_1 x, \qquad c_2 = d_2 x, \qquad c_3 = d_3 x. \tag{8}$$

If we expand the parentheses in the expression for y in (7) and collect terms of the same degree in x, we obtain

$$y = (d_1^2 + d_2^2 + d_3^2)x^2 - 2(c_1 d_1 + c_2 d_2 + c_3 d_3)x + (c_1^2 + c_2^2 + c_3^2). \tag{9}$$

Thus we see that y is a quadratic expression in x of the type $y = ax^2 + bx + c$ where

$$\begin{aligned} a &= d_1^2 + d_2^2 + d_3^2, \\ b &= -2(c_1 d_1 + c_2 d_2 + c_3 d_3), \\ c &= c_1^2 + c_2^2 + c_3^2. \end{aligned} \tag{10}$$

Since the numbers d_1, d_2, d_3 are not all 0, it follows that $a > 0$. And since $y \geq 0$ for all x, the graph of this quadratic expression is one of the two types shown in Figure II.38. For the Figure II.38(a) $\Delta < 0$ [see Figure II.33(a)]; for Figure II.38(b), $\Delta = 0$ [see Figure II.32(a)]. Thus in any case, $\Delta \leq 0$. That is, $b^2 - 4ac \leq 0$. If we substitute the expressions for a, b, c given in (10) we obtain

$$4(c_1 d_1 + c_2 d_2 + c_3 d_3)^2 - 4(c_1^2 + c_2^2 + c_3^2)(d_1^2 + d_2^2 + d_3^2) \leq 0. \tag{11}$$

Dividing by 4 and making a transposition, we obtain the Cauchy Inequality. Note that if $\Delta = 0$, then, for a certain x, one has $y = 0$, and this gives the proportionality relationship given in (8).

We have stated that the Cauchy Inequality is very closely related to the Pythagorean Theorem and hence to Euclidean geometry. This statement will become somewhat clearer when we study the circular functions. See also the exercises below.

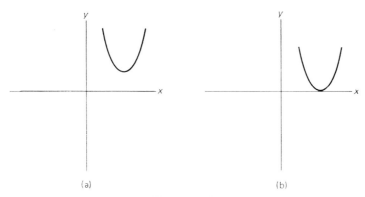

(a)   (b)

Figure II.38

Exercises II.7.a

1. Verify the Cauchy Inequality for the pair of n-tuples below.

   (a) 3, 2 and 4, -7;   (b) 0, 0 and 2, 5;
   (c) 2, 4, -2 and -3, -6, 3;   (d) 1, c and $2c + 1$, 2;
   (e) 3, 2, 1 and -2, 3, 0.

2. Given the two pairs of n-tuples below, find out for what values of c the left side of the Cauchy Inequality equals 0; for what value of c, if any, is there equality in the Cauchy Inequality:

   (a) 1, c and $2c$, 1;   (b) 1, c, 2 and $2c$, 1, 0.

3. Let A_i represent the n-tuple all of whose numbers are 0 except the one in the ith place which is equal to 1 (for example, for $n = 4$, A_3 is 0, 0, 1, 0). Calculate the two sides of the Cauchy Inequality for the n-tuples A_i and A_j where i and j can have any of the values 1, 2, $\cdots$, n. (To get the proof mechanism and notation lubricated, start off by proving this for $n = 4$.)

4. Prove that for any numbers $x_1, x_2, \cdots, x_n$,

$$\frac{x_1 + x_2 + \cdots + x_n}{n} \leq \left(\frac{x_1^2 + x_2^2 + \cdots + x_n^2}{n}\right)^{1/2}.$$

   [*Hint*: Use the Cauchy Inequality on the n-tuples $x_1, x_2, \cdots, x_n$ and 1, 1, $\cdots$, 1.]

5. (a) Prove that for any two pairs a, b and c, d one has

$$\sqrt{(a + c)^2 + (b + d)^2} \leq \sqrt{a^2 + b^2} + \sqrt{c^2 + d^2}$$

   [*Hint*: Square both sides and apply the Cauchy Inequality.]

   (b) Graph the points $P: (a, b)$, $Q: (c, d)$, and $R: (a + c, b + d)$. Note that the above inequality shows that the length of one side of a triangle is less than the sum of the other two lengths. The triangle is OPR where O is the origin $(0, 0)$. Note also that use is being made of the distance formula which will be developed in Chapter IV. That is, the distance $\overline{OP} = \sqrt{a^2 + b^2}$ and similarly $\overline{OR} = \sqrt{(a + c)^2 + (b + d)^2}$; finally $\overline{PR} = \overline{OQ} = \sqrt{c^2 + d^2}$.

6. Prove that for two n-tuples $x_1, x_2, \cdots, x_n$ and $y_1, y_2, \cdots, y_n$,

$$\sqrt{(x_1 + y_1)^2 + (x_2 + y_2)^2 + \cdots + (x_n + y_n)^2}$$
$$\leq \sqrt{x_1^2 + x_2^2 + \cdots + x_n^2} + \sqrt{y_1^2 + y_2^2 + \cdots + y_n^2}.$$

   If $n = 2$, this gives the inequality in Problem 5. For that reason, it is called the Euclidean triangle inequality in n dimensions. [*Hint*: Proceed as in Problem 5; square both sides and use the Cauchy Inequality.]

7. A study of Chapters VI and VIII shows that if for the points $P: (a, b)$ and $Q: (c, d)$ one has $ac + bd = 0$, then the segment OP is perpendicular to the segment OQ [here O is $(0, 0)$]. Show that if $ac + bd = 0$, then

$$(a^2 + b^2) + (c^2 + d^2) = (a - c)^2 + (b - d)^2.$$

Using the distance formula given in Chapter IV we may interpret this as the Pythagorean Theorem for right triangles. Make a diagram. See also the note given in Problem 5.

8. Show that if for a pair of n-tuples $x_1, x_2, \cdots, x_n$ and $y_1, y_2, \cdots, y_n$,

$$x_1 y_1 + x_2 y_2 + \cdots + x_n y_n = 0,$$

then

$$(x_1^2 + x_2^2 + \cdots + x_n^2) + (y_1^2 + y_2^2 + \cdots + y_n^2)$$
$$= (x_1 - y_1)^2 + (x_2 - y_2)^2 + \cdots + (x_n - y_n)^2.$$

This is called the Pythagorean Theorem for right triangles in n dimensions. Notice that this problem and the preceding one are not difficult to solve. What is difficult here is the interpretation as a right triangle.

9. Write out the proof of the Cauchy Inequality for the general case. (Remember that the proof given above treats only the case $n = 3$.)

Historical Note. Augustin Louis Cauchy (1789–1857) is known principally for his contributions to the theory of functions of a complex variable. He was one of the pioneering advocates of rigor in mathematical proof.

Hermann Amandus Schwarz (1843–1921) was one of the outstanding analysts of the end of the last century. He is best known for his work in the theory of functions of a complex variable.

We turn our attention now to another inequality whose proof is of quadratic character, the inequality concerning arithmetic and geometric means. This inequality is much older than the Cauchy Inequality, having already attracted much attention from the Greek philosophers.

Let us give some preliminary definitions. To start, consider two positive numbers x_1 and x_2. Thus $x_1 > 0$ and $x_2 > 0$. Then by a *mean* of x_1 and x_2 is meant some sort of average of these numbers. There are many such averages but the most important by far are the *arithmetic* mean and the *geometric* mean. Since it is natural to denote a mean by the letter m, we shall denote the arithmetic mean by m_a (read: m sub a) and the geometric mean by m_g (read: m sub g). Here are the definitions:

$$m_a = \frac{x_1 + x_2}{2}; \qquad m_g = \sqrt{x_1 \cdot x_2}. \tag{12}$$

If $x_1 = 4$ and $x_2 = 9$, then $m_a = \frac{1}{2}(4 + 9) = 6\frac{1}{2}$; also, $m_g = \sqrt{4 \times 9} = 6$. Note that in this case $m_g \leq m_a$. We shall prove shortly that this is always true.

The notion of these means goes over to an arbitrary collection of positive numbers. For example, for a triple of positive numbers x_1, x_2, and x_3,

$$m_a = \frac{x_1 + x_2 + x_3}{3}; \qquad m_g = \sqrt[3]{x_1 \cdot x_2 \cdot x_3}. \tag{13}$$

In general, consider an n-tuple of positive numbers, $x_1 > 0, x_2 > 0, \cdots, x_n > 0$. Then by definition

$$m_a = \frac{x_1 + x_2 + \cdots + x_n}{n}; \qquad m_g = \sqrt[n]{(x_1 \cdot x_2 \cdot \cdots \cdot x_n)}. \tag{14}$$

The quantity on the right is the nth root of the product.

We are now ready to state the inequality between the arithmetic and the geometric mean:

II–3 Theorem

If $x_1, \cdots, x_n$ is an n-tuple of positive numbers, then

$$\frac{x_1 + x_2 + \cdots + x_n}{n} \geq \sqrt[n]{(x_1 \cdot x_2 \cdot \cdots \cdot x_n)}. \tag{15}$$

That is, $m_a \geq m_g$. Equality holds only if

$$x_1 = x_2 = \cdots = x_n. \tag{16}$$

We shall give the proof of this theorem for the cases $n = 2$ and $n = 4$. In the exercises we suggest what is necessary to carry out a general proof. The complete proof is rather complicated and will not be given. The case $n = 1$ is taken up in Exercise 3.

Consider the case $n = 2$. We are given $x_1 > 0$ and $x_2 > 0$. Thus there exist numbers $t_1 > 0$ and $t_2 > 0$ such that $t_1^2 = x_1$, $t_2^2 = x_2$, namely, $t_1 = \sqrt{x_1}, t_2 = \sqrt{x_2}$.

Since the square of a real number is not negative,

$$(t_1 - t_2)^2 \geq 0. \tag{17}$$

Expand the expression in parentheses, transpose, and divide by 2. This gives

$$\frac{t_1^2 + t_2^2}{2} \geq t_1 t_2. \tag{18}$$

Substituting $x_1 = t_1^2$ and $x_2 = t_2^2$ gives

$$\frac{x_1 + x_2}{2} \geq \sqrt{x_1} \sqrt{x_2}. \tag{19}$$

Since $\sqrt{x_1}\,\sqrt{x_2} = \sqrt{x_1 x_2}$, this gives the desired inequality: $m_a \geq m_g$. Note that if there is equality in (19), there is equality in (18) and (17). This implies that $t_1 = t_2$; hence $t_1^2 = t_2^2$; hence $x_1 = x_2$. This completes the proof of the inequality for the case $n = 2$.

The remainder of this section is a little more complicated and detailed reading of it may be put off. Consider the inequality for the case $n = 4$. We shall handle this case by making use of the result for the case $n = 2$. In fact, we shall use it three times.

Write

$$y_1 = \frac{x_1 + x_2}{2}, \quad y_2 = \frac{x_3 + x_4}{2}. \tag{20}$$

It is not difficult to check the following relations:

$$m_a = \frac{x_1 + x_2 + x_3 + x_4}{4} = \frac{(x_1 + x_2)/2 + (x_3 + x_4)/2}{2} \tag{21}$$

$$= \frac{y_1 + y_2}{2} \geq \sqrt{y_1 y_2}.$$

Now

$$y_1 = \frac{x_1 + x_2}{2} \geq \sqrt{x_1 x_2} \quad \text{and} \quad y_2 = \frac{x_3 + x_4}{2} \geq \sqrt{x_3 x_4}, \tag{22}$$

so that

$$\sqrt{y_1} \geq \sqrt[4]{x_1 x_2} \quad \text{and} \quad \sqrt{y_2} \geq \sqrt[4]{x_3 x_4}.$$

Thus

$$\sqrt{y_1 y_2} \geq \sqrt[4]{x_1 x_2}\,\sqrt[4]{x_3 x_4} = \sqrt[4]{x_1 x_2 x_3 x_4} = m_g. \tag{23}$$

Using (21) and (23) we obtain $m_a \geq m_g$. Once more, equality holds only in the case $x_1 = x_2 = x_3 = x_4$ (see Exercise 4). This completes the proof of the theorem for the case $n = 4$.

It is indicated in Exercise 5 how to prove the theorem for the case $n = 2 \times 4$; that is, $n = 8$; $n = 2 \times 8$, that is, $n = 16$, and so on. Finally Exercises 6 and 7 show how to carry out the proof for natural numbers which are not powers of 2 (2, 4, 8, 16, 32, $\cdots$) such as $n = 3, 5, 6, 7$, and so on.

Exercises II.7.b

1. Calculate m_a, m_g for the following n-tuples:

(a) 9, 16;

(b) 1, 25;

(c) 1, 12, 18;

(d) 1^4, 2^4, 3^4, 4^4.

2. A teacher had the practice of awarding first prize in his mathematics class to the student whose average (arithmetic mean) on 4 quizzes was the highest. In case of a tie, he used geometric means to determine the winner. In a given year, there was a triple tie for first place by students A, B, C. Here were their grades:

$$A:\quad 9, 10, 8, 9;$$
$$B:\quad 10, 10, 9, 7;$$
$$C:\quad 10, 10, 10, 6.$$

Who received the prize?

3. Prove the inequality between arithmetic and geometric means for the case $n = 1$. (Use the definition: $\sqrt[1]{x} = x$. Note that this case actually gives equality.)

4. Show in the case $n = 4$ that $m_a = m_g$ only if $x_1 = x_2 = x_3 = x_4$.

5. Using the method outlined in the text for $n = 4$, show that if the inequality between the two means is known for a positive integer m, it can be demonstrated for the integer $2m$. This thus gives a proof for the cases $n = 8$, 16, 32, and so on.

6. Prove the inequality for the case $n = 3$ as follows: Write as usual

$$m_a = \frac{x_1 + x_2 + x_3}{3}.$$

Then we have

$$m_a = \frac{x_1 + x_2 + x_3 + m_a}{4} \geq (x_1 x_2 x_3 m_a)^{1/4} = (x_1 x_2 x_3)^{1/4} m_a^{1/4};$$

$$m_a^{3/4} = m_a^{1 - 1/4} \geq (x_1 x_2 x_3)^{1/4}$$

or

$$m_a \geq (x_1 x_2 x_3)^{1/3} = m_g.$$

Exponents and their properties will be taken up in detail in Chapter V.

7. Using the ideas of the preceding problem, prove the inequality for $n = 5$ assuming it for $n = 8$ (Exercise 5). This gives the idea of the proof in general.

Historical Note. The arithmetic, geometric, and other means received an enormous amount of attention from the early Greek philosophers. A list of names here represents a veritable Who's Who of the intellectual leaders of Greek culture. Pythagoras (about 569–500 B.C.) and his followers probably lead the way. The Pythagoreans devoted all their energies to the study of the natural numbers, simple geometric configurations, and their interrelations.

8. FUNCTIONAL EQUATIONS

Let us consider the very simple function f defined by $f(x) = ax$. Here a is some fixed number. Consider two values x_1 and x_2 of the variable. One has

$$f(x_1 + x_2) = a(x_1 + x_2) = ax_1 + ax_2, \tag{1}$$

and since $f(x_1) = ax_1$ and $f(x_2) = ax_2$, this shows that

$$f(x_1 + x_2) = f(x_1) + f(x_2). \tag{2}$$

This is an example of a *functional equation*. We say that the function f above *satisfies* the given functional equation.

Note in passing that functions picked at random do not satisfy this functional equation. For example, if $f(x) = x^2$, then $f(3 + 4) = f(7) = 49$ whereas $f(3) + f(4) = 9 + 16 = 25$ and since $25 \neq 49, f(3 + 4) \neq f(3) + f(4)$. We shall show immediately that very few functions satisfy the above functional equation.

Suppose now that f is a function about which nothing is known except that it satisfies the above functional equation. What can be said about it? To start with let us represent the real number $f(1)$ by a. Then since $f(2) = f(1 + 1) = f(1) + f(1)$, one has $f(2) = 2a$. For any positive integer n, this calculation shows that

$$f(n) = f(1 + \cdots + 1) = f(1) + \cdots + f(1) = a + \cdots + a = na. \tag{3}$$

Next, since

$$f(1) = f(1 + 0) = f(1) + f(0), \tag{4}$$

we have $f(0) = 0$. Also, for every natural number m,

$$0 = f(0) = f[m + (-m)] = f(m) + f(-m). \tag{5}$$

Thus $f(-m) = -f(m) = -am$ for all natural numbers m. Hence for any integer n, positive or negative,

$$f(n) = an. \tag{6}$$

Now consider the behavior of f for rational numbers. To begin with, if n is a positive integer, write $1 = 1/n + \cdots + 1/n$ (n times). Thus,

$$a = f(1) = f\left(\frac{1}{n} + \cdots + \frac{1}{n}\right)$$

$$= f\left(\frac{1}{n}\right) + \cdots + f\left(\frac{1}{n}\right) \tag{7}$$

$$= nf\left(\frac{1}{n}\right).$$

Hence

$$f\left(\frac{1}{n}\right) = \frac{1}{n} \cdot a. \tag{8}$$

From this it is not difficult to derive the fact that for any rational number r ($r = p/q$ where p and q are integers, $q \neq 0$),

$$f(r) = ar. \tag{9}$$

This proof is conveniently carried out in two steps. First, consider positive rational numbers; then, negative ones. For example, $f(\frac{2}{5}) = f(\frac{1}{5} + \frac{1}{5})$ $= f(\frac{1}{5}) + f(\frac{1}{5}) = \frac{1}{5}f(1) + \frac{1}{5}f(1) = \frac{1}{5}a + \frac{1}{5}a = \frac{2}{5}a$. If, more generally, p and q are positive integers, it is easy to show that $f(p/q) = (p/q)a$. The case of negative rational numbers is handled as is that of negative integers. (See Exercise 9.)

This is the end of the road. It is not possible to conclude from the functional equation above that $f(x) = ax$ for *all* real numbers x unless we have some other information about f. (The usual additional information about f that is required is that f is continuous. This means essentially that the graph of f is a smooth curve.) However, the discussion above shows clearly the importance of the notion of functional equation. In fact, if it is known that a function f satisfies some functional equation it is possible in many cases to derive much information about f merely from this fact. Do not conclude that all functions satisfy some functional equation. There are relatively few functions that satisfy interesting functional equations.

In considering the next example, a certain facility in manipulating exponents is assumed. (Questions concerning exponents are taken up in detail in Chapter V.) Take a positive number a, not equal to 1 ($a > 0$, $a \neq 1$). Consider the function defined by

$$g(x) = a^x. \tag{10}$$

Let us first determine for which values of x this function is defined. Certainly g is defined for all integers, positive and negative. It is also defined for rational numbers. For example, $a^{1/2}$, $a^{3/5}$, have clear meanings: $a^{3/5} = (\sqrt[5]{a})^3$. For real x which are not rational, the meaning of a^x is much more complicated. For the time being, let us consider that g is defined for rational numbers only. For this domain of definition, the going is not difficult.

It is easy to see that g satisfies the functional equation

$$g(x_1 + x_2) = g(x_1) \cdot g(x_2). \tag{11}$$

For in fact

$$g(x_1 + x_2) = a^{x_1 + x_2} = a^{x_1} \cdot a^{x_2} = g(x_1) \cdot g(x_2). \tag{12}$$

To say that g satisfies the above functional equation *is equivalent to stating a law of exponents*. Another law of exponents which will be recalled is: $(a^{x_1})^{x_2} = a^{x_1 x_2}$. This leads to a second functional equation which g satisfies, namely,

$$(g(x_1))^{x_2} = g(x_1 x_2). \tag{13}$$

Note that (11) is a much nicer looking equation than (13). The point is merely that a given function may satisfy several functional equations.

It may be shown that if g satisfies Equation (11) and if $g(1) \neq 0$, then $g(x) = a^x$ for some $a > 0$. The proof follows. In the first place, let us write $g(1) = a$. Then since

$$a = g(1) = g\left(\frac{1}{2} + \frac{1}{2}\right) = g\left(\frac{1}{2}\right) \cdot g\left(\frac{1}{2}\right), \tag{14}$$

we see that a is the square of a number; hence $a > 0$. Furthermore, $g(2) = g(1 + 1) = g(1) \cdot g(1) = a^2$.

For a natural number m,

$$g(m) = g(1 + \cdots + 1) = g(1) \cdots g(1)$$
$$= a \cdots a = a^m. \tag{15}$$

From the fact that $1 + 0 = 1$, it follows that

$$g(1) = g(1 + 0) = g(1) \cdot g(0); \tag{16}$$

hence $g(0) = 1$. If m is a natural number, then

$$1 = g(0) = g[m + (-m)] = g(m) \cdot g(-m)$$
$$= a^m \cdot g(-m). \tag{17}$$

Hence

$$g(-m) = \frac{1}{g(m)} = \frac{1}{a^m} = a^{-m}. \tag{18}$$

Use has been made here of the fact that if m is a natural number, the definition of a^{-m} is: $a^{-m} = 1/a^m$. Thus for any integer n, positive or negative,

$$g(n) = a^n. \tag{19}$$

If n is a positive integer,

$$a = g(1) = g\left(\frac{1}{n} + \cdots + \frac{1}{n}\right) = g\left(\frac{1}{n}\right) \cdots g\left(\frac{1}{n}\right) = \left[g\left(\frac{1}{n}\right)\right]^n. \tag{20}$$

Hence

$$g\left(\frac{1}{n}\right) = a^{1/n}. \tag{21}$$

Finally, it may be shown (see Exercise 10) that for any rational number r

$$g(r) = a^r.$$

Once more, therefore, we see that a function is largely determined by its functional equation. The functional equations discussed above are exceptionally important.

There are two other functional equations that come up repeatedly. They are

$$f(x) = f(-x);$$ (22)

$$f(x) = -f(-x).$$ (23)

Functions that satisfy the first equation are called *even* functions. Those that satisfy the second equation are called *odd* functions. For example, if $f(x) = x^2 + 5$, f is even since $(-x)^2 + 5 = x^2 + 5$. Whereas if $f(x) = x^5 - x^3$, then f is odd since $(-x)^5 - (-x)^3 = -x^5 - (-x^3) = -x^5 + x^3 = -(x^5 - x^3)$. Most functions are neither even nor odd. For example, if $f(x) = 1 + x$, then f is neither even nor odd.

Exercises II.8.a

1. Write a functional equation satisfied by a constant function $f(x) = c$.

2. Show that if f satisfies the equation $f(x_1 + x_2) = 2f(x_1) + f(x_2)$, then $f(x) = 0$ for all x.

3. Show that if $f(x) = x^2$, then $f(\sqrt{f(x)}) = f(x)$.

4. Show that if f satisfies $f(x_1 + x_2 + x_3) = f(x_1) + f(x_2) + f(x_3)$, then f satisfies $f(x_1 + x_2) = f(x_1) + f(x_2)$.

5. Which of the following functions are even? Which are odd? Which are neither? Which are both?

   (a) $f(x) = x^6 - 2|x|$;   (b) $f(x) = x^5 - \dfrac{1}{x}$;

   (c) $g(x) = 2x^2 + x - 1$;   (d) $f(x) = 0$;

   (e) $h(x) = a_0 + a_1 x + a_2 x^2$;   (f) $\varphi(u) = \dfrac{1 + u^2}{1 - u^2}$;

   (g) $h(x) = 3x^4 + cx^3 + 2x^2$;   (h) $\psi(t) = \left(t + \dfrac{1}{t}\right)\left(t - \dfrac{1}{t}\right)$.

6. Show that if f is an arbitrary function, then $f = g + h$ where

   $$g(x) = \frac{f(x) + f(-x)}{2} \quad \text{and} \quad h(x) = \frac{f(x) - f(-x)}{2}.$$

   Show that g is even and h is odd.

7. Calculate g and h (Problem 6) for the function f defined by

(a) $f(x) = x^2 + 2x - 3$;

(b) $f(x) = \dfrac{x^2 - 1}{x + 1}$;

(c) $f(x) = |x|$;

(d) $f(x) = 0$.

8. Show that the sum and difference of even or odd functions is even or odd. Show that the product and quotient of two even functions or of two odd functions is an even function. Show that if f is an even function and g is arbitrary, then $g \circ f$ is even. Make appropriate statements for $g \circ f$ and $f \circ g$ for the various possibilities for f and g.

9. Show that if r is a negative rational number and if f satisfies Equation (2), then $f(r) = rf(1)$.

10. Show that if r is a rational number and if the function g satisfies (11), then

$$g(r) = a^r.$$

11. Prove that if f is both an even function and an odd function, then $f = 0$.

9. PERIODIC FUNCTIONS

We now introduce the notion of a *periodic function* which is defined by a type of functional equation. Suppose f is a function and let us suppose that there exists some real number $p \neq 0$ such that

$$f(x + p) = f(x) \tag{1}$$

for all numbers x. Such a function is called *periodic*. The number p is called a *period* of the function; f is also said to have period p.

Here is an example. Consider the wheel of an automobile and let us focus our attention on a fixed point located on the outside of the tire. Assume that a small nail is in the tire. Call the distance that the car moves along the road x and designate by y the height above the road of this point on the tire. The distance x can be conveniently measured from some starting point, preferably one for which the point is in contact with the road. The graph of the function given by $y = f(x)$ is indicated in Figure II.39. Here r represents the radius of

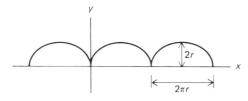

Figure II.39

the wheel; hence the circumference of the wheel is $2\pi r$. It is clear that the height of the nail off the road at the distance x is the same as that at the distance $x + 2\pi r$ (the wheel has made exactly one revolution between the two points.) Thus we have for all x,

$$f(x + 2\pi r) = f(x).$$

That is, f is periodic and has period $p = 2\pi r$. Incidentally, the curve above given by f is called a *cycloid*. [*Note*: It can be argued that the automobile will ultimately stop—the tire will wear out, the car will break down, etc., hence there is no real periodicity. In this and the following examples we are idealizing the situation so that this eventuality does not occur.]

One of the oldest references to periodicity concerns the role of Sisyphus in mythology. Sisyphus had displeased Pluto, the god of the underworld, and had been sentenced to roll a heavy stone up a steep hill. This stone unfortunately tumbled back down the hill as soon as he reached its crest and he was forced to run after the stone to the bottom and start all over. Let us consider the function f which gives for any time t the height h of the stone above the starting point. We shall assume that the effort of our friend Sisyphus is constant over time. The graph of $h = f(t)$ is given in Figure II.40. It is clearly periodic. The period is the time t_0 of a complete cycle. For convenience, we have set $f(0) = 0$. Note incidentally that curves of this sort occur frequently in situations controlled by certain types of machinery. The temperature of a thermostatically controlled house on a cold winter night is one such.

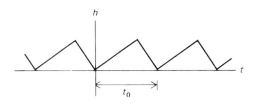

Figure II.40

Let us now consider a third example leading to what is called sinusoidal motion. Little Donatella is sitting in her swing in the orchard and dreamily swinging in constant small arcs. Let s denote the distance of the swing from the vertical position, say in feet, and let t denote the time in seconds. Then we have $s = g(t)$ for some g. The graph is given in Figure II.41 [we started the clock when the swing was at the bottom; thus $g(0) = 0$]. Note from the graph that the period of the swing is 3 seconds and that its amplitude (maximum distance from vertical position) is 2 feet. This example of periodicity is at the base of most repetitive phenomena including those found in sound, light, radio, and many electrical phenomena (alternating currents).

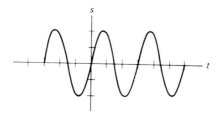

Figure II.41

Exercises II.9.a

1. Show that if a function f admits all real numbers p as periods, then f is a constant.

2. Show that if f is periodic with period p, then it is periodic with period np where n is an integer.

3. Show that the length of the day (hours, minutes, seconds from sunrise to sunset) at any fixed spot on the earth is a periodic function. What is its period?

4. A very important periodic function f is the following: $f(t) = 1$ for $0 < t < 1$; $f(t) = -1$ for $1 < t < 2$; $f(0) = 0 = f(1)$; f has period 2. Graph the function. Note that $f(-t) = -f(t)$.

5. The German philosopher Immanuel Kant (1724–1804) was said to be so regular in his habits that the townspeople of Königsberg could set their clocks by his afternoon walks. Show that if f represents the distance of Kant to his home, then f is a periodic function. What is the period?

6. Give two examples of periodic functions not treated so far.

7. If f and g are periodic, what about $f + g$ and $f \cdot g$? If g is periodic, show that $f \circ g$ is periodic for any f.

8. It will be shown later that if

$$f(x) = a_1 x + \cdots + a_n x^n, \qquad a_n \neq 0, \qquad n \geq 1,$$

then there are at most n numbers b such that $f(b) = 0$. Show that f is not periodic. After reading Chapter III, we can devise a proof not using the existence of the numbers b.

9. Define a function g similar to the one in Exercise 4 having period p instead of period 2. For example, a moderately good computer could be "pulsed" by a function g of this type with p equal to one millionth of a second. Write down the rule for forming g in this case.

10. Prove that if f is an even function of period p, then $f(p - x) = f(x)$. If f is an odd function of period p, then $f(p - x) = -f(x)$.

10. SOME SPECIAL METHODS IN GRAPHING

Earlier in this chapter we introduced the concept of the graph of a function given to us in the form $y = f(x)$. As will be recalled, the graph of the function consists of all pairs of numbers $(x, f(x))$. This means that in principle we must let x have every possible value and then we must calculate the corresponding value of y, namely, $f(x)$. This is, of course, an impossible task. What we decided to do earlier was to obtain a few points on the graph by letting x have a few values and then make a guess as to where the other points of the graph are. This guessing procedure is sometimes described as "drawing a smooth curve through the given points." It is important that this guess be well made for otherwise the results obtained may be far from correct. It is the purpose of this section to indicate special devices to help in graphing. Thus a preliminary study of the given function f may result in a plan for selecting some tell-tale values x thus obtaining a few points on the curve which tell us what is going on. Naturally this list of special devices neither is nor could be complete.

Consider first the question of *symmetry*. Suppose f has the property that for any x, $f(x) = f(-x)$; in other words, f is an even function. This is the case, for instance, for

$$f(x) = x^4 - 3x^2 + 2 \tag{1}$$

since

$$f(-x) = (-x)^4 - 3(-x)^2 + 2 = x^4 - 3x^2 + 2 = f(x). \tag{2}$$

Clearly, if (x, y) is a point of the graph, then $(-x, y)$ is also such a point. Thus it is sufficient to graph points (x, y) with $x \geq 0$. Each point so obtained gives a new point $(-x, y)$ which is on the graph. We say that the graph is symmetric about the y-axis.

We have spoken so far of symmetry about the y-axis. However, symmetry may exist with respect to any line. For example, the function

$$f(x) = 2(x - 1)^2 + 1 \tag{3}$$

has a graph which is symmetric about the line $x = 1$. This means that

$$f(1 + a) = f(1 - a) \tag{4}$$

for all a (check this in the present instance). The graph of this function is indicated in Figure II.42.

Next, consider the question of what is sometimes called the *behavior at infinity*. This phrase means the behavior of y for large values of $|x|$. The question can be asked this way: What happens to y when $|x|$ becomes large? There is a somewhat similar question: Are there numbers a such that when x is close to a, $|y|$ is large? These questions are formulated somewhat loosely, but

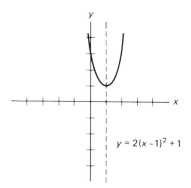

Figure II.42

their meaning should become clear from an example. Suppose a function is defined by

$$y = \frac{1}{x - 1}.$$ (5)

Then it is clear that if x is positive and very large, y is positive and very small (close to zero). If x is negative and $|x|$ is very large, then y is negative and $|y|$ is very small. These two facts show up clearly in Figure II.43. Furthermore, it is clear that if x is close to 1, in other words, if $|x - 1|$ is small, then $|y|$ is large. Specifically, if x is slightly larger than 1, then y is large and positive. If x is slightly less than 1, then y is negative and $|y|$ is large. The fact that $|y|$ is large when x is close to 1 should be immediately apparent from the appearance of the equation connecting y and x.

The lines $x = 1$ and $y = 0$ play a special role in the above examples. They are called *asymptotes* of the curve $y = 1/(x - 1)$. Specifically, the line $y = 0$ (the x-axis) is called a *horizontal* asymptote. The line $x = 1$ is called a *vertical* asymptote.

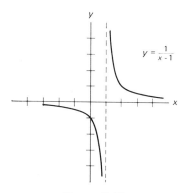

Figure II.43

Exercises II.10.a

1. Graph the following functions.

(a) $f(x) = x$;

(b) $g(x) = \dfrac{1}{x}$;

(c) $f(x) = x + \dfrac{1}{x}$;

(d) $f(u) = u^2$;

(e) $h(t) = t^2 + \dfrac{1}{t}$;

(f) $f(x) = \dfrac{1}{x^2}$;

(g) $f(x) = x + \dfrac{1}{x^2}$;

(h) $f(x) = x^2 + \dfrac{1}{x^2}$;

(i) $f(x) = \dfrac{1}{x^3}$.

2. Graph the following functions.

(a) $f(x) = \dfrac{1}{x^2 - 1}$;

(b) $h(x) = \dfrac{1}{x^2 + 1}$;

(c) $f(x) = \dfrac{1}{|x|}$;

(d) $\varphi(x) = \dfrac{1}{(x - 3)^2}$;

(e) $f(x) = x^2(x^2 - 4)$;

(f) $f(x) = |x| + \dfrac{1}{|x|}$;

(g) $f(x) = |x - 3|$;

(h) $f(x) = |x - 3| + \dfrac{1}{|x - 3|}$.

3. Graph the following functions.

(a) $f(x) = \sqrt[3]{x}$;

(b) $f(x) = \dfrac{\sqrt{x^2 - 1}}{x^2}$;

(c) $f(x) = \dfrac{\sqrt{1 - x^2}}{x^2}$;

(d) $f(x) = x\sqrt{1 - x^2}$;

(e) $f(x) = \dfrac{\sqrt{1 - x^2}}{x}$.

4. Show that the graphs of the following equations are symmetric with respect to the line $y = x$.

(a) $y = \dfrac{1}{x}$;

(b) $y = -x$;

(c) $y = \sqrt{1 - x^2}, 0 \le x \le 1$;

(d) $y = -\dfrac{1}{x}$.

11. IMPLICIT FUNCTIONS

We have had considerable experience with functions up to this point. We know, for example, that if f is a function, we may write the functional dependence in the form $y = f(x)$. That is, we are given an explicit method or formula for calculating y for any allowable value of x. Now there are certain situations involving pairs of numbers (x, y) where a relation is given between these numbers which is not explicit. For example, suppose someone is interested in pairs (x, y) such that

$$x^2 + y^2 = 25. \tag{1}$$

We yield to our first temptation to solve this expression for y. This gives

$$y = \pm\sqrt{25 - x^2}. \tag{2}$$

We are now in a position to surmise that Equation (1) defines a function given in (2) and that in fact (1) defines two functions, namely $y = \sqrt{25 - x^2}$ and $y = -\sqrt{25 - x^2}$. The above reasoning is partly correct. It is correct that there exist functions that satisfy (1). And it is also correct that there are two "interesting" functions that satisfy (1). However, there happen to be many others, less interesting if you wish. For example, $y = \sqrt{25 - x^2}$ for $0 \le x \le 5$ and $y = -\sqrt{25 - x^2}$ for $-5 \le x < 0$ defines a function that satisfies (1).

We shall be concerned only with the two functions

$$y = \sqrt{25 - x^2}, \qquad -5 \le x \le 5, \tag{3}$$

and

$$y = -\sqrt{25 - x^2}, \qquad -5 \le x \le 5. \tag{4}$$

We shall say that (1) defines the functions (3) and (4) *implicitly*. This shows that equations in x and y can define one or more functions. These functions are obtained by "solving" the given expression for y in terms of x. The functions so obtained satisfy the given initial equation. For example, if one writes $\sqrt{25 - x^2}$ instead of y in Equation (1) one obtains

$$x^2 + (\sqrt{25 - x^2})^2 = 25 \tag{5}$$

and this statement is correct for all values of x. One may also say that Equation (3) or (4) gives the function in *explicit* form.

It is to be expected that the graphs of the two functions (3) and (4) which are defined by (1) should bear a close relation to one another. In fact, if we are interested in all number pairs (x, y) that satisfy (1) we must look to both (3) and (4). More precisely, if (x, y) satisfies (1), then it will satisfy (3) or it will satisfy (4). It has already been seen that any (x, y) which satisfies (3) will also satisfy (1). The same is true for (4). Thus we can obtain all (x, y) satisfying (1) by superimposing the graphs of (3) and (4). The resulting figure is the graph of (1). In Figures II.44, II.45, and II.46 are shown the graphs of (3), (4), and (1).

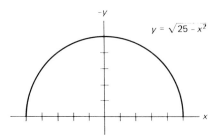

Figure II.44

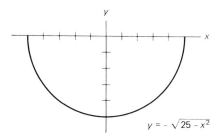

Figure II.45

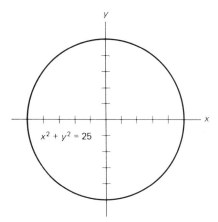

Figure II.46

Having studied this special example, we now generalize this procedure. Given an equation in x and y, it defines (by the process of solving for y) one or more functions of x. The graph of the given equation is defined to be the collection of all pairs (x, y) which satisfy the equation. This graph is obtained by the superposition of the graphs of the several functions obtained by solving for y. It may be added that the process of solving may be arduous, as for example in $x^{27}y^{15} - y^7 + 2xy^{12} = 1$; or it may be impossible, as in $xy - x - x(y - 1) = 0$, where the equation contains y in an illusory way. We shall only consider situations in which the solution for y is feasible.

Let us consider a second example. We are to find the graph of

$$\frac{x^2}{9} - \frac{y^2}{16} = 1. \tag{6}$$

Solving for y, the following two functions are obtained:

$$y = \frac{4}{3}\sqrt{x^2 - 9} \quad \text{and} \quad y = -\frac{4}{3}\sqrt{x^2 - 9}. \tag{7}$$

The second function is the same as the first except for sign. To find the graph it will be sufficient to graph the first of these and to take the mirror image of this graph in the x-axis. Let us examine the function f defined by

$$f(x) = \frac{4}{3}\sqrt{x^2 - 9}. \tag{8}$$

Since $x^2 - 9$ cannot be negative, $x^2 - 9 \geq 0$, that is, $x^2 \geq 9$, and this means that either $x \geq 3$ or $x \leq -3$. Thus the function is not defined for values of x in the interval from -3 to 3. Next, note that $f(-x) = f(x)$; hence, the graph is symmetric with respect to the y-axis. Finally, if x is positive and large, y is also positive and large although it is not clear how y grows with x. We shall examine this point in an exercise below. At this stage it is advisable to keep an open mind and to obtain a fair number of points on the graph. In addition to obtaining values y for $x = 3, 4, 5$, it is suggested to try also $x = 3\frac{1}{2}$ and $x = 10$. This gives Table II.7.

Table II.7

x	3	4	5	$\frac{7}{2}$	10	
y	0	$\frac{4}{3}\sqrt{7}$	$\frac{16}{3}$	$\frac{2}{3}\sqrt{13}$	$\frac{4}{3}\sqrt{91}$	

For our purposes, $\sqrt{7} = 2.6$, $\sqrt{13} = 3.5$, and $\sqrt{91} = 9.5$ (obtained by making a rough guess and following it by a quick multiplication). This gives: $\frac{4}{3}\sqrt{7} = 3.5$, $\frac{2}{3}\sqrt{13} = 2.3$, $\frac{4}{3}\sqrt{91} = 12.7$. The graph of $y = f(x)$ for $x \geq 3$ is shown in Figure II.47. This gives for our original equation, Figure II.48.

This curve is called a hyperbola.

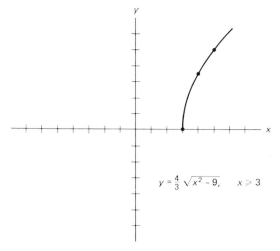

Figure II.47

Let us try another example, one that is not easy. The example may be skipped at first reading. The discussion will suggest that each problem is special and yields to rather special methods that do not necessarily apply to another problem. Let it be required to find the graph of

$$(x^2 + y^2)^2 = x^2 - y^2. \tag{9}$$

Our first thought is to solve this for y. This calls for the solution of a fourth degree equation, something in which we are not expert. However, we

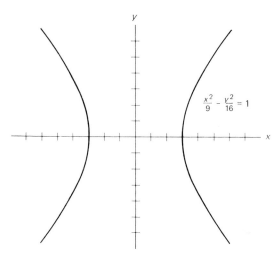

Figure II.48

note that the equation is really of the second degree in x^2 and y^2. Let us make the substitution

$$x^2 = u \quad \text{and} \quad y^2 = v. \tag{10}$$

Note that u equals the square of a real number, $u \geq 0$; also, $v \geq 0$. Now we obtain a quadratic equation in u and v, namely,

$$(u + v)^2 = u - v, \tag{11}$$

which can be solved, obtaining

$$v = \frac{-2u - 1 + \sqrt{8u + 1}}{2}. \tag{12}$$

This gives

$$y = \pm\sqrt{\frac{-2x^2 - 1 + \sqrt{8x^2 + 1}}{2}}. \tag{13}$$

Note that in Equation (12), we do not have the choice $-\sqrt{8u + 1}$ as is customary in the quadratic formula. This is due to the fact that $v \geq 0$ while $-2u - 1 < 0$. Since the result (13) is not very useful for getting points on the graph we discard it. However, we note from it that the graph is symmetric with respect to both axes.

It can be seen that the graph lies inside or on the circle

$$x^2 + y^2 = 1. \tag{14}$$

Because, if for some x and y, $x^2 + y^2 > 1$, then $(x^2 + y^2)^2 > x^2 + y^2 \geq x^2 - y^2$ and hence (x, y) is not on the graph. In view of this result, we shall use a large scale in graphing.

Note that the point $(0, 0)$ lies on the graph. So do $(1, 0)$ and $(-1, 0)$. In order to find further points proceed as follows: Consider the line $y = mx$ which passes through the origin with a slope m, and calculate where this line cuts the graph. This gives

$$(x^2 + m^2x^2)^2 = x^2 - m^2x^2, \tag{15}$$

that is,

$$x^4(1 + m^2)^2 = x^2(1 - m^2). \tag{16}$$

Leaving out the possibility $x = 0$, this gives

$$x^2(1 + m^2)^2 = (1 - m^2), \tag{17}$$

and hence

$$x = \pm\frac{\sqrt{1 - m^2}}{1 + m^2}. \tag{18}$$

This tells us that if $m > 1$ or $m < -1$, there is no value of x. In other words, lines $y = mx$ with $m > 1$ or $m < -1$ do not intersect the graph (except at the origin). If we give the values $m = 0, \frac{1}{4}, \frac{1}{2}, \frac{3}{4}, 1$, we obtain after some calculations $x = \pm 1, \pm 0.9, \pm 0.6, \pm 0.4, 0$ and $y = 0, \pm 0.2, \pm 0.3, \pm 0.3, 0$. This finally gives the graph shown in Figure II.49, where we have indicated the circle and the two lines which limit the graph. The curve is called a *lemniscate*.

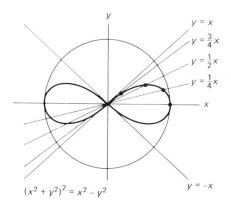

$$(x^2 + y^2)^2 = x^2 - y^2$$

Figure II.49

As an example involving implicit functions consider the following problem in astronautics: At what velocity will a spaceship travel in order to go in circles about the earth?

If one assumes that the ship is at a distance of 4000 miles from the center of the earth and has a horizontal velocity of x miles per second, then according to the Pythagorean Theorem the square of the distance to the center of the earth at the end of 1 second would seem to be $4000^2 + x^2$. Actually, gravity makes the spaceship fall approximately 16 feet, that is, the ship falls $16/5280 = 1/330$ miles during that second. Thus for the distance y to the center of the earth we have (see Figure II.50)

$$\left(y + \frac{1}{330} \right)^2 = 4000^2 + x^2. \tag{19}$$

[Note that the graph of this curve is of the type $y^2 - x^2 = a^2$ except for the translation of the x-axis. See also Problem 4(c).] We are of course interested in the value $y = 4000$ since this means that the distance of the spaceship from the earth's center has not altered in the elapsed second. This gives, leaving out the trivial quantity $(1/330)^2$,

$$4000^2 + \frac{8000}{330} = 4000^2 + x^2. \tag{20}$$

Hence $x^2 = 24.2$ or $x = 4.9$. This is the speed in miles per second. In miles per hour we get $3600 \times 4.9 = 17,640$. The time for one revolution is

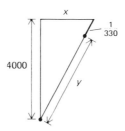

Figure II.50

$(2\pi \times 4000)/17,640$. This gives approximately 1.4 hours or 84 minutes. Do you agree?

A note on the problems that follow: Equations of the type appearing in Problems 1 through 4 will be considered in great detail in sections of Chapter IV devoted to the study of circles, ellipses, and hyperbolas. It is possible at this point to obtain the graphs involved but the task will be somewhat simpler later on after a complete study of all the points involved has been made.

Exercises II.11.a

1. Find the graph determined by the equations below.

(a) $u^2 + v^2 = 25$;

(b) $(x - 1)^2 + (y + 2)^2 = 16$;

(c) $\dfrac{x^2}{4} + \dfrac{y^2}{9} = 1$;

(d) $\dfrac{x^2}{4} - \dfrac{y^2}{9} = 1$;

(e) $\dfrac{y^2}{9} - \dfrac{x^2}{4} = 1$;

(f) $u^2 v^2 - 1 = 0$.

2. Find the graph determined by the equations below.

(a) $x^2 + y^2 = a^2$;

(b) $\dfrac{x^2}{a^2} + \dfrac{y^2}{b^2} = 1$;

(c) $\dfrac{x^2}{a^2} - \dfrac{y^2}{b^2} = 1$;

(d) $(x - h)^2 + (y - k)^2 = 25$.

3. Find the graph determined by the equations below.

(a) $\dfrac{(x - 2)^2}{9} + \dfrac{(y + 3)^2}{4} = 1$;

(b) $\dfrac{(x + 1)^2}{4} - \dfrac{(y - 2)^2}{9} = 1$;

(c) $\dfrac{(y + 1)^2}{9} - \dfrac{(x + 1)^2}{4} = 1$;

(d) $(x - 1)(y + 2) = 1$.

4. Find the graph determined by the equations below.

(a) $\dfrac{(x - h)^2}{9} + \dfrac{(y - k)^2}{4} = 1$;　　(b) $\dfrac{(x - h)^2}{9} - \dfrac{(y - k)^2}{4} = 1$;

(c) $\dfrac{(y - k)^2}{9} - \dfrac{(x - h)^2}{4} = 1$.

5. Find the graph determined by the equations below.

(a) $x^2 = y^2$;　　　　　　　　(b) $x = y^2$;
(c) $x^4 + y^4 = 1$;　　　　　　(d) $|x| + |y| = 1$;
(e) max $(|x|, |y|) = 1$. Here max (a, b) means the larger of a and b.

6. Find the graph determined by the equations below.

(a) $(x^2 + y^2)^2 = 2xy$;　　　　(b) $(x^2 + y^2)^3 = x^2$.

7. Given the graph of $y = f(x)$, show how to obtain the graph of $x = f(y)$.

8. Indicate the points of the plane for which $x^2 + y^2 > 25$; for which $x^2 + y^2 < 25$.

9. Consider each equation given in Problems 1 through 6 and determine the regions of the plane where we have "$>$" instead of "$=$"; where we have "$<$" instead of "$=$". For example, for Problem 5(a) determine the portion of the plane in which $x^2 > y^2$; for which $x^2 < y^2$.

10. Obtain the graph of $x^2/9 - y^2/16 = 1$ by calculating the intersection of the curve with the line $y = mx$ for various values of m. (See the discussion of the lemniscate given in the text.)

11. Solve the following problem in astronautics: At what velocity must a spaceship travel to go in circles about the moon? Assume that the radius of the moon is 1100 miles (assume the same radius for the orbit) and assume that the force of gravity on the moon is 1/6 of that of the earth, hence that in 1 second, a body falls $16/6 = 8/3$ feet.
Answers: Velocity needed for a circular orbit is 1.05 miles per second or 3780 miles per hour, duration of one revolution is 1.83 hours or 1 hour 50 minutes. (Newspapers reported on July 20, 1969 that the orbital speed of the lunar module at 69 miles above surface of the moon was 5660 feet per second. Since 1.05 miles per second equals 5540 feet per second, our result agrees very closely with that given.)

Chapter III

POLYNOMIAL FUNCTIONS

1. THE UNIQUE REPRESENTATION PROPERTY

This chapter is devoted to a study of polynomial functions. Such functions were already briefly discussed (Chapter II, Section 2). In a sense, these are the very simplest functions that one can construct. And, as will be seen later, they serve to "get close" to more general functions; in other words, general functions can be approximated by polynomials in a variety of ways. In addition to their importance in analysis, polynomials play a predominant role in the study of modern algebra. Some portions of the theory of polynomials are very deep. The so-called fundamental theorem of algebra, stated later, is a good example of a deep result. Fortunately, all the results we shall need are readily provable. (In other words, we do not need the fundamental theorem.)

We have repeatedly studied functions f, g, h, and so on, defined by expressions such as

$$f(x) = 5; \qquad g(x) = 3 - 2x; \qquad h(x) = \sqrt{2} - 2x^2 + x^3 - 3x^7.$$

These are examples of polynomials. In general, we have:

III–1 Definition

A function f defined by an equation of the type

$$f(x) = a_0 + a_1 x + a_2 x^2 + \cdots + a_n x^n, \qquad n \geq 0, \tag{1}$$

is called a polynomial function (also, a polynomial). The numbers a_0, a_1, $a_2, \cdots, a_n$ are called the coefficients of the polynomial.

It is assumed, naturally, that the coefficients are real numbers. Many of the polynomials appearing in examples below have integer coefficients. This will make them easier to handle.

Consider the polynomial f given by

$$f(x) = 1 - 7x + 3x^2 + x^4. \tag{2}$$

Its coefficients are $a_0 = 1$, $a_1 = -7$, $a_2 = 3$, $a_3 = 0$, and $a_4 = 1$. (Be sure to include a_3 in the list.)

Given a polynomial such as f above, we may also write it as

$$f(x) = 1 - 7x + 3x^2 + 0x^3 + x^4 + 0x^5 + 0x^6. \tag{3}$$

We won't usually do this but it might be useful—for example, if we wanted to add f to the polynomial g given by $g(x) = 3x^6$.

We are going to define the *degree* of a polynomial function. For example, it will turn out that the degree of the polynomial function in (2) is 4. The entire development of the theory of polynomials depends on the notion of degree. The material that follows will lead to the required definition. The student is advised not to allow previously acquired notions concerning degree to obscure what is going on.

If all the coefficients of the polynomial function f in (1) are 0 we are dealing with the function $f = 0$. (This function $f = 0$ is the function such that $f(x) = 0$ for all x.) This raises the following important question at the very outset. If the question is not answered satisfactorily, we cannot proceed.

QUESTION: *Is it possible that a polynomial f defined by*

$$f(x) = a_0 + a_1x + \cdots + a_nx^n, \tag{4}$$

where not all the coefficients are 0, represents the function $f = 0$?

We shall show that the answer to this question is a decisive "no." This implies that if one of your friends tells you that he has in mind a polynomial function f such that for all x, $f(x) = 0$, you can tell him right away that all the coefficients are zero.

The proof of the needed result uses an essentially new type of argument. We shall use this argument in a variety of forms to obtain very interesting information about polynomials. We shall establish the answer "no" if we prove the following.

If f is a polynomial given by

$$f(x) = a_0 + a_1x + \cdots + a_nx^n, \tag{5}$$

where not all of $a_0, a_1, \cdots, a_n$ are 0, then there are values of x such that $f(x) \neq 0$.

There are two cases to consider. In case (1), it is assumed that $a_0 \neq 0$ and that all the other coefficients equal zero; that is, $a_1 = 0, a_2 = 0, \cdots, a_n = 0$. Then for any value of $x, f(x) = a_0$, hence for any $x, f(x) \neq 0$. This gives the result in case (1).

So now we are confronted with case (2): Some one of the coefficients other than a_0 is not 0. In this case we select in the string of numbers $a_1, a_2, \cdots,$ a_n the last one that is different from zero. We may assume that this last one is a_n itself. Thus we have $a_n \neq 0$ with $n \geq 1$. To understand what is meant refer to Equations (2) and (3). In (3), the last nonzero coefficient is $a_4 = 1$. One can replace (3) by (2) and then $n = 4$. What we shall prove for the polynomial f is not merely that there are values of x such that $f(x) \neq 0$. We shall prove that there are values of x which make $f(x)$ arbitrarily large in absolute value.

Let us state the general theorem and then we shall consider examples to clarify its meaning.

III–2

Let f be a polynomial function defined by

$$f(x) = a_0 + a_1 x + \cdots + a_n x^n, \qquad n \geq 1 \qquad (6)$$

where $a_n \neq 0$. Then for $|x|$ large, $|f(x)|$ is also large. More precisely, given a number $M > 0$, there exists a number $L > 0$ such that if $|x| \geq L$, then $|f(x)| \geq M$.

Thus the function f in (6) is not the zero function.

First, what does the theorem say? It says: "Then for $|x|$ large, $|f(x)|$ is also large." Now the first intuitive meaning of this is reasonably clear. And if we go along with this understanding, the conclusion of the last sentence springs up immediately: If for $|x|$ large, $|f(x)|$ is large, then in particular, $f(x) \neq 0$. "Thus the function f is not the zero function" because there are values of x such that $f(x) \neq 0$.

The only thing to understand more clearly is what is meant by "$|x|$ is large and $|f(x)|$ is large." The meaning of that is given in the middle part of the theorem. The answer is put in the form of a contest between two people: A and B. A is to say what he considers large. For instance A might use the figure 100. This is the number M of the theorem. Then B's job is to find a number L which depends of course on f and also on M, such that if $|x| > L$, then $|f(x)| > 100 = M$. According to the theorem, B can always do this.

As we said above, for $M = 100$ we can find an L. If instead of $M = 100$ we start with $M = 1000$, we can still find an L, this time bigger than the first L. That is part of the game. It is not asserted that no matter what M is, we can always find one value of L which works in all cases. In fact this is not so. What is claimed is that for each M there is an L. It is not said that for each M there is just one L. That also is false. It is asserted that for each M there is *at least* one L. Note that in this discussion the polynomial function f lurking in the background is fixed. If one wishes to switch over to another polynomial, one starts all over to find L.

In other words, the theorem states that for a given polynomial f, and for a given number M, at least one number L can be found such that if $|x| > L$, then $|f(x)| > M$.

Parenthetically, there is something to be learned from the explanation given above of the meaning of the theorem. The explanation is nothing but the restatement of the theorem in slow motion. It also adds a few statements as to what the theorem does not say. This is characteristic of almost all mathematical explanations of this kind. An explanation is a slow rerun of the original. The reason for adding statements as to what the theorem didn't say is so as to check that the reader has made the right mental maneuvers at the critical points on the road, that he has not been lured into making the wrong turn. But when one is through, the conclusion is that the theorem says just what it means. If it is well stated, it is terse, accurate, clear, and to the point. It may be complicated. What does one do? One rereads it slowly, twice, three times if necessary, until the mystery disappears.

To prove the theorem, it must be shown that for *every* f and *every* M one can find an L. A single proof must do simultaneously for all cases. Thus the proof will be exclusively given in abstract terms and this makes it a bit hard. In order to motivate it, we consider a specific case.

Suppose that f is the special function defined by

$$f(x) = x^3 - x^2 \tag{7}$$

and let $M = 100$. It will be shown that if x satisfies $|x| > 10$, then $|f(x)| > 100$. (So $L = 10$.)

First write (7) in the equivalent form

$$f(x) = x^3 \left(1 - \frac{1}{x} \right). \tag{8}$$

We remind the reader that for any real numbers a and b, $|a - b| \geq |a| - |b|$. [See I.2.b, Exercise 4(c).] Choose x so that $|x| \geq 2$. Then for such a choice,

$$\left| 1 - \frac{1}{x} \right| \geq 1 - \frac{1}{|x|} \geq 1 - \frac{1}{2} = \frac{1}{2}. \tag{9}$$

Therefore, if $|x| \geq 2$ then from (8),

$$|f(x)| \geq \frac{1}{2} |x^3|. \tag{10}$$

Now we wish to ensure that x is so chosen that $|f(x)| \geq 100$. Then all we need to do is to choose x so that $|x| \geq 10$. This can be seen as follows: Note that if $|x| \geq 10$, then $|x^3| \geq 1000$. Next note that if $|x| \geq 10$, then $|x| \geq 2$; hence (10) holds. Thus, for $|x| \geq 10$,

$$|f(x)| \geq \frac{1}{2} \times 1000 = 500 > 100. \tag{11}$$

This shows how the statement of the theorem is proved for the special case: $f(x) = x^3 - x^2$ and $M = 100$; an answer is $L = 10$. (Another answer is $L = 21$, because if $|x| \geq 21$ then $|x| \geq 10$ and hence $|f(x)| \geq 100$.)

Suppose that for the same polynomial f given in (7), the value of M equals one billion, that is, $M = 10^9$ ($10^9 = 1,000,000,000$). Returning to our two contestants A and B, we can see that A is trying to make the going hard for B. However, B will meet the challenge with ease.

Going back to (10), it may be seen that for any $|x| \geq 2$, $|f(x)| \geq \frac{1}{2}|x^3|$. Thus to make $|f(x)| \geq 10^9$, all that is needed is $|x| \geq 10^4$; because if $|x| \geq 10^4$, then $|x^3| \geq 10^{12}$ and $\frac{1}{2}10^{12} \geq \frac{1}{10}10^{12} = 10^{11}$ and finally $10^{11} \geq 10^9$. Thus if $|x| \geq 10^4$, then $|f(x)| \geq 10^9$.

A note on inequalities. The student should feel lavish in his handling of inequalities. If he wishes to make some quantity > 100 and it is easier to make it $> 10,000$ he should go right ahead and make it $> 10,000$. There is no use penny pinching in this game.

Since the proof of the theorem is a bit more difficult than the calculation of specific examples, it is left for the Appendix to this chapter. This Appendix proves some results showing how $f(x)$ behaves when x is large. The technical language for "x is large" is "x is close to infinity." For that reason the Appendix is called "The behavior of polynomials at infinity." Before reading the Appendix, some of the exercises at the end of this section should be worked out.

If f is the polynomial function given in (6) (remember that $a_n \neq 0$ and $n \geq 1$), then for $x \neq 0$, $f(x)$ may be written as indicated below:

$$f(x) = a_n x^n \left(1 + \frac{a_{n-1}}{a_n x} + \frac{a_{n-2}}{a_n x^2} + \cdots + \frac{a_0}{a_n x^n} \right). \tag{12}$$

Consider now just the quantity in parentheses

$$w = 1 + \frac{a_{n-1}}{a_n x} + \frac{a_{n-2}}{a_n x^2} + \cdots + \frac{a_0}{a_n x^n}. \tag{13}$$

If $|x|$ is large then $|a_{n-1}/a_n x|$ is small. That is, by looking at the magnitude of a_{n-1} and of a_n, we can choose $|x|$ so large that $|a_{n-1}/a_n x|$ is small. This means that $a_{n-1}/a_n x$ is close to 0. The quantity may be positive or negative, but in any case it is close to 0.

Similarly, for $|x|$ large, $a_{n-2}/a_n x^2$ is close to 0. Finally $a_0/a_n x^n$ is close to 0.

Now if 1, 2, or 3 or even if n quantities are close to 0, their sum is close to 0. Since for $|x|$ large, w is the sum of 1 plus n quantities close to 0, w is itself close to 1. The important fact is that for $|x|$ large, $w > 0$.

The above argument is important for the proof of the preceding theorem and of the next theorem. The validity of the argument is shown in the Appendix. We shall assume it at this point and proceed.

Let us suppose that it has been shown that if $|x| > L$, then $w > 0$. Then since $f(x) = a_n x^n \cdot w$, $f(x)$ has the same sign as $a_n x^n$. Since $a_n \neq 0$, either $a_n > 0$ or $a_n < 0$. Suppose first that $a_n > 0$. Then for $x > 0$, $x^n > 0$ and $a_n x^n > 0$; thus if $|x|$ is large, $f(x) > 0$. Suppose now that $x < 0$. Then if n is even $x^n > 0$ and $a_n x^n > 0$. If n is odd $x^n < 0$ and $a_n x^n < 0$. Thus for $x > 0$, $|x|$ large, $f(x) > 0$; for $x < 0$, $|x|$ large, $f(x) < 0$.

In the case $a_n < 0$, results of a similar nature can be obtained. We state this in the form of a theorem. To make matters a little more simple we assume that $a_n = 1$. Keep in mind that according to Theorem III–2, $|f(x)|$ is large when $|x|$ is large.

III–3 Theorem
If f is defined by

$$f(x) = a_0 + a_1 x + \cdots + x^n, \qquad n \geq 1, \tag{14}$$

then

    (a) *if n is even, $f(x) > 0$ for $|x|$ large;*
    (b) *if n is odd, $f(x) > 0$ for x positive and $|x|$ large and $f(x) < 0$ for x negative and $|x|$ large.*

Theorems III–2 and III–3 show that if a polynomial function f is the 0 function, that is, if $f(x) = 0$ for all x, then all the coefficients of f are zero. We state this result formally.

III–4 Theorem
Let f be defined by

$$f(x) = a_0 + a_1 x + \cdots + a_n x^n \tag{15}$$

and suppose $f(x) = 0$ for all x. Then $a_0 = 0$, $a_1 = 0$, $\cdots$, $a_n = 0$.

Note that Theorem III–4 is logically equivalent to the statement: *If the coefficients of f are not all zero, there exists an x such that $f(x) \neq 0$.* Thus we have answered the question at the beginning of this section.

A numerical example follows to show how to prove that w is close to 1 for $|x|$ large [see (13)].

Given that

$$w = 1 + \frac{2}{x} - \frac{3}{x^2} + \frac{1}{x^5}, \tag{16}$$

find L so that if $|x| \geq L$, then $w \geq \frac{1}{2}$.

First remember that if a, b, c are any real numbers $|a \pm b \pm c| \leq |a| + |b| + |c|$ [see I.2.b, Exercises 4(b) and 5(a)]. Also, if $|d| < \frac{1}{2}$, then $-\frac{1}{2} < d < \frac{1}{2}$ and $1 + d$ satisfies $\frac{1}{2} < 1 + d < \frac{3}{2}$.

Going back to (16), we shall make each of the quantities $|2/x|$, $|3/x^2|$, $|1/x^5|$ less than $1/6$. Then their sum is less than $\frac{1}{2}$.

In order that $|2/x| < 1/6$, it suffices that $|x| > 12$.

In order that $|3/x^2| < 1/6$, it suffices that $|x^2| > 18$. Thus it suffices that $|x| > 5$.

In order that $|1/x^5| < 1/6$, it suffices that $|x^5| > 6$, hence it suffices that $|x| > 2$.

Thus if x is so chosen that $|x|$ is larger than each of 12, 5, 2, each of the above quantities is less than $1/6$. This will be true if $|x| > 12$.

This shows that for $|x| > 12$,

$$\left|\frac{2}{x}\right| + \left|\frac{3}{x^2}\right| + \left|\frac{1}{x^5}\right| < \frac{1}{6} + \frac{1}{6} + \frac{1}{6} = \frac{1}{2}. \tag{17}$$

Also,

$$\left|\frac{2}{x} - \frac{3}{x^2} + \frac{1}{x^5}\right| \le \left|\frac{2}{x}\right| + \left|\frac{3}{x^2}\right| + \left|\frac{1}{x^5}\right|, \tag{18}$$

hence, finally, by the discussion in a previous paragraph,

$$\frac{1}{2} < 1 + \frac{2}{x} - \frac{3}{x^2} + \frac{1}{x^5} < \frac{3}{2}. \tag{19}$$

Exercises III.1.a

1. For each of the functions f below, find L such that if $|x| > L$, $|f(x)| > M$.

(a) $f(x) = x^3$, $\qquad M = 100$;

(b) $f(x) = -2x^4$, $\qquad M = 1000$;

(c) $f(x) = x^n$, $n \ge 3$, $\qquad M = 10$;

(d) $f(x) = \dfrac{1}{10} x^{10}$, $\qquad M = 10^{10}$.

2. Prove that if $|x| < \frac{1}{2}$, then

(a) $\dfrac{1}{2} < 1 - x < \dfrac{3}{2}$;

(b) $\dfrac{1}{4} < 1 - 3x^2 < \dfrac{7}{4}$;

(c) $\dfrac{1}{4} < 1 - x^2 + x^3 - x^4 < \dfrac{7}{4}$.

3. Prove that if $|x| > 2$, then

(a) $|x^3 - x^2| > 4$;
(b) $|x^5 - x^3 + x| > 16$;
(c) $|x^7 - 2x^4 + 7x^2| > 64$.

4. Show that for $|x| > 10^4$,

$$\left|\frac{x^5}{10^5} - 10^8 x\right| > 10^{14}.$$

5. Find L so that if $|x| > L$, then the function f below satisfies $|f(x)| < \frac{1}{2}$.

(a) $f(x) = \frac{1}{x} + \frac{1}{x^2}$;

(b) $f(x) = \frac{1}{x} - \frac{2}{x^2} + \frac{3}{x^3}$;

(c) $f(x) = \frac{10}{x} + \frac{1}{100x^2} + \frac{1}{x^5}$.

6. In Problem 5, find L so that if $|x| > L$, then $|f(x)| < \frac{1}{10}$.

7. Find a natural number k such that if $|x| > 10^k$, then

$$|x^7 - 10x^2 + 30x - 14| > 10^{100}.$$

2. THE DEFINITION OF DEGREE

Suppose that we have two polynomials f and g defined by

$$f(x) = a_0 + a_1 x + \cdots + a_n x^n, \tag{1}$$

and

$$g(x) = b_0 + b_1 x + \cdots + b_n x^n. \tag{2}$$

We have used the same integer n for both expressions by adding 0 coefficients to one or the other according to need. [For example, if $f(x) = 1 + x + x^2$ and $g(x) = 2 - x$, then g is written in the form $g(x) = 2 + (-1)x + 0x^2$. Thus in both f and g the same number of coefficients is used.] Suppose that

$$f(x) = g(x) \qquad \text{for all } x.$$

Then, as will be shown, $a_0 = b_0, a_1 = b_1, \cdots, a_n = b_n$.

The proof is straightforward: Seeing that $f = g$, we have $f - g = 0$. Now $f - g$ is given by

$$(f - g)(x) = f(x) - g(x) = (a_0 - b_0) + \cdots + (a_n - b_n)x^n. \tag{3}$$

Then, since $f - g = 0$, the last theorem of Section 1 states that all the coefficients of $f - g$ are 0. Thus

$$a_0 - b_0 = 0, \qquad a_1 - b_1 = 0, \qquad \cdots \quad, \qquad a_n - b_n = 0. \qquad \text{(4)}$$

This gives the desired equality of the coefficients of f and g. *Notice that we do not insist that $a_n \neq 0$ or $b_n \neq 0$.* We give this important result an explicit formulation:

III–5 Unique Representation Theorem

If f and g are polynomial functions defined by

$$f(x) = a_0 + a_1 x + \cdots + a_n x^n,$$
$$g(x) = b_0 + b_1 x + \cdots + b_n x^n,$$

and if $f = g$ [that is, $f(x) = g(x)$ for all x], then the coefficients of f are the same as those of g; that is,

$$a_0 = b_0, \qquad a_1 = b_1, \qquad \cdots \quad, \qquad a_n = b_n.$$

According to this theorem, if we are given a polynomial function f, the coefficients of f are determined uniquely. This is a fact of capital importance. Everything we do from now on depends on it.

Suppose now that f is a polynomial function different from the zero function. Then we may write it as

$$f(x) = a_0 + a_1 x + \cdots + a_n x^n$$

with $a_n \neq 0$. In other words we use the minimal length required for writing f [see Equations (2) and (3) of Section 1]. The integer n is called the *degree* of f. If $f = 0$, that is, if f is the zero polynomial function, we do not assign a degree to it (for reasons that will be apparent later). The term $a_n x^n$ is called the *leading term* of the polynomial. Thus:

III–6 Definition

If $f \neq 0$ is a polynomial function defined by

$$f(x) = a_0 + a_1 x \cdots + a_n x^n, \qquad a_n \neq 0,$$

then the integer $n \geq 0$ is called the degree of f. If $f = 0$, f does not have a degree.

At first reading, one may be somewhat mystified by the long and some-what difficult considerations that precede the definition of degree. After much work we seem to have reached a conclusion that many might have been ready to accept at the outset. There are several answers to such an attitude. In the first place, the objection amounts to this: If something can be proved to be true, it is a waste of time to so prove it! Another fact about this situation is the following: Our results concern polynomial functions defined over the field of real numbers. The results are false for polynomials defined over other fields; for example, the finite fields. This is the substance of Exercise 5 in I.1.a.

Polynomial functions of degree 2, 3, 4, 5, 6 are called quadratics, cubics, quartics, quintics, sextics. A polynomial of degree 1 is described as linear. The amount of complication to be expected from polynomials goes up sharply with the degree. Roughly speaking a sextic is $1 \cdot 2 \cdot 3 \cdot 4 \cdot 5 \cdot 6 = 720$ times as complicated as a linear polynomial.

We show now how to add and multiply polynomials. More precisely, we show what addition and multiplication of polynomials do to the coefficients. That is, we show how to get the coefficients of the sum or product of f and g from the coefficients of f and g.

Consider the case of addition. Let f and g be defined by

$$f(x) = a_0 + a_1 x + \cdots + a_n x^n, \qquad a_n \neq 0;$$
$$g(x) = b_0 + b_1 x + \cdots + b_m x^m, \qquad b_m \neq 0,$$

Then

$$(f + g)(x) = f(x) + g(x) = (a_0 + b_0) + (a_1 + b_1)x + \cdots, \qquad \textbf{(5)}$$

where the last term to be written down in (5) depends on the relationship between n and m. Thus it is evident that the coefficients of $f + g$ are obtained by adding the respective coefficients of f and of g. Note also that the degree of $f + g$ (assuming that $f + g \neq 0$) is at most equal to the larger of the degrees of f and of g.

For example, let us add the two polynomials f and g defined by

$$f(x) = 2 - x^2 \quad \text{and} \quad g(x) = 2x^2 + 3x^3 + x^4.$$

First "fill in" with the necessary zeros. This gives

$$f(x) = 2 + 0x - x^2 + 0x^3 + 0x^4;$$
$$g(x) = 0 + 0x + 2x^2 + 3x^3 + x^4,$$

Hence

$$f(x) + g(x) = 2 + 0x + (2 - 1)x^2 + 3x^3 + x^4$$

or $f(x) + g(x) = 2 + x^2 + 3x^3 + x^4$.

The following example shows that the degree of $f + g$ can be less than the degree of either f or g. Let $f(x) = 2 - x^2$ and $g(x) = 1 + 3x + x^2$. Then $f(x) + g(x) = 3 + 3x$.

Consider now the case of multiplication. If either $f = 0$ or $g = 0$, then $f \cdot g = 0$. Suppose now that neither $f = 0$ nor $g = 0$. Thus we suppose that both f and g have a degree. Let us start off with an example. If we have

$$f(x) = 3 - 2x + x^2 \quad \text{and} \quad g(x) = 2 - 2x^2 + x^3,$$

then, by the definition of the multiplication of functions,

$$\begin{aligned}(f \cdot g)(x) = f(x) \cdot g(x) &= (3 - 2x + x^2)(2 - 2x^2 + x^3) \\ &= 6 - 4x + (2 - 6)x^2 + (3 + 4)x^3 + (-2 - 2)x^4 + x^5 \\ &= 6 - 4x - 4x^2 + 7x^3 - 4x^4 + x^5.\end{aligned}$$

This shows that the product $f \cdot g$ is a polynomial of degree 5, that is, of degree equal to the sum of the degrees of f and g. The coefficients of $f \cdot g$ are obtained as follows: For a given power of x, say x^3, consider all combinations of powers of x, one from f and one from g, whose product is x^3. These are $x^0 \cdot x^3$, $x^1 \cdot x^2$, $x^2 \cdot x^1$. The corresponding products of coefficients are 3, 4, and 0. Adding, we obtain the coefficient of x^3 in the product of f and g: this coefficient is $3 + 4 + 0 = 7$.

In general, for the two polynomials f and g defined by

$$f(x) = a_0 + a_1 x + \cdots + a_n x^n, \qquad a_n \neq 0, \tag{6}$$

$$g(x) = b_0 + b_1 x + \cdots + b_m x^m, \qquad b_m \neq 0, \tag{7}$$

we have for the product $f \cdot g$

$$(f \cdot g)(x) = f(x) \cdot g(x) = c_0 + c_1 x + \cdots + c_{n+m} x^{n+m}, \tag{8}$$

where the coefficients $c_0, c_1, \cdots, c_{n+m}$ are given by the expressions

$$\begin{aligned}
c_0 &= a_0 b_0, \\
c_1 &= a_0 b_1 + a_1 b_0, \\
c_2 &= a_0 b_2 + a_1 b_1 + a_2 b_0, \\
c_3 &= a_0 b_3 + a_1 b_2 + a_2 b_1 + a_3 b_0,
\end{aligned} \tag{9}$$

and so on up to c_{n+m} for which

$$c_{n+m} = a_n b_m. \tag{10}$$

From the fact that $a_n \neq 0$ and $b_m \neq 0$, follows that $a_n \cdot b_m \neq 0$; thus $c_{n+m} \neq 0$ and $f \cdot g$ has the degree $n + m$.

The latter result indicates why it is not desirable to give the polynomial 0 a degree. If $f = 0$ had a degree (presumably 0) then the degree of the product of f and g would not equal the sum of the degrees of f and g.

The method of composing the a's with the b's in order to obtain the c's arises frequently and in more sophisticated forms in advanced mathematics. It is called *convolution*.

If for three nonzero polynomials f, g, h one has $h = f \cdot g$, it is said that f and g are *factors* of h and h is divisible by f and by g.

We are now in possession of the following information and skills: Given two polynomial functions f and g we know how to recognize whether $f = g$ by looking at the coefficients. Given two such polynomials, we know how to add them and multiply them and we know that the result of these operations is again a polynomial. We know that addition and multiplication have a variety of properties, including associativity, commutativity, and distributivity. (These properties are valid for all functions, not merely for polynomials.) In other words, the set of polynomials, with the operations of addition and multiplication, forms a ring. We met another example of a ring, namely the integers. The polynomials have properties very similar to the integers. For example, they can be factored into prime factors in one and only one way (we shall not need this result in what follows).

We repeat once more that a polynomial function is completely determined by its coefficients. The various powers of x just act as "place holders." Thus the polynomial f given by $f(x) = 3 + 2x - x^2$ is completely determined by the ordered triple $(2, 3, -1)$. This observation leads to the conclusion that polynomials have a "life" independent of their life as functions. For example, it is quite possible and easy to prove that the set of polynomials is a ring without referring to the fact that one is dealing with functions. We shall exploit these ideas in a subsequent chapter on polynomials when we deal with abstract power series.

Exercises III.2.a

1. Find the sum $f + g$ and the product $f \cdot g$ of the polynomial functions f and g defined by

   (a) $f(x) = 2 - x^2 + 3x^3$, $g(x) = 4 - 2x - x^5$;
   (b) $f(x) = x^2(x - 2)$, $g(x) = (x - 1)^2 + 2x$;
   (c) $f(x) = x^3 + x^2 + x + 1$, $g(x) = x(x - 1)$;
   (d) $f(x) = x^2 + 2x + 1$, $g(x) = x^2 - 2x + 1$;
   (e) $f(x) = x^3 - 1$, $g(x) = x^3 + 1$;
   (f) $f(x) = x^3 - x$, $g(x) = x^4 - 2x^2 + 1$;
   (g) $f(x) = 4x^2 - 4x + 1$, $g(x) = 2x - 1$.

2. Find the coefficient of x^3, x^4, x^5 in the product of the polynomial functions defined by

   (a) $f(x) = 3x^3 - 2$, $g(x) = 6 - 2x + x^4$;
   (b) $f(x) = (x + 2)^5$, $g(x) = 2x^2$;
   (c) $f(x) = (x + 1)^3$, $g(x) = x^2 - 1$;
   (d) $f(x) = x^3 - x + 1$, $g(x) = x^2 + x - 2$;
   (e) $f(x) = x^4 + x^2 + 1$, $g(x) = x^2 - 1$;
   (f) $f(x) = (2x - 1)^3$, $g(x) = (2x + 1)(2x - 1)$.

3. Obtain the coefficients of

   (a) $(x + 1)^5$;   (b) $(x + 2)^6$;
   (c) $(x - 1)^4$;   (d) $(2x - 1)^3$.
   Obtain the sum of the coefficients in two distinct ways.

4. Prove that if the product of two polynomials is the zero polynomial, then one of the polynomials in the product is itself the zero polynomial.

5. Find for which values of s the polynomials below are of degree 2:

(a) $f(x) = (s^2 - 3s + 2)x^3 + (s - 5)x^2 + 2sx - 1$;

(b) $f(x) = (s^2 - 1)x^3 + (s + 1)x^2 + 3x - (2s + 3)$;

(c) $f(x) = (s + 2)x^3 + (s^2 + 4s + 4)x^2 + 2$;

(d) $f(x) = (s^2 - 1)x^4 + (s - 1)x^3 + 2x^2 - 1$;

(e) $f(x) = (s^3 - s)x^5 + sx^4 + (s + 1)x^2 - sx - 3$.

3. THE DIVISION ALGORITHM

It has been proved (Chapter I, Section 1) that the set of natural numbers has the following property: If a and b are natural numbers with $b \neq 0$, then there exist natural numbers c and d with $0 \leq d < b$ such that

$$a = bc + d.$$

This is the division algorithm for the natural numbers. It is the basic tool in the entire theory of factorization. A similar algorithm holds for polynomials.

It has been seen that the product of two polynomials is a polynomial. It is not true that the quotient of two polynomials is a polynomial in all cases. Suppose, for example, that two polynomials f and g are defined by $f(x) = 1$, $g(x) = x$. Suppose that

$$\frac{1}{x} = \frac{f(x)}{g(x)} = h(x),$$

where $h(x)$ is a polynomial.

Now, h is obviously not constant. Thus h is a polynomial of degree ≥ 1. However, all such polynomials h have the property that when $|x|$ is large, $|h(x)|$ is large (Theorem III–2). This is clearly not the case here; if $|x| \geq 1$, $|h(x)| \leq 1$. Thus h is not a polynomial.

It has been seen earlier that the polynomials form a ring. The above result shows that they do not form a field.

We shall now show that if f and g are polynomials with $g \neq 0$, then there exist two polynomials q and r such that

$$f = g \cdot q + r, \tag{1}$$

and such that either $r = 0$, or else $r \neq 0$ and r has a degree that is less than the degree of g. In the case $r = 0$, we shall say that g is a factor of f (also, g divides f exactly). The polynomial r is called the remainder after dividing f by g.

Before writing out the proof in general, let us consider an example. Suppose f and g are two polynomials given by

$$f(x) = 2x^4 - 6x^3 + 5x^2 - 2x - 7,$$
$$g(x) = x^2 - 3x + 2. \tag{2}$$

We wish to find the polynomials q and r for this special pair f and g. We proceed as if g actually divided f to find the quotient q. It will turn out that our assumption on division is wrong. There is something left over, namely, r.

If g divides f, then since f is of degree 4 and g is of degree 2, the quotient q must be of degree $4 - 2 = 2$. Thus q is given by an expression

$$q(x) = b_0x^2 + b_1x + b_2. \tag{3}$$

Since we assume that g divides f, or to put it more precisely, it comes close to dividing f, we have

$$f(x) = g(x) \cdot q(x) + r(x), \tag{4}$$

that is,

$$
\begin{aligned}
2x^4 - 6x^3 + 5x^2 - 2x - 7 &= (x^2 - 3x + 2)(b_0x^2 + b_1x + b_2) + r(x) \\
&= b_0x^4 + (b_1 - 3b_0)x^3 + (b_2 - 3b_1 + 2b_0)x^2 \\
&\quad + (-3b_2 + 2b_1)x + 2b_2 + r(x).
\end{aligned}
$$

Now, if g is to divide f exactly, then $r = 0$ and we can appeal to the theorem about equal polynomials having equal coefficients. This gives five equations in the unknowns b_0, b_1, b_2. Usually these five equations cannot be solved; they are inconsistent. But the first three of these equations can most certainly be solved. They are

$$
\begin{aligned}
b_0 &= 2, \\
b_1 - 3b_0 &= -6, \\
b_2 - 3b_1 + 2b_0 &= 5.
\end{aligned}
$$

The solutions are $b_0 = 2$, $b_1 = 0$, $b_2 = 1$. With these values we have $q(x) = 2x^2 + 1$. And thus $f - g \cdot q$ is a polynomial r of degree 1, that is, of degree lower than that of g. Indeed, $r(x) = x - 9$.

This is, for a special example, the method for proving the result in the general case.

It is apparent from the example that in all cases we shall have success in solving the equations for the coefficients of q. The solutions give a polynomial q such that the polynomial $f - g \cdot q$ has a degree less than the degree of g, or is the polynomial 0.

Going back to the example, the correct and the understandable way of obtaining the polynomials q and r is that which is indicated above. However, in the interest of efficiency, and for those who have to perform many divisions, the above proof can be schematized as follows:

$$
\begin{array}{r}
2x^2 + 0x + 1 = q(x) \\
g(x) = x^2 - 3x + 2 \overline{)2x^4 - 6x^3 + 5x^2 - 2x - 7} = f(x) \\
\underline{2x^4 - 6x^3 + 4x^2} \\
0x^3 + x^2 - 2x - 7 \\
\underline{0x^3 + 0x^2 + 0x} \\
x^2 - 2x - 7 \\
\underline{x^2 - 3x + 2} \\
x - 9 = r(x)
\end{array}
$$

The above scheme reflects faithfully if not with complete transparency, the steps of the solution we have given earlier. This fact can be checked by rewriting the scheme line by line and comparing the results obtained here with those we obtained above.

Let us now turn to the general problem. Suppose f and g are given by

$$f(x) = a_0 x^m + a_1 x^{m-1} + \cdots + a_m, \qquad a_0 \neq 0,$$
$$g(x) = b_0 x^n + b_1 x^{n-1} + \cdots + b_n, \qquad b_0 \neq 0, \tag{5}$$

and let us assume $m \geq n$. (If $m < n$, then $q = 0$ and $r = f$.)
Write

$$q(x) = c_0 x^{m-n} + c_1 x^{m-n-1} + \cdots + c_{m-n}. \tag{6}$$

Then, multiplying g by q and writing down as many equations involving the a's, the b's, and the c's as q has coefficients (there are $m - n + 1$ of them), we obtain

$$\begin{aligned}
b_0 c_0 &= a_0, \\
b_0 c_1 + b_1 c_0 &= a_1, \\
b_0 c_2 + b_1 c_1 + b_2 c_0 &= a_2,
\end{aligned} \tag{7}$$

$$b_0 c_{m-n} + \cdots + b_{m-n} c_0 = a_{m-n}.$$

Remember that the a's and b's are assumed known and the c's are the unknowns. Since $b_0 \neq 0$ we solve the first equation for c_0. Substitute this value in the second equation and solve that equation for c_1. Continue in this way to solve all equations. These values of $c_0, c_1, \cdots, c_{m-n}$ determine q completely (and uniquely). We thus find that $f - g \cdot q$ is a polynomial r of degree less than n or $r = 0$. This completes the proof. For the sake of completeness and emphasis, this result is stated explicitly:

III–7 Division Algorithm
Let f and g be polynomials, $g \neq 0$. Then there exist unique polynomials q and r such that

$$f = gq + r,$$

and such that either $r = 0$ or the degree of r is less than the degree of g.

We shall now derive a theorem that can be obtained at trivial cost from the division algorithm. This result is known by the romantic name of:

III–8 The Principal Ideal Theorem
Let $\mathscr{F}$ be a family of polynomials having the property that:

(a) *if f and g are polynomials in the family $\mathscr{F}$, then $f + g$ is also in $\mathscr{F}$;*
(b) *if f is in $\mathscr{F}$ and k is any polynomial, then $k \cdot f$ is in $\mathscr{F}$.*

Then there exists a single polynomial h in $\mathscr{F}$ which divides exactly every other polynomial in $\mathscr{F}$.

PROOF: Each of the nonzero polynomials in $\mathscr{F}$ has a degree. Of all the natural numbers that appear as a degree, there is a least one (by the well-ordering property of the natural numbers, Theorem I–2). Let h be any polynomial in $\mathscr{F}$ having this least degree. Now suppose f is any polynomial in $\mathscr{F}$. Then by the division algorithm,

$$f = hq + r \qquad \text{or} \qquad f - hq = r, \tag{8}$$

where either $r = 0$ or the degree of r is less than that of h. Because h is in $\mathscr{F}$, $-hq = (-q) \cdot h$ is in $\mathscr{F}$ by condition (b) in the theorem. By condition (a), $f - hq = f + (-q)h$ is also in $\mathscr{F}$. This means that r is in $\mathscr{F}$. Now, the degree of r cannot be less than that of h by the choice of h. Thus $r = 0$. This proves the theorem. The alert reader will note that we have made a very mild assumption about $\mathscr{F}$ which belongs in the theorem. We have assumed that $\mathscr{F}$ contains nonzero polynomials.

The Principal Ideal Theorem for the integers **Z** is given in Exercise 3 of I.2.a.

If one is working in a ring (such as the ring of integers or the ring of polynomials), families $\mathscr{F}$, which have properties (a) and (b), are called ideals. The theorem states that all ideals in the ring of polynomials are of a special kind; they consist of the polynomial multiples of a fixed polynomial h. For example, all the multiples of $x - 1$ form an ideal. [This ideal contains $x^2 - 1 = (x + 1)(x - 1)$; it contains $x^3 - 1 = (x^2 + x + 1)(x - 1)$; it contains many other polynomials.] There are many ideals of polynomials. There are many ideals of integers.

Now the rational numbers **Q** form a field, hence also a ring. In **Q** there are only two ideals: the ideal consisting of the number 0 only and the ideal consisting of all the numbers in **Q**. Try to prove this. A complete proof is five lines long but the thinking required here is a bit new.

Exercises III.3.a

1. Find the quotient q and the remainder r in the equation $f = gq + r$ where

(a) $f(x) = x^3 + x^2 + x + 1,$ $\qquad\qquad$ $g(x) = x - 1;$
(b) $f(x) = x^5 - 1,$ $\qquad\qquad$ $g(x) = x - 1;$
(c) $f(x) = x^3 - 2x^2 + 3x,$ $\qquad\qquad$ $g(x) = x - 2;$
(d) $f(x) = x^3 + 3x^2 + 3x + 1,$ $\qquad\qquad$ $g(x) = x + 1;$
(e) $f(x) = x^5 + x^4 - x^3 + 2x^2 + 5x - 2,$ $\quad$ $g(x) = x^2 + 1;$
(f) $f(x) = x^4 - 3x^2 + x - 2,$ $\qquad\qquad$ $g(x) = 2x^2 + x - 4;$
(g) $f(x) = 3x^2 - 2x + 1,$ $\qquad\qquad$ $g(x) = x^4 + 6x.$

2. Find the quotient q and the remainder r in the equation $f = gq + r$ where

(a) $f(x) = x^3 + 2x^2 - 3x + 1,$ $\quad$ $g(x) = x - 1;$
(b) $f(x) = x^4 - 1,$ $\qquad\qquad\quad$ $g(x) = x + 1;$

(c) $f(x) = 2x^3 + 4x^2 - 1$, $g(x) = 4x^2 + 2$;
(d) $f(x) = x^2 + 3x + 2$, $g(x) = x^3 + 3x^2 + 2x$;
(e) $f(x) = x^3 + 8$, $g(x) = x + 2$;
(f) $f(x) = x^5 - x^3 + x^2 - 1$, $g(x) = x - 1$.

3. Write down three distinct polynomial ideals. For each ideal, indicate three polynomials that belong to the ideal. [*Note*: Ideals of polynomials are defined by conditions (a) and (b) of the Principal Ideal Theorem III–2. The definition of an ideal in **Z** is analogous.]

4. For every natural number n, write down an ideal such that all nonzero polynomials in the ideal have degree at least n. What happens for the case $n = 0$?

5. Prove that in **Q** there are only two ideals. Same problem for **R**.

Historical Note. Ideals were introduced into mathematics by two great German algebraists, Ernst Eduard Kummer (1810–1893) and J. W. R. Dedekind (1831–1916). Kummer's work was earlier (1846). There is unique factorization into primes for the integers and for the polynomials because the principal ideal theorem holds.

4. THE REMAINDER THEOREM AND THE FACTOR THEOREM

Suppose f is a polynomial of degree at least equal to 1 and suppose c is some fixed number. Then if the polynomial g is defined by $g(x) = x - c$ it is of special interest to apply the division algorithm to the pair f and g. What, in this case, will the polynomials q and r be? About q, nothing of note can be said at this moment. But for r we have a special situation. Either $r = 0$ and in this case $x - c$ divides $f(x)$ exactly. Or $r \neq 0$. In this case, the degree of r is less than the degree of $x - c$ which is 1. Thus the degree of r is 0 and r is a constant. Question: What constant? Obviously, it is a constant that has something to do with the polynomial f and something to do with the number c. The Remainder Theorem states that this constant is $f(c)$.

III–9 Remainder Theorem
Let f be a polynomial function of degree $n \geq 1$. Let c be a constant. Then if $f(x)$ is divided by $x - c$, the remainder is the constant $f(c)$. That is,

$$f(x) = (x - c)q(x) + f(c). \tag{1}$$

The proof is almost trivial. By the division algorithm,

$$f(x) = (x - c)q(x) + r, \tag{2}$$

where r is a constant. This equation is valid for all x. In particular, it is valid for $x = c$. Thus,

$$f(c) = (c - c)q(c) + r = 0 \cdot q(c) + r = 0 + r = r. \qquad (3)$$

This finishes the proof.

Consider an example. Let f be given by

$$f(x) = x^4 - 2x^3 + x^2 + x - 4$$

and consider the case $c = 2$. The division is carried out below.

$$
\begin{array}{r}
x^3 + 0x^2 + x + 3 \qquad = q(x) \\
g(x) = x - 2 \overline{)x^4 - 2x^3 + x^2 + x - 4} = f(x) \\
\underline{x^4 - 2x^3} \\
0 + 0 \quad + x^2 + x - 4 \\
\underline{x^2 - 2x} \\
3x - 4 \\
\underline{3x - 6} \\
2 = r(x)
\end{array}
$$

Thus $r = 2$. Also

$$f(2) = 2^4 - 2 \times 2^3 + 2^2 + 2 - 4 = 2.$$

This verifies the Remainder Theorem in this case.

Consider now a slightly deeper and more instructive example. Let f be as defined below

$$f(x) = x^3 + x^2 + x + 1,$$

and let us not specify the value of c. According to the theorem, the remainder after dividing $f(x)$ by $x - c$ is $f(c)$. That is, the remainder is $c^3 + c^2 + c + 1$. The division is actually carried out below and the correct answer is obtained.

$$
\begin{array}{r}
x^2 + (1 + c)x + (1 + c + c^2) \qquad = q(x) \\
g(x) = x - c \overline{)x^3 + \quad x^2 \qquad + \quad x + 1} = f(x) \\
\underline{x^3 - \quad cx^2} \\
(1 + c)x^2 \qquad + \quad x + 1 \\
\underline{(1 + c)x^2 \quad - \quad (c + c^2)x} \\
(1 + c + c^2)x + 1 \\
\underline{(1 + c + c^2)x - \quad (c + c^2 + c^3)} \\
1 + c + c^2 + c^3 = r(x)
\end{array}
$$

This example not only merely verifies the Remainder Theorem but it indicates how the remainder evolves, step by step, in the process of division. The Remainder Theorem has this important corollary:

III–10 Corollary

If f is any polynomial and c is any constant, then $f(x) - f(c)$ is exactly divisible by $x - c$.

The proof (which is immediate) is left as an exercise (see Exercise 3).

Exercises III.4.a

1. Verify the Remainder Theorem in the following cases by actually carrying out the division of $f(x)$ by $(x - c)$.

   (a) $f(x) = x^2 - 4x + 5$, $c = 2$;
   (b) $f(x) = x^3$, $c = 1$;
   (c) $f(x) = x^4 + 3x^3 - x^2 - 3x$, $c = 1$;
   (d) $f(x) = x^5 - 7x^3 + x^2 - 4$, $c = 0$.

2. Do the same as in Exercise 1 for

   (a) $f(x) = x^3 - 27$, $c = -3$;
   (b) $f(x) = x^4 - 1$, $c = 1$;
   (c) $f(x) = x^3 + x^2 + x + 1$, $c = -1$;
   (d) $f(x) = x^4 - 4x^3 + 6x^2 - 4x + 1$, $c = 1$.

3. Prove Corollary III–10.

4. In this exercise $f(x)$ is a polynomial, c and d are numbers. Calculate $f(c)$ and $f(d)$ and show that $f(c) = f(d)$. Obtain the quotient $q(x)$ after dividing $f(x)$ by $(x - c)$. Show that $q(d) = 0$.

   (a) $f(x) = x^2 + 14x + 49$, $c = -5$, $d = -9$;
   (b) $f(x) = x^3 - 6x^2 + 11x - 6$, $c = 1$, $d = 2$;
   (c) $f(x) = x^4 - 4x^3 + 6x^2 - 4x + 6$, $c = 3$, $d = -1$;
   (d) $f(x) = x^3 - 7x$, $c = 1$, $d = -3$.

5. Using the equation $f(x) = (x - c)q(x) + f(c)$, show that $f(d) = f(c)$ whenever $q(d) = 0$.

We come to an important definition. Suppose f is any function (not merely a polynomial function) and c is a constant such that

$$f(c) = 0.$$

Then we say that c is a *zero* of f. Thus if f is given by $f(x) = x^3 - 3x^2 + 2x$, it has three zeros, $x = 0$, $x = 1$, and $x = 2$. For polynomial functions f, an alternative and older name for zero is *root* (presumably because one has to dig down to get it). Thus the cube root of 3 means the root of the polynomial $x^3 - 3$ and this in turn is the same as the zero of $x^3 - 3$.

We can now state:

III–11 Factor Theorem

If the polynomial function f has the zero c, then f(x) has the factor x − c. Conversely, if f(x) has the factor x − c, then c is a zero of f.

The proof is simple. By the Remainder Theorem,

$$f(x) = (x − c)q(x) + f(c),$$

where q is some polynomial. Now if c is a zero of f, then $f(c) = 0$ and

$$f(x) = (x − c)q(x),$$

that is, $f(x)$ has the factor $x − c$.

Conversely, if $f(x)$ has the factor $x − c$, write

$$f(x) = (x − c)q(x),$$

Then, clearly,

$$f(c) = (c − c)q(c) = 0 \cdot q(c) = 0.$$

Thus c is a zero of f.

With the help of the Factor Theorem we can prove:

III–12 Theorem

If f is a polynomial function of degree n ≥ 1, then f can have at most n distinct zeros.

PROOF: Let c_1 be a zero of f. Then by the Factor Theorem, one has

$$f(x) = (x − c_1)q_1(x), \tag{4}$$

where $q_1(x)$ is some polynomial. The degree of q_1 is $n − 1$. If $n = 1$ then q_1 is of degree 0; that is, q_1 is a constant, say, $a \neq 0$. In this case f cannot have another zero c_2 distinct from c_1. For, if $c_2 \neq c_1$,

$$f(c_2) = (c_2 − c_1) \cdot a,$$

and since $c_2 − c_1 \neq 0$ and $a \neq 0, f(c_2) \neq 0$. Thus c_2 is not a zero of f. Thus, for the case $n = 1$, f has at most one zero (in fact it has exactly one zero).

Suppose now that $n > 1$. Let c_2 be a second zero of f distinct from c_1. Then

$$f(c_2) = (c_2 − c_1)q_1(c_2).$$

Since $f(c_2) = 0$ and $c_2 \neq c_1$, we have $q_1(c_2) = 0$. Thus c_2 is a zero of q_1. Hence by the Factor Theorem

$$q_1(x) = (x − c_2)q_2(x), \tag{5}$$

where q_2 has degree $n − 2$. Since $f(x) = (x − c_1)q_1(x)$, this gives

$$f(x) = (x − c_1)(x − c_2)q_2(x). \tag{6}$$

If $n = 2$ then q_2 is a constant. Once more we call it a and clearly $a \neq 0$. Proceeding as before, it may be seen that in this case (the case $n = 2$) the polynomial f cannot have more than 2 distinct zeros.

It is now clear how to proceed in general. For a polynomial f of degree n, which has distinct zeros $c_1, c_2, \cdots, c_n$, we factor out the linear terms $(x - c_1)$, $(x - c_2)$, and so on, obtaining finally,

$$f(x) = (x - c_1)(x - c_2) \cdots (x - c_n) \cdot a, \tag{7}$$

where a is a constant, $a \neq 0$. If c is a number distinct from $c_1, c_2, \cdots, c_n$ then

$$f(c) = (c - c_1)(c - c_2) \cdots (c - c_n) \cdot a,$$

and since $c \neq c_1, \cdots, c \neq c_n$, and $a \neq 0$, clearly $f(c) \neq 0$ and thus c is not a zero of f.

From the above theorem it follows very simply that if f is a polynomial of degree $n \geq 0$, then in any interval $a \leq x \leq b$, there exist numbers c such that $f(c) \neq 0$. The proof lies in the fact that no matter what n is, there are more than n real numbers in any given interval. Another way of looking at it is that for a polynomial f of degree $n \geq 1$ the occurrence $f(c) = 0$ is exceedingly rare.

Exercises III.4.b

1. Write down a polynomial of degree 2 which has the zeros 2 and -3. A polynomial of degree 4 which has the zeros 2, 3, -1, and -2.

2. Write down a polynomial of degree 3 which has the zeros 4 and 5 and no others; a polynomial of degree 8 which has the zeros 3 and 7 and no others. How many such polynomials can you find? [*Hint*: Use the notion of repeated roots.]

3. Show that $x + a$ is a factor of $x^3 + a^3$, $x^5 + a^5$. Show that $x - a$ is a factor of $x^3 - a^3$, $x^4 - a^4$, $x^5 - a^5$. Find the quotient in each case.

4. Show that $x - a$ is a factor of $x^n - a^n$ for any natural number n. Find the quotient.

5. Find all distinct zeros of the following polynomials.

(a) $f(x) = x^4 - 3x^2 + 2$;
(b) $f(x) = x^3 - 3x + 2$;
(c) $f(x) = x^3 - 3x^2 + 3x - 1$;
(d) $f(x) = x^4 - 2x^2 + 1$;
(e) $f(x) = 4x^3 - 12x^2 - x + 3$;
(f) $f(x) = 12x^3 - 19x^2 + 5x$.

6. Prove that $f(x) = x^5 + 6x^4 + 13x^3 + 14x^2 + 12x + 8$ is divisible by $(x + 2)^3$. What is the quotient?

7. The polynomial $f(x)$ below is divisible by $x - 2$. Find possible values for s.

(a) $f(x) = x^2 - sx + 2$;
(b) $f(x) = x^2 - 2x + 3s^2 + 2s - 1$;
(c) $f(x) = (sx)^3 - 2sx + s$.

8. The polynomial $f(x)$ below is divisible by $x + 1$. Find the possible values for s.

(a) $f(x) = x^4 + 4x^3 + (3s + 3)x^2 + 4x + s$;
(b) $f(x) = x^2 + (s^2 - 2)x + s - 3$;
(c) $f(x) = x^3 + (s^2 - s - 2)x^2 + (s^2 - 4)x + 2s - 1$.

9. Find a polynomial $f(x)$ having among its zeros $\sqrt{2}$ and $\sqrt{3}$. Find one with integer coefficients.

10. Prove that if c is an integer which is a zero of the polynomial $f(x) = x^n + a_{n-1}x^{n-1} + \cdots + a_0$, where $a_0, a_1, \cdots, a_{n-1}$ are integers, then c divides a_0.

5. THE FUNDAMENTAL THEOREM OF ALGEBRA

The zeros of a polynomial f are not casual numbers without importance. On the contrary, they give a highly incisive type of information about f: If $f(c) = 0$ then $x - c$ is a factor of $f(x)$. This suggests that one should try to determine all the zeros of f. Or possibly, before finding all zeros, one might try to discover whether f has any zeros at all.

We state the question: If f is a polynomial, does f have any zeros? Before attempting to answer the question, it should be made precise.

We are considering a polynomial f. This polynomial may have integral coefficients; it may have rational coefficients; it may have real coefficients. Thus we have three reasonable interpretations to our question: Does f have an integral zero; does it have a rational zero; does it have a real zero?

For example, if f is defined by $f(x) = 3x - 8$, then f is a polynomial with integral coefficients and it has no integral zeros. If f is defined by $f(x) = x^2 - 2$, then f has rational coefficients (it also has integral coefficients) yet f has no rational zero, since there is no rational number whose square is 2. Note that for $f(x) = 3x - 8$ we have a rational zero, namely, $\frac{8}{3}$. For $f(x) = x^2 - 2$, we have a real zero, namely, $\sqrt{2}$.

In the present book we are interested mainly in real functions. Thus we can raise the question: Does a real polynomial f have real zeros? The answer to this is very simple. Consider the real polynomial f defined by

$$f(x) = x^2 + 1. \tag{1}$$

Then f has no real zeros. To see this, consider any real number c. Then $c^2 \geq 0$. Adding 1 to both sides of this inequality, $c^2 + 1 \geq 1$. Thus $c^2 + 1 > 0$. This means that $f(c) \neq 0$. Hence f has no real zeros.

There is a theorem to the effect that if f is a real polynomial of *odd* degree, then f has at least one real root. The proof depends on the structure of the real number system and on the fact that f is a "continuous" function. We shall not go into it here more than to give a breezy sketch of the ideas involved.

Suppose f has leading coefficient 1 (this cleans up the problem a bit). Now, it was shown in Theorem III–3 that for x positive and $|x|$ very large, $f(x)$ is also positive and large; and that for x negative and $|x|$ large, $f(x)$ is negative and $|f(x)|$ is large. Note that we use the fact that f has odd degree. Thus there exist two numbers a and b such that $a < 0$ and $|a|$ is large, $b > 0$ and $|b|$ is large for which $f(a) < 0$ and $f(b) > 0$. Consider the graph of f. Near $x = a$, the graph lies below the x-axis. Near $x = b$ the graph lies above the x-axis. Then in traveling from a to b, the graph must cut the x-axis because f is continuous and hence the graph of f has no jumps. This cut-point is a zero of f. This is all picturesque. In point of fact, neither does x travel nor does the graph of f do any cutting. However, the explanation is interesting in that it indicates precisely what has to be done in order to make the result rigorous: (1) Set down the fundamental properties of the real number system; (2) define continuity of functions and obtain the properties of such functions; (3) prove that polynomials are continuous. We shall not pursue this matter further.

We saw above that the polynomial f defined by $f(x) = 3x - 8$ has no zeros if only integral values for x are allowed. However, if a larger set of values, namely rational values, is allowed then f does have a zero ($x = \frac{8}{3}$). Similarly, the polynomial f defined by $f(x) = x^2 - 2$ has no zeros if x is allowed to have only rational values. However, if the domain over which x is defined is extended to the real numbers, then f does have a zero ($x = \sqrt{2}$). Thus the question can be raised: Is it possible to extend the field of real numbers over which the polynomial f given by $f(x) = x^2 + 1$ has no zeros to a larger field over which it does have a zero? The answer to this question is "yes" and it has been known since the eighteenth century although mathematicians of that period were much puzzled by the properties of this new number system. The zero of $x^2 + 1$ is called i (thus $i^2 = -1$) and the complex numbers are numbers of the form $a + bi$ where a and b are real. The complex numbers are denoted by $\mathbf{C}$. Note that every real number is complex (set $b = 0$). This fact is important.

The big question at this point in mathematical history was to determine whether all polynomials with real or complex coefficients have at least one complex zero (perhaps real). This problem was solved affirmatively by a German mathematician, C. F. Gauss (1777–1855), at the beginning of the last century. Although this result was beyond the comprehension of all but expert mathematicians when it was given some 170 years ago, our mathematical advances have been such in the intervening years that many beautiful proofs of this now standard result are given in courses at the upper college and university level. We state the result below. It is convenient to know it for some of the problems that are considered below but none of our future results depends on it. Remember that the complex zero it mentions could be real.

III–13 Fundamental Theorem of Algebra

Let f be a polynomial function with complex coefficients and of degree $n \geq 1$. Then f has at least one complex zero.

We are not interested in developing the theory of complex numbers here. However, it may be stated that the principal results so far obtained hold for complex as well as for real numbers. These include the Division Algorithm, the Remainder Theorem, and the Factor Theorem.

Now it is quite clear from the Fundamental Theorem of Algebra that if a polynomial f is of degree $n \geq 1$, it has exactly n zeros (repeated zeros are counted once for each occurrence). For, if f has the zero c_1, then by the Factor Theorem (which holds for complex numbers),

$$f(x) = (x - c_1)q_1(x),$$

where q_1 is of degree $n - 1$. If $n \geq 2$, then $n - 1 \geq 1$ and q_1 has a zero; call it c_2. Note that it is conceivable that $c_2 = c_1$. Then

$$f(x) = (x - c_1)(x - c_2)q_2(x).$$

We proceed in this way and show that

$$f(x) = a(x - c_1)(x - c_2) \cdots (x - c_n),$$

where a is some constant.

If $f(x)$ is divisible by $(x - c)^k$ but not by $(x - c)^{k+1}$—here k is a natural number ≥ 1—then c is said to be a zero of multiplicity k.

Exercises III.5.a

1. Find the zeros of the following polynomials indicating their multiplicities.
   (a) $f(x) = x^2 - 5x + 6$;
   (b) $f(x) = x^3 - 17x$;
   (c) $f(x) = (x + a)^{15}$;
   (d) $f(x) = 8x^3 + 12x^2 + 6x + 1$;
   (e) $f(x) = x^4 - 5x^3 + x^2$;
   (f) $f(x) = 4x^4 - 16x^2 + 21x^2 - 11x + 2$;
   (g) $f(x) = (x^4 - 2x^2 + 1)^2$.

2. Give three distinct examples of polynomials having no real zeros.

3. Give an example of a polynomial of degree 4 having two real zeros and two complex zeros that are not real.

Historical Note. Carl Friedrich Gauss (1777–1855) published the first rigorous proof of the Fundamental Theorem of Algebra at the age of 22. He gave three additional proofs of the theorem, spaced over the years. Gauss was pre-eminent in many branches of mathematics: number theory, differential geometry, non-Euclidean geometry. He was famous also for his work in physics and astronomy.

6. RATIONAL FUNCTIONS

As has been mentioned before, a rational function f is one of the form p/q where p and q are polynomials. If p and q have a factor in common, it is divided out. Thus it can be assumed that p and q have no factor in common. One implication of this decision is that if $x = c$ is a zero of q, then it is not a zero of p. For if $q(c) = 0$ and $p(c) = 0$, then both $q(x)$ and $p(x)$ are divisible by $x - c$.

We have seen that the rational functions constitute a field. That is, the sum, difference, product, and quotient of rational functions are rational functions. A subset of the set of rational functions is the ring of polynomials. For if p is a polynomial, then $p = p/q$ where $q(x) = 1$ for all x. Thus each polynomial function is a rational function. Note that a rational function p/q is defined for all x except the finite number of zeros of the denominator q.

We shall consider in this section the graphing of a rational function $f = p/q$. Special values of x to single out are the zeros of p and those of q. If c is a zero of p then $p(c) = 0$ and hence $f(c) = 0$. If c is a zero of q we have quite another phenomenon, namely, $f(c)$ is not defined. But if x is close to c, that is, if $|x - c|$ is small, then $|q(x)|$ is small and hence $|p(x)/q(x)|$ is large. Thus the line through the point $(c, 0)$ and parallel to the y-axis is a vertical asymptote to the graph of f. In graphing, it is important to ascertain carefully the sign of f to the right and to the left of c.

Consider for example the function f defined by

$$f(x) = x + \frac{1}{x} = \frac{x^2 + 1}{x}. \tag{1}$$

Here $x = 0$ gives a vertical asymptote. Note that if $x > 0$ then $f(x) > 0$; and if $x < 0$ then $f(x) < 0$. The graph is given in Figure III.1. The graph reveals another asymptote: the line $y = x$. However, we shall not study asymptotes of this kind here.

Now consider a rational function f in which the degree of the denominator q exceeds that of the numerator p. Then the x-axis is a horizontal asymptote of the graph. This phenomenon is illustrated in the following example. Suppose f is given by

$$f(x) = \frac{x}{1 + x^2}. \tag{2}$$

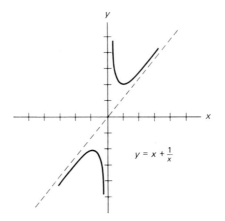

Figure III.1

Then, dividing the numerator and denominator by x gives

$$f(x) = \frac{1}{1/x + x}.$$

Now, when $|x|$ is large $|1/x|$ is small and $|1/x + x|$ is large. Thus $|f(x)|$ is small. The graph is given in Figure III.2. Note that f is an odd function.

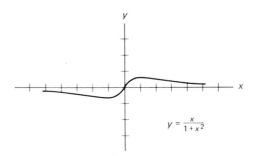

Figure III.2

It is interesting to compare the above function with the function f given by

$$f(x) = \frac{x}{1 - x^2} = \frac{x}{(1 - x)(1 + x)}. \tag{3}$$

This function is again odd. Note that:

If $1 < x$,   then $f(x) < 0$, since: $x > 0$, $1 - x < 0$, and $1 + x > 0$.
If $0 < x < 1$, then $f(x) > 0$, since: $x > 0$, $1 - x > 0$, and $1 + x > 0$.
If $-1 < x < 0$, then $f(x) < 0$, since: $x < 0$, $1 - x > 0$, and $1 + x > 0$.
If $x < -1$,   then $f(x) > 0$, since: $x < 0$, $1 - x > 0$, and $1 + x < 0$.

The graph follows in Figure III.3. Note that the lines $y = 0, x = 1, x = -1$ are asymptotes of the graph.

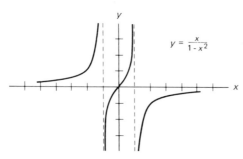

$$y = \frac{x}{1-x^2}$$

Figure III.3

Exercises III.6.a

1. For the function f below indicate the behavior of f for $|x|$ large in case (i) $x > 0$; (ii) $x < 0$. Indicate the behavior of f when $|x|$ is small in case (i) $x > 0$, (ii) $x < 0$.

   (a) $f(x) = \dfrac{1}{x}$;

   (b) $f(x) = 2x^2 - 17x + 35$;
   (c) $f(x) = x^5 - x^3 + 60x^2 + 117$;

   (d) $f(x) = \dfrac{1}{x^2}$;

   (e) $f(x) = x^3 + \dfrac{1}{x^3}$;

   (f) $f(x) = x + \dfrac{1}{x^2}$;

   (g) $f(x) = x^2 + \dfrac{1}{x^2}$.

2. Find the graph of the function f given below.

   (a) $f(x) = x^2 + \dfrac{1}{x}$;   (b) $f(x) = \dfrac{1}{1 + x^2}$;

   (c) $f(x) = \dfrac{1}{1 - x^2}$;   (d) $f(x) = \dfrac{1}{x^2}$;

   (e) $f(x) = \dfrac{1}{x^3}$.

3. Find the graph of the function f given below.

(a) $f(x) = \dfrac{3 - x}{3 + x}$

(b) $f(x) = \dfrac{x}{x^2 - 2x + 1}$;

(c) $f(x) = \dfrac{x^2 + 2}{x^2 - 2}$;

(d) $f(x) = \dfrac{x^2 - 2}{x^2 + 2}$.

4. Which of the functions in Problems 1 and 2 are even? Which are odd?

5. Give the equations of the asymptotes to each of the functions in Problems 2 and 3. Do this without referring to the graphs.

6. Discuss the problem of graphing the function given by (2) by noting that it is the reciprocal of that given by (1) and using the information in Figure III.1.

7. Show that if r is a rational function then for $|x|$ large, either $|r(x)|$ is large or $|r(x)|$ is close to some constant. [*Hint*: write $r = p/q$ where p and q are polynomials of degree m and n respectively; then consider the cases $m > n$, $m \leq n$.]

THE BEHAVIOR OF POLYNOMIALS AT INFINITY

The purpose of this appendix is to give proofs of Theorems III–2 and III–3. For the sake of ease in reference, the theorems are restated below.

III–2 Theorem

Let f be a polynomial function defined by

$$f(x) = a_0 + a_1x + \cdots + a_nx^n, \qquad n \geq 1, \tag{1}$$

where $a_n \neq 0$. Then for $|x|$ large, $|f(x)|$ is also large. More precisely, given a number $M > 0$, there exists a number $L > 0$ such that if $|x| \geq L$, then $|f(x)| \geq M$.

Thus the function f in (1) is not the zero function.

III–3 Theorem

If f is defined by

$$f(x) = a_0 + a_1x + \cdots + x^n, \qquad n \geq 1, \tag{2}$$

then

(a) *if n is even, $f(x) > 0$ for $|x|$ large;*

(b) *if n is odd $f(x) > 0$ for x positive and $|x|$ large and $f(x) < 0$ for x negative and $|x|$ large.*

The proof is easier to follow if some of the exercises in III.1.a are worked out. We shall need the following inequalities: If $b_1, b_2, \cdots, b_n$ are real numbers then

$$|b_1 + b_2 + \cdots + b_n| \leq |b_1| + |b_2| + \cdots + |b_n|. \tag{3}$$

This was proved for $n = 2, 3, 4$. The general case is treated by the same method. Next, if b is a real number such that $|b| \leq \frac{1}{2}$, then $-\frac{1}{2} \leq b \leq \frac{1}{2}$, and $\frac{1}{2} \leq 1 + b \leq \frac{3}{2}$. Thus

$$|b| \leq \frac{1}{2} \qquad \text{implies} \qquad \frac{1}{2} \leq 1 + b \leq \frac{3}{2}. \tag{4}$$

Now for the polynomial f defined by (1) write

$$f(x) = a_nx^n\left(1 + \frac{a_{n-1}}{a_nx} + \frac{a_{n-2}}{a_nx^2} + \cdots + \frac{a_0}{a_nx^n}\right). \tag{5}$$

Note that $a_n \neq 0$. Furthermore write

$$b = \frac{a_{n-1}}{a_n x} + \frac{a_{n-2}}{a_n x^2} + \cdots + \frac{a_0}{a_n x^n}. \tag{6}$$

We shall show that there exists a positive number c such that if $|x| \geq c$, then

$$\left| \frac{a_{n-1}}{a_n x} \right| \leq \frac{1}{2n}, \quad \left| \frac{a_{n-2}}{a_n x^2} \right| \leq \frac{1}{2n}, \quad \cdots, \quad \left| \frac{a_0}{a_n x^n} \right| \leq \frac{1}{2n}. \tag{7}$$

Thus for $|x| \geq c$, using (3), it may be seen that

$$|b| = \left| \frac{a_{n-1}}{a_n x} + \frac{a_{n-2}}{a_n x^2} + \cdots + \frac{a_0}{a_n x^n} \right| \leq \frac{1}{2n} + \cdots + \frac{1}{2n} = \frac{1}{2}. \tag{8}$$

Note that the number of terms in the absolute value sign is n and that each one is less than $1/2n$.

Using (4),

$$1 + b = 1 + \frac{a_{n-1}}{a_n x} + \cdots + \frac{a_0}{a_n x^n} \geq \frac{1}{2}. \tag{9}$$

Now (5) gives

$$|f(x)| = |a_n x^n||1 + b|. \tag{10}$$

Hence, for $|x| \geq c$,

$$|f(x)| \geq \frac{1}{2} |a_n x^n|. \tag{11}$$

Return to the number M given in the theorem. We wish to make the quantity on the right larger than M. This is easy. Choose L so that

$$L \geq 1, \quad L \geq c, \quad L \geq \frac{2M}{|a_n|}. \tag{12}$$

Then if $|x| \geq L$, $|x| \geq c$; hence, (11) holds. Since $L \geq 1$, $|x^n| \geq L^n \geq L$. Also

$$\frac{1}{2} |a_n x^n| = \frac{1}{2} |a_n||x^n| \geq \frac{1}{2} |a_n| L^n$$

$$\geq \frac{1}{2} |a_n| L \geq \frac{1}{2} |a_n| \frac{2M}{|a_n|} = M. \tag{13}$$

This is the number L mentioned in Theorem III–2. In order to finish the proof of the theorem, it is necessary to prove the existence of a number c such that $|x| \geq c$ makes (7) valid. First, find a number c_1 such that $|x| \geq c_1$ implies that

$$\left| \frac{a_{n-1}}{a_n x} \right| \leq \frac{1}{2n}. \tag{14}$$

This is very easy. It suffices to choose c_1 such that

$$c_1 \geq \frac{2n|a_{n-1}|}{|a_n|}. \tag{15}$$

Next we find c_2 such that $|x| \geq c_2$ implies that

$$\left|\frac{a_{n-2}}{a_n x^2}\right| \leq \frac{1}{2n}. \tag{16}$$

To do this, choose c_2 so that

$$c_2 \geq 1, \qquad c_2 \geq \frac{2n|a_{n-2}|}{|a_n|}. \tag{17}$$

Then we may check that $|x| \geq c_2$ implies (15). Use the fact that $|x^2| \geq c_2^2 \geq c_2$.

We may proceed in this way to find the numbers $c_3, c_4, \cdots, c_n$. For example, for c_n choose a number satisfying

$$c_n \geq 1, \qquad c_n \geq \frac{2n|a_0|}{|a_n|}. \tag{18}$$

The number c wanted above is then chosen to be any number larger than each of $c_1, c_2, \cdots, c_n$. For example, a possible selection is $c = c_1 + c_2 + \cdots + c_n$. This finishes the proof of Theorem III–2.

In proving Theorem III–2, we have obtained the main inequalities that are needed for the proof of Theorem III–3. Note that for the sake of convenience, we have set $a_n = 1$. This being the case, we rewrite (5) in the form

$$f(x) = x^n \left(1 + \frac{a_{n-1}}{x} + \frac{a_{n-2}}{x^2} + \cdots + \frac{a_0}{x^n}\right)$$

$$= x^n(1 + b). \tag{19}$$

In the preceding theorem, it is shown that there is a number c such that $|x| \geq c$ implies that

$$\frac{1}{2} \leq 1 + b \leq \frac{3}{2}. \tag{20}$$

This means that for $|x| \geq c$, $f(x)$ has the *same sign* as x^n. The sign of x^n is positive if x is positive. If x is negative, the sign of x^n is positive if n is even and is negative if n is odd.

The proof above implies that not only does $f(x)$ have the same sign as x^n if $|x| \geq c$, but also $f(x)$ and x^n are of comparable size. In fact $f(x)$ is at least one half as large as x^n and at most three halves as large as x^n.

The big lesson to be drawn from all this is that for big values of x, a polynomial is dominated by its highest power. In our proof, we have chosen c so that $|x| \geq c$ implies [see (6) and (8)] $|b| \leq \frac{1}{2}$. We could just as well have chosen c so that $|x| \geq c$ implies $|b| \leq \frac{1}{4}$, or $|b| \leq 1/1000$. This means that $1 + b$ is very close to 1 and hence $f(x)$ is very close to x^n; in fact it can be made as close as we want to 1. This fact is used in one of the proofs of the Fundamental Theorem of Algebra. Since x^n is very close to $f(x)$, they should have the same number of zeros. Now x^n has n zeros, namely $0, 0, \cdots, 0$. Thus $f(x)$ has n zeros also. The proof based on this argument is quite deep.

Exercises III-Appendix

1. Find c such that $|x| \geq c$ implies that

(a) $\left| \dfrac{2}{x} - \dfrac{3}{x^2} + \dfrac{1}{x^5} \right| \leq \dfrac{1}{4}$;

(b) $\left| \dfrac{2}{x} - \dfrac{3}{x^2} + \dfrac{1}{x^5} \right| \leq \dfrac{1}{1000}$.

2. Show that given any polynomial f of degree ≥ 1, a number c can be calculated such that all the real zeros of the polynomial lie in the interval $-c < x < c$.

3. Show that if f is a polynomial of degree ≥ 1, the graph of $y = 1/f(x)$ has the x-axis as an asymptote.

4. Show that if f is a nonconstant periodic function, it is not a polynomial.

5. Prove that the function f defined by $f(x) = |x|$ is not a polynomial.

Chapter **IV**

ALGEBRAIC FUNCTIONS

1. SQUARE ROOTS AND *n*th ROOTS

As we already know, the square root of a number $a \geq 0$ means a number $b \geq 0$ such that $b^2 = a$. It is written $b = \sqrt{a}$. (Note that the statement $\sqrt{4} = 2$ is correct while the statement $\sqrt{4} = -2$ is incorrect, because -2 is not a positive number.) Our intuition tells us that for every $a \geq 0$ there is such a number $b \geq 0$. The existence of b can be demonstrated by using the least upper bound principle. This is done in the short appendix to this chapter.

That the square root of a number $a > 0$ is unique can be seen as follows: Suppose that b and c are square roots of a; that is,

$$b^2 = a \quad \text{and} \quad c^2 = a.$$

Then $b^2 = c^2$ or $b^2 - c^2 = 0$. Thus,

$$0 = b^2 - c^2 = (b - c)(b + c). \tag{1}$$

Since $b > 0$ and $c > 0$, $b + c > 0$, and dividing both sides of (1) by $b + c$, we obtain $0 = b - c$; hence $b = c$. Thus the square root is unique.

Suppose $b_1 = \sqrt{a_1}$ and $b_2 = \sqrt{a_2}$ where $a_1 > 0$ and $a_2 > 0$. Suppose that $a_1 < a_2$. Then $b_1 < b_2$. This can be seen as follows: Either $b_1 = b_2$;

143

$b_1 > b_2$; or $b_1 < b_2$. If $b_1 = b_2$, then $a_1 = b_1^2 = b_2^2 = a_2$, which contradicts $a_1 < a_2$. If $b_1 > b_2$, then, multiplying this inequality by b_1 and by b_2 (remember that $b_1 > 0, b_2 > 0$),

$$b_1^2 > b_1 b_2,$$
$$b_1 b_2 > b_2^2, \tag{2}$$

and this leads to the conclusion that $b_1^2 > b_2^2$, that is, $a_1 > a_2$. This is again a contradiction. Thus, we conclude that $b_1 < b_2$.

Changing the letters from a and b to x and y, we have therefore that given any number $x > 0$ there is a unique number $y > 0$ such that

$$y = \sqrt{x}. \tag{3}$$

Using the notation of exponents which will be examined in more detail later, this is also written

$$y = x^{1/2}. \tag{4}$$

If a function f has the property that whenever $x_1 < x_2$, then $f(x_1) < f(x_2)$, f is said to be a *monotone increasing* function. If f has the property that whenever $x_1 < x_2$, then $f(x_1) > f(x_2)$, f is said to be a *monotone decreasing* function. In both cases f is referred to as a *monotone* function. We see then that the square root function is monotone increasing.

The graph of the equation $y = \sqrt{x}$ is given in Figure IV.1.

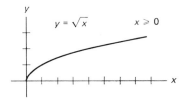

Figure IV.1

Suppose now that n is an arbitrary positive integer. Suppose that $a \geq 0$. Let it be required to find a number $b \geq 0$ such that $b^n = a$. We write this in the form

$$b = \sqrt[n]{a} \quad \text{or} \quad b = a^{1/n}. \tag{5}$$

Once more our intuition tells us correctly that such a number b always exists (see Appendix). The number b must be a root of the polynomial equation $x^n - a = 0$. This polynomial equation is of degree n and has at most n real roots. It will be seen immediately that in the present situation ($a > 0$) there is only one root $b > 0$.

Suppose we have $b^n = a$ and $c^n = a$. Then $b^n - c^n = 0$. Using the algebraic identity,

$$b^n - c^n = (b - c)(b^{n-1} + b^{n-2}c + \cdots + bc^{n-2} + c^{n-1}), \tag{6}$$

we obtain

$$0 = b^n - c^n = (b - c) \cdot A, \tag{7}$$

where A stands for $b^{n-1} + b^{n-2}c + \cdots + bc^{n-2} + c^{n-1}$. The relation $b > 0$ gives $b^2 > 0$, $b^3 > 0$, $\cdots$, $b^{n-1} > 0$. Similarly, since $c > 0$, $c^2 > 0, \cdots, c^{n-1} > 0$. Next $b^{n-1}c > 0$. In other words, all the terms in A are greater than 0 and thus their sum A satisfies $A > 0$. Divide the two sides of $0 = (b - c) \cdot A$ by A and obtain: $b - c = 0$ or $b = c$. Thus, given $a \geq 0$, there is a unique $b \geq 0$ such that $b = \sqrt[n]{a}$.

Consider now the function

$$f(x) = \sqrt[n]{x} \quad \text{or} \quad f(x) = x^{1/n}. \tag{8}$$

It is readily seen, using the same type of argument as that used above for square roots, that if $x_1 < x_2$ then $\sqrt[n]{x_1} < \sqrt[n]{x_2}$. Thus the nth root function (also called the $(1/n)$th power function) is monotone increasing. We set down the details for $n = 4$.

Suppose $a_1 < a_2$ and $b_1^4 = a_1$, $b_2^4 = a_2$. We wish to show that $b_1 < b_2$. As before there are three possibilities: $b_1 = b_2$; $b_1 > b_2$; $b_1 < b_2$. The case $b_1 = b_2$ gives $b_1^4 = b_2^4$, that is, $a_1 = a_2$, which is impossible since $a_1 < a_2$. Thus the only possibilities left are $b_1 < b_2$ and $b_1 > b_2$. Assume that $b_1 > b_2$. Since $b_1 > 0$ and $b_2 > 0$, the inequality $b_1 > b_2$ may be multiplied by itself two, three, four times, obtaining $b_1^2 > b_2^2$, $b_1^3 > b_2^3$, $b_1^4 > b_2^4$ (see properties of inequalities, Chapter I). Thus $b_1 > b_2$ leads to the conclusion that $b_1^4 > b_2^4$, that is, $a_1 > a_2$. This contradicts our supposition that $a_1 < a_2$; hence we discard the case $b_1 > b_2$ and the only possibility left is $b_1 < b_2$.

We graph in Figure IV.2 the nth root function for various values of n. Note that the interest is centered about the points $(0, 0)$ and $(1, 1)$.

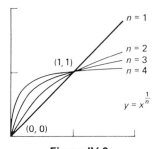

Figure IV.2

A word about finding nth roots. This is essentially a very simple matter. It may try your patience but it will not try your intelligence. We show how this is to be done. We propose to obtain the nth root with any desired degree of accuracy. The method explained below is that which a computer would use. It is based solely on the fact that the nth root function is monotone increasing.

Let it be required to find $b = \sqrt[3]{1162}$ to one decimal place. Start with some simple cubes: $1^3 = 1$, $10^3 = 1000$, $100^3 = 1,000,000$, etc. We see right away (by monotonicity) that $b > 10$ and $b < 100$.

Next locate b more closely by calculating $10^3 = 1000$, $20^3 = 8000$, $30^3 = 27,000$, etc. It is quickly seen that $b > 10$ and $b < 20$ (since $1000 < 1162 < 8000$).

Now calculate $10^3 = 1000$, $11^3 = 1331$. Since $1000 < 1162 < 1331$, we see that $10 < b < 11$.

Finally, we find that $10.5^3 = 1157.625$ and that $10.6^3 = 1191.016$. Thus $\sqrt[3]{1162} = 10.5$ correct to one decimal place and therefore to three significant figures in the present case. It is quite apparent that we could have gone on for some time. It is also apparent that the process is slow and tiring. The above program for calculating nth roots is a very feasible one for a computer. In the absence of a computer, it is preferable to calculate nth roots by some other means. This can be done in a variety of ways such as referring to tables of nth roots, using logarithms, trying it on a slide rule. Tables are to be found in the rear of the book; logarithms will be developed in Chapter V. In that same chapter, it will be shown how to construct an inexpensive (one cent) slide-rule.

Some of the exercises below require the use of Table I at the end of the book.

Exercises IV.1.a

1. Verify in Table I the statement that "the functions $f(x) = \sqrt{x}$, $g(x) = \sqrt[3]{x}$ are monotone increasing."

2. Using Table I find

(a) $\sqrt{7}$;   (b) $\sqrt{13}$;
(c) $\sqrt{69}$;   (d) $\sqrt[3]{2}$;
(e) $\sqrt[3]{9}$;   (f) 29^2;
(g) 33^3.

3. Using the approximation method described in the text (the slavish computer method), find to one decimal place

(a) $\sqrt{5}$;   (b) $\sqrt[3]{7}$;
(c) $\sqrt{10}$;   (d) $\sqrt{19}$;
(e) $\sqrt[3]{25}$;   (f) $\sqrt[5]{38}$.

4. Show that for $0 < x < 1$, one has $\sqrt{x}/x > 1$. Show that for small values of x, the ratio is large. For example, find a value k such that the ratio > 100 if $x < k$.

5. Show that for $x > 1$, one has $\sqrt{x}/x < 1$. Show that for large values of x, the ratio can be made small. For example, find a value of k such that the ratio $< 1/100$ if $x > k$.

6. Show that for all x, $\sqrt{x^2} = |x|$.

7. Let x be fixed, $0 < x < 1$. Suppose $n > m$. Compare $x^{1/n}$ and $x^{1/m}$. Do the same for $x > 1$. Check the results by referring to Figure IV.2.

8. Let b_1 and b_2 be positive numbers and let n be an integer ≥ 1. It is shown in the text that if $b_1 > b_2$, then $b_1^n > b_2^n$. How does this show the uniqueness of nth roots?

2. THE CIRCLE

Consider a plane equipped with coordinate axes. As was pointed out in Chapter II in the sections on graphing, there is no reason why the axes should be chosen perpendicular to each other. In fact, the statement that one line is perpendicular to another is a statement made in the language of Euclidean geometry. Given a plane, there is no special reason why it should be Euclidean. For example, if the distance s is graphed against the time t in the equation $s = 16t^2$, it does not add to our understanding that the s-axis and the t-axis are perpendicular to each other. Similarly, we would not be interested in the length of a segment in the (s, t) plane.

If we wish to consider the length of segments in a plane, we have to have the notion of distance. Now the concept of distance is one that, by universal agreement, has certain fundamental properties. Let P, Q, R be points in a plane and let $d(P, Q)$ stand for the distance from P to Q. Then $d(P, Q)$ is a number ≥ 0; it is 0 only if P and Q coincide, that is, $P = Q$. Furthermore,

$$d(P, Q) = d(Q, P);$$
$$d(P, R) \leq d(P, Q) + d(Q, R). \tag{1}$$

The first of these relations is the relation of symmetry. The second relation is called the *triangle inequality*. These relations have already occurred in Chapter I, Section 2, Equation (17). Be sure to make a diagram that will throw light on (1).

Nothing has been said so far to ensure that the distance being talked about is identical with the distance in the ordinary world of physics or business. This latter distance is a very special one called Euclidean distance. What is being said here is that there are many possible kinds of distance. Consider the following example, which is very instructive. Suppose that for any two elements P and Q of some set (the U.S. Senate, if you wish), we write $d(P, Q) = 1$ if $P \neq Q$ and $d(P, Q) = 0$ if $P = Q$. It is easy to check that with this definition, (1) is satisfied. Thus we have a distance. We may at first decide to call it a "distance," but after awhile, the idea of using quotation marks is put aside.

As has just been suggested, it is possible to introduce distance into the plane in many ways. Putting aside the method given above, there are three ways which are particularly interesting. One of these is the Euclidean distance. The other two are discussed in the exercises; they will not be used in this book. This being the case, from now on, every time that distance is mentioned, it means Euclidean distance. We now proceed to find a formula giving the distance between two points.

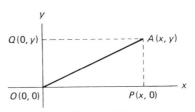

Figure IV.3

Consider a plane equipped with rectangular coordinate axes. (See Figure IV.3.) Take any point A in the plane and let its coordinates be (x, y). Let us find the distance from the origin O of coordinates to the point A. We project a perpendicular AP to the x-axis. The coordinates of P are $(x, 0)$. Similarly, if we draw AQ perpendicular to the y-axis, the coordinates of Q are $(0, y)$. The figure $OPAQ$ is a rectangle. The sides of the rectangle have lengths $|x|$ and $|y|$ respectively. We wish to find the length l of diagonal OA. By the Pythagorean Theorem for right triangles we see that

$$l^2 = |x|^2 + |y|^2. \tag{2}$$

Since $|x|^2 = x^2$ and $|y|^2 = y^2$,

$$l = \sqrt{x^2 + y^2}. \tag{3}$$

In Figure IV.3 the point (x, y) is in the first quadrant, that is, $x > 0$ and $y > 0$. An excellent exercise consists in making three other diagrams showing (x, y) successively in the second, third, and fourth quadrants. Does the proof above apply to each diagram? It should.

Consider now the following problem: Let $A(x_1, y_1)$ and $B(x_2, y_2)$ be two points of the plane. Let it be required to find the length l of the segment AB. The procedure is essentially the same as before (see Figure IV.4). The figure $APBQ$ is a rectangle whose sides have lengths $|x_2 - x_1|$ and $|y_2 - y_1|$. Using the Pythagorean Theorem once more, we obtain for the length l of AB

$$l^2 = |x_2 - x_1|^2 + |y_2 - y_1|^2, \tag{4}$$

hence

$$l = \sqrt{(x_2 - x_1)^2 + (y_2 - y_1)^2}. \tag{5}$$

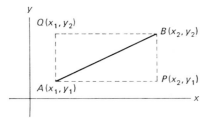

Figure IV.4

Several things should be noted in this proof. First of all, $|x_2 - x_1| = |x_1 - x_2|$ and $(x_2 - x_1)^2 = (x_1 - x_2)^2$. Thus it doesn't matter which point is considered first and which is considered second. Next, Figure IV.4 represents the two points in the first quadrant and furthermore, in the diagram $x_2 > x_1$ and $y_2 > y_1$. It is advisable to make four or five different diagrams and to become convinced that every statement of the proof applies to each diagram. In other words, no matter what points $A(x_1, y_1)$ and $B(x_2, y_2)$ are chosen, the above proof gives correctly the length l of AB.

The distance from A to B, hence the length of the segment AB, is denoted by $\overline{AB}$. Thus

$$\overline{AB} = \sqrt{(x_2 - x_1)^2 + (y_2 - y_1)^2}, \qquad A(x_1, y_1) \qquad \text{and} \qquad B(x_2, y_2). \quad \textbf{(6)}$$

Note that $\overline{AB} = \overline{BA}$; this is the first property in (1). The second property in (1) is established with the help of the Cauchy Inequality (Chapter II, Section 7, Exercise 5). It is clear now why the Cauchy Inequality is closely related to Euclidean geometry.

We are about to solve one of the principal problems of analytic geometry. In order to do so, we remind the reader of the definition of a circle.

Definition

Let there be given a plane, a point C in that plane, and a number $r > 0$. The set of all points P lying in the plane such that

$$\overline{CP} = r$$

is called a *circle*. The point C is the *center* of the circle. The number r is the *radius* of the circle.

Any collection of points in the plane which is of special interest is called a *curve*. Examples of curves are circles, parabolas, ellipses, and hyperbolas; also lines.

A curve is said to have an equation $F(x, y) = 0$ providing that the graph of $F(x, y) = 0$ is the given curve. It isn't clear that curves should have equations. However in all cases we treat, they do have them. If a curve has an equation, it will have many. For example, $F(x, y) = 0$, $[F(x, y)]^2 = 0$, and so on all have the same graph. We should speak of *an* equation for a curve, but being mortal sinners, we shall occasionally slip and say *the* equation of the curve. We now come to our problem, and its solution.

Find an equation of a circle whose center is at the point C(h, k) and whose radius is r.

Note that what is wanted is an equation in *x* and *y* such that:

(i) If a point $P(x, y)$ is on the circle, then the equation is valid for that *x* and *y*.

(ii) If the equation is valid for a given *x* and *y*, then the point *P* whose coordinates are (x, y) lies on the circle (that is, the distance from *C* to *P* is *r*).

SOLUTION: First find an equation in *x* and *y* which each point (x, y) on the circle satisfies. Next show that if a point (x, y) satisfies this equation, then (x, y) is on the circle.

(a) Let $P(x, y)$ lie on circle.

(b) Then the length of the segment *PC* is *r*.

(c) The length of *PC* is $\sqrt{(x - h)^2 + (y - k)^2}$ [see Equation (6)].

(d) Hence

$$\sqrt{(x - h)^2 + (y - k)^2} = r. \tag{7}$$

(e) That is,

$$(x - h)^2 + (y - k)^2 = r^2. \tag{8}$$

This is the promised equation in *x* and *y*.

Now, suppose a point $P:(x, y)$ satisfies Equation (8). Then taking the square root of both sides, we obtain (7). This equation states that the distance from *C* to *P* is *r*. Hence *P* lies on the circle. See Figure IV.5.

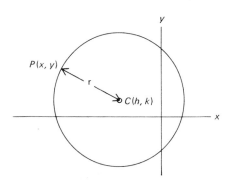

Figure IV.5

Exercises IV.2.a

1. Find the distance from the origin *O* $(0, 0)$ to the point *P* whose coordinates are

(a) $(3, 4)$;

(b) $(5, -12)$;

(c) $(6, -7)$;

(d) (x, y);

(e) $(0, 0)$;   (f) $(a + b, a - b)$;
(g) (cx, cy);   (h) (y, x);
(i) $(x, -y)$;   (j) $(-2, -3)$.

2. Draw Figure IV.3 showing the point A in the second, third, and fourth quadrants. In each case indicate the points O, A, P, Q and write their coordinates.

3. Draw Figure IV.3 showing the point A on the x-axis; on the y-axis. Indicate the points O, A, P, Q and write down their coordinates. (Note that these points will not be distinct.)

4. Find the distance between the indicated pairs of points. Make a diagram.

(a) $(2, 4)$, $(5, 8)$;   (b) $(2, 4)$, $(7, -8)$;
(c) $(3, 2)$, $(-4, 4)$;   (d) $(-3, 0)$, $(2, -5)$;
(e) $(3, 6)$, (x, y);   (f) (a, b), (c, d);
(g) $(5, 8)$, $(2, 4)$;   (h) $(-2, -4)$, $(-7, 8)$;
(i) $(3, 6)$, $(-x, -y)$;   (j) (a, b), $(-c, -d)$.

5. Draw Figure IV.4 showing the point A in the first quadrant and the point B in the second; A in the second and B in the fourth. Indicate the points A, B, P, Q and their coordinates. Check the fact that formulas (4) and (5) hold for each of your diagrams.

6. Prove that the points $(-4, 7)$, $(2, 4)$, and $(4, 8)$ are the vertices of a right triangle (use the Pythagorean Theorem).

7. Prove that the points $(1, 0)$, $(4, 3)$, $(6, -2)$ are vertices of an isosceles triangle.

8. Find all numbers a such that the points $(0, 2)$, $(2, 0)$, and (a, a) are vertices of an equilateral triangle.

9. Consider the parallelogram with vertices O, A, B, C where the coordinates are given by $O(0, 0)$; $A(x_1, y_1)$; $B(x_2, y_2)$; $C(x_1 + x_2, y_1 + y_2)$. Prove that

$$\overline{OA}^2 + \overline{AC}^2 + \overline{CB}^2 + \overline{BO}^2 = \overline{OC}^2 + \overline{BA}^2.$$

This is called the *parallelogram identity*. Make a diagram. State the identity in words.

10. A plane is given with x- and y-axes which coordinatize it. If $A(x_1, y_1)$ and $B(x_2, y_2)$ are any two points, define $D(A, B)$ by

$$D(A, B) = |x_2 - x_1| + |y_2 - y_1|.$$

Prove that D has the properties given in (1) and hence is a distance.

11. Let the coordinatized plane and the points A, B be as in Problem 10. Define

$$\mathscr{D}(A, B) = \text{the larger of } |x_2 - x_1| \text{ and } |y_2 - y_1|.$$

Prove that $\mathscr{D}$ has the properties given in (1) and hence is a distance.

12. Write the equation of a circle given its center and radius in each case below.

(a) center $(4, 3)$, radius 2;   (b) center $(-4, 3)$, radius $\sqrt{2}$;
(c) center $(-2, 6)$, radius 1;   (d) center $(0, 0)$, radius $2a$;

(e) center $\left(\dfrac{a}{2}, \dfrac{b}{2}\right)$, radius $\dfrac{a^2 + b^2}{4}$;   (f) center $(-h, -k)$, radius $2r$.

We have seen above that the equation of a circle is given by $(x - h)^2 + (y - k)^2 = r^2$. Expanding this, one obtains

$$x^2 - 2hx + h^2 + y^2 - 2ky + k^2 = r^2, \tag{9}$$

which is an equation of the form

$$x^2 + y^2 + Dx + Ey + F = 0, \tag{10}$$

where

$$D = -2h, \qquad E = -2k, \qquad \text{and} \qquad F = h^2 + k^2 - r^2.$$

We shall now show that within a slight limitation, every Equation (8) represents a circle. We have already used the technique of "completing a square" (see Chapter II, Section 5). It will be used again here.

It is clear that

$$x^2 + Dx = x^2 + Dx + \frac{D^2}{4} - \frac{D^2}{4} = \left(x + \frac{D}{2}\right)^2 - \frac{D^2}{4}. \tag{11}$$

Similarly,

$$y^2 + Ey = \left(y + \frac{E}{2}\right)^2 - \frac{E^2}{4}.$$

Hence

$$x^2 + y^2 + Dx + Ey + F = \left(x + \frac{D}{2}\right)^2 + \left(y + \frac{E}{4}\right)^2 - \left(\frac{D^2}{4} + \frac{E^2}{4} - F\right).$$

This means that (10) can be written in the form

$$\left[x - \left(-\frac{D}{2}\right)\right]^2 + \left[y - \left(-\frac{E}{2}\right)\right]^2 = \frac{D^2 + E^2 - 4F}{4}. \tag{12}$$

It is clear that Equation (12) and hence Equation (10) represent a circle with center $(-D/2, -E/2)$ and radius $r = \frac{1}{2}\sqrt{D^2 + E^2 - 4F}$. What then is the limitation mentioned above? It is obviously that the quantity $D^2 + E^2 - 4F$ should be positive!

Consider an example:

Obtain the center and radius of the circle.

$$x^2 + y^2 - 8x + 6y = 0. \tag{13}$$

We write

$$x^2 + y^2 - 8x + 6y = x^2 - 8x + 16 + y^2 + 6y + 9 - 16 - 9$$
$$= (x - 4)^2 + (x + 3)^2 - 25.$$

Thus Equation (13) is equivalent to

$$(x - 4)^2 + (y + 3)^2 = 25. \tag{14}$$

This is a circle with center $(4, -3)$ and radius 5.

Up to this point, when we have considered a graphing problem, we have considered only graphs defined by equalities. However, graphs can equally well be defined by inequalities. For example:

Find the graph of the inequality

$$x^2 + y^2 < 4.$$

The answer is obvious. The graph consists of the points interior to the circle $x^2 + y^2 = 4$. Similarly, the graph of $x^2 + y^2 > 4$ consists of the points exterior to the circle $x^2 + y^2 = 4$. Notice that there is a difference between the graph of $x^2 + y^2 < 4$ and that of $x^2 + y^2 \leq 4$. Be sure to indicate this in some way on the drawing.

In this section, we recall two fundamental formulas: The length (circumference) L of a circle of radius r is given by

$$L = 2\pi r. \tag{15}$$

The area A enclosed by a circle of radius r (the area inside the circle) is given by

$$A = \pi r^2. \tag{16}$$

Here π is a real number, whose decimal expansion is $\pi = 3.1415928\cdots$. The number π is not rational, nor even algebraic. (A number is called algebraic if it is the root of a polynomial with integral coefficients. For example, $\sqrt{2}$ is algebraic, since it is a root of $x^2 - 2 = 0$.) This fact was proved in 1882 by Lindemann. The infinite decimal expression for π has always been of interest. Archimedes proved that $3.1408 < \pi < 3.1429$. Around 1600, Ludoff calculated π to 20 decimals using regular polygons having up to 60×2^{29} sides. The decimals were carved on his tombstone. In 1873, Shanks gave 707 places of which 527 are correct. In 1949 one of the first electronic computers obtained 2039 digits in 70 hours of work. Finally, in 1961 in 8 hours, a computer calculated 100,000 digits!

Exercises IV.2.b

1. Write in the expanded form (10) the equations of the following circles.

   (a) center $(3, 4)$,   radius 5;   (b) center $(2, -6)$,   radius 1;
   (c) center $(a, 3a - 2)$,   radius $2c^2$;   (d) center $(0, 0)$,   radius r;
   (e) center $(-1, 2)$,   radius 3;   (f) center $(-3, -2)$,   radius 5;
   (g) center $(2, -1)$,   radius r;   (h) center (h, k),   radius $\sqrt{h^2 + k^2}$.

2. Find the center and radius of the circle whose equation is given below.

   (a) $x^2 + y^2 + 4x - 6y + 12 = 0$;
   (b) $x^2 + y^2 + 6x - 8y + 22 = 0$;
   (c) $x^2 + y^2 - 3x + 5y = 0$;
   (d) $2x^2 + 2y^2 + 4x - 3y = 0$;
   (e) $x^2 + y^2 - 2ax + 2y - 2ay + a^2 - 2a + 1 = 0$.

3. Find the graph of the inequalities below.

   (a) $x^2 + y^2 < 16$;
   (b) $(x - a)^2 + (y + 3)^2 \leq 9$;
   (c) $x^2 + y^2 + 6x - 8y \geq 0$;
   (d) $x^2 + y^2 \leq 16$ and $(x - 4)^2 + y^2 \leq 1$;
   (e) $x^2 + y^2 < 1$ and $(x - 1)^2 + (y - 1)^2 < 1$;
   (f) $x^2 + y^2 - 6x - 2y + 6 \leq 0$ and $x^2 + y^2 + 2x - 2y - 2 \leq 0$;
   (g) $x^2 + y^2 < 9$ and $x^2 + y^2 > 4$.

4. For the circle $x^2 + y^2 + 4x - 6y + F = 0$ find the value of F given that

   (a) the circle passes through the origin;
   (b) the circle passes through the point $(1, 2)$;
   (c) the circle is tangent to the x-axis.

5. For the circle $x^2 + y^2 + 2ax - 2y + a^2 - 8 = 0$, find the value of a given that

   (a) the center of the circle is $(1, 1)$;
   (b) the circle passes through the point $(3, 1)$.

3. THE ELLIPSE

In Chapter II, Section 11, we studied implicit functions. Roughly speaking, an implicit function is given by an expression in x and y set equal to 0. If one solves for y, one or more functions of x are obtained. The graph of the implicit function is the collection of all points (x, y) which satisfy the given equation. An example of an implicit function is $x^2 + y^2 - 25 = 0$. The graph of this is a circle of radius 5 and center $(0, 0)$. Other examples that were examined are $x^2/9 - y^2/16 = 1$ whose graph is given in Figure II.48 and $(x^2 + y^2)^2 = x^2 - y^2$ whose graph is given in Figure II.49. In each case the graph of the function is an interesting collection of points. As has been stated before, such collections are called curves.

We turn to a converse problem. Suppose one is given an interesting collection of points; in other words, suppose a curve is given. For example, the given curve could be a circle with some radius and some center. The problem is to find the equation of this curve. This means finding an equation in x and y whose graph is the given curve.

In the last section, it was seen that the equation of a circle with radius 2 and center $(3, -1)$ is $(x - 3)^2 + (y + 1)^2 = 4$. This means that if a point (x, y) in the plane lies on the circle, then it satisfies the given equation; and if a point (x, y) satisfies the given equation, it lies on the circle.

In the present chapter we consider the problem of finding the equations of certain well-known curves. The case of the circle has already been handled in Section 2. In this section we study ellipses. In Section 4 the attention is focused on hyperbolas.

The curves that are studied have to be adequately defined. The given curve is the collection of points having a certain property. For example, the circle of radius 2 and center $(3, -1)$ is the collection of points (x, y) whose distance to $(3, -1)$ equals 2. Thus each curve studied will be defined to be the collection of points having some special property.

To introduce the ellipse, consider an example. Let there be given two points F_1 and F_2 whose coordinates are $(-3, 0)$ and $(3, 0)$ respectively. Let there be given a constant, say, 10. Consider the curve consisting of all points P such that for the two distances $\overline{PF_1}$ and $\overline{PF_2}$,

$$\overline{PF_1} + \overline{PF_2} = 10. \tag{1}$$

The given curve is called an *ellipse*.

Let the point P have coordinates (x, y). By the equation of the ellipse is meant an equation in x and y such that

(i) if a point P with coordinates (x, y) is such that (1) is true, then x and y satisfy the given equation;

(ii) if the equation is valid for a given x and y, then the point P with coordinates (x, y) is such that (1) is true.

We repeat some facts about equations for curves. The three equations $x^2 + y^2 = 4$, $2x^2 + 2y^2 = 8$, $y^2 = 4 - x^2$ all define the same curve. That is, a point (x, y) satisfies one if and only if it satisfies them all. Thus there is no such thing as *the* equation of the curve. What is wanted is *an* equation for the curve. However, it may be that of the several possible equations for the curve, one of them looks more satisfactory than the others. This will be the case for the ellipse. We shall not be satisfied with the very first equation that comes up.

We shall *transform* this first equation into another one that looks more attractive. The final result will be called the equation of the ellipse. The problem is restated:

Find an equation in x and y for the set of all points $P(x, y)$ satisfying (1).

SOLUTION: The diagram of the situation is represented in Figure IV.6.

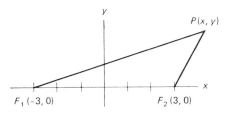

Figure IV.6

By the distance formula (Section 2),

$$\overline{PF_1} = \sqrt{(x + 3)^2 + y^2}; \qquad \overline{PF_2} = \sqrt{(x - 3)^2 + y^2}.$$

Since (1) is true for P, this gives

$$\sqrt{(x + 3)^2 + y^2} + \sqrt{(x - 3)^2 + y^2} = 10. \qquad \textbf{(2)}$$

Now (2) is an equation in x and y having the properties given in (i) and (ii). Thus (2) is an equation of the given curve. However, as suggested above, (2) is not a very attractive equation. For that reason it will be transformed. The important thing to watch is that the transformed equation also has the properties given in (i) and (ii).

Write (2) in the equivalent form

$$\sqrt{(x + 3)^2 + y^2} = 10 - \sqrt{(x - 3)^2 + y^2}.$$

Square both sides of the above. This gives

$$x^2 + 6x + 9 + y^2 = 100 - 20\sqrt{(x - 3)^2 + y^2} + x^2 - 6x + 9 + y^2.$$

Simplifying this yields

$$12x - 100 = -20\sqrt{(x - 3)^2 + y^2},$$

and hence

$$3x - 25 = -5\sqrt{(x - 3)^2 + y^2}.$$

Squaring the above once more gives

$$9x^2 - 150x + 625 = 25x^2 - 150x + 225 + 25y^2,$$

that is,

$$16x^2 + 25y^2 = 400,$$

hence,

$$\frac{x^2}{25} + \frac{y^2}{16} = 1.$$ (3)

This is the desired equation. It is clear that if (x, y) satisfies (2), then it satisfies (3).

It is a fact that if a point (x, y) satisfies (3) then it satisfies (2) also (see Exercise 5).

The above curve is a particular ellipse.

In general, an ellipse is defined as follows: Two positive numbers a and c are given with $a > c$, and two fixed points F_1 and F_2 such that the distance $\overline{F_1F_2} = 2c$. The ellipse is the set of all points P such that

$$\overline{PF_1} + \overline{PF_2} = 2a.$$

To find an equation for this ellipse it is convenient to choose coordinate axes as in Figure IV.7.

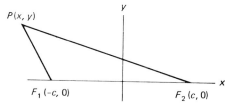

Figure IV.7

Then

$$\overline{PF_1} + \overline{PF_2} = 2a$$ (4)

or

$$\sqrt{(x + c)^2 + y^2} + \sqrt{(x - c)^2 + y^2} = 2a.$$ (5)

Transposing one square root, squaring, and simplifying gives

$$cx - a^2 = -a\sqrt{(x - c)^2 + y^2}.$$

Squaring again and simplifying, one obtains

$$\frac{x^2}{a^2} + \frac{y^2}{a^2 - c^2} = 1.$$ (6)

As before, every point (x, y) satisfying (6) satisfies (5) (Exercise 6). Therefore, this is the desired equation. We add some remarks: The ellipse may be defined in other ways that we shall not examine here. If $c = 0$, a circle of radius a is obtained; also, the points F_1 and F_2 coincide. Finally, $a > c$ gives $a^2 > c^2$ or $a^2 - c^2 > 0$. Thus there exists a number b such that

$b^2 = a^2 - c^2$. Therefore the equation of the ellipse can be written as

$$\frac{x^2}{a^2} + \frac{y^2}{b^2} = 1. \tag{7}$$

The graph of the ellipse is given in Figure IV.8 (see Exercise 2b, Chapter II, Section 11).

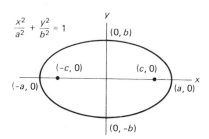

Figure IV.8

Solving for y in (7) gives

$$y = \pm \frac{b}{a} \sqrt{a^2 - x^2}. \tag{8}$$

If we consider the circle $x^2 + y^2 = a^2$ and solve for y, we obtain

$$y = \pm\sqrt{a^2 - x^2}.$$

The relationship between the circle and the ellipse is illustrated in Figure IV.9.

The fact that is graphically represented in the figure allows us to find the formula for the area bounded by an ellipse. Let A_e denote the area of the ellipse (7) and let A_c denote the area of the circle $x^2 + y^2 = a^2$. Then Figure

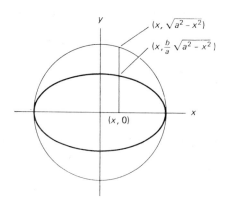

Figure IV.9

IV.9 shows that

$$\frac{A_e}{A_c} = \frac{b}{a}. \tag{9}$$

This can be made evident from Figure IV.10.

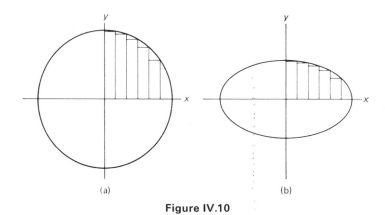

(a)   (b)

Figure IV.10

The area bounded either by the circle or the ellipse is approximately the sum of the areas of the many thin rectangles inscribed by them. The approximation is good if the rectangles are very thin. Now each rectangle in the ellipse has a height which is b/a times the height of the corresponding rectangle for the circle. This leads to formula (9).

Since the area bounded by the circle is πa^2 and since by (9) $A_e = (b/a)A_c$, we obtain finally

$$A_e = \pi ab. \tag{10}$$

The formula for the length of a piece of arc of an ellipse is enormously more complicated than that for a circle and cannot be set down here.

The equation given in (7) is for an ellipse whose center is at the origin. If the center of the ellipse is located at the point (h, k) and if the points F_1 and F_2 lie on the line $y = k$, then the equation of the ellipse is (see Exercise 3)

$$\frac{(x - h)^2}{a^2} + \frac{(y - k)^2}{b^2} = 1. \tag{11}$$

An example with $(h, k) = (2, -1)$, $a = 3$ and $b = 2$ is given in Figure IV.11.

We close by introducing some vocabulary. The points F_1 and F_2 in (1) are called the *foci* of the ellipse. The singular is *focus*. The origin in Figure IV.8 is the center of the ellipse. The number a represents the length of the *semimajor axis*. The number b represents the length of the *semiminor axis*. The number c is called the *focal distance*. Line segments joining two points of the ellipse are called *chords* and chords that pass through the center are called *diameters*.

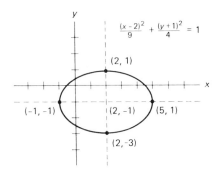

Figure IV.11

There is a largest diameter of length $2a$ and a shortest one of length $2b$. The number c/a is called the *eccentricity*. The literal meaning of eccentricity is: measure of noncircularity. If the eccentricity equals 0, then $c = 0$ and the ellipse is a circle. Note that $0 \le c \le 1$.

Exercises IV.3.a

1. Find the equation of an ellipse having its center at the origin and its foci on the y-axis. [Repeat the argument appearing in Equations (4) to (7), making the necessary changes.]

2. Graph the ellipses whose equations are given below. Indicate the semimajor axis, semiminor axis, center, foci, eccentricity, and area.

   (a) $\dfrac{x^2}{9} + \dfrac{y^2}{4} = 1$;

   (b) $\dfrac{x^2}{4} + \dfrac{y^2}{9} = 1$;

   (c) $4x^2 + 9y^2 - 8x + 18y - 11 = 0$;
   (d) $5x^2 + 2y^2 + 30x - 4y + 37 = 0$;
   (e) $4x^2 + y^2 - 8x - 12 = 0$;

   (f) $\dfrac{(x + 1)^2}{9} + \dfrac{(y - 1)^2}{25} = 1$;

   (g) $4x^2 + 25y^2 + 100y = 0$;
   (h) $9x^2 + 4y^2 + 36x - 24y + 36 = 0$.

3. Prove directly from the definition (or by some other acceptable means) that the equation of an ellipse with center at the point (h, k) and with foci on the line $y = k$ is given by Equation (11).

4. Find the equation of an ellipse with center at the origin, foci at $(1, 1)$ and $(-1, -1)$, and with $a = 2$. (Use the definition.)

5. Prove that if (x, y) satisfies Equation (3), then it satisfies Equation (2). [*Hint*: In establishing the equations in reverse order, there is one delicate point where in taking a square root one needs the fact that $25 - 3x \geq 0$. This follows from $25 \geq x^2$.]

6. Prove that if (x, y) satisfies (6), it satisfies (5). [*Hint*: See Exercise 5.]

7. (a) Find the equation of the ellipse with foci at $(-1, 1)$ and $(3, 1)$ and with $a = 4$.
   (b) Find the equation of the ellipse with foci at $(1, -1)$ and $(1, 3)$ with $a = 4$.

8. Find an equation for the ellipse with foci at $(-1, 0)$ and $(3, 4)$ and with $a = 4$. [*Hint*: Start from the definition.] What new phenomenon do you notice?

9. The German astronomer Johann Kepler (1571–1630) showed that the earth travels around the sun in an elliptic path with the sun at one focus. The major diameter is the chord joining the summer solstice (June 21) with the winter solstice (December 21). Assuming that its length $(2a)$ is 184,000,000 miles and that $c = 1,000,000$, calculate b. Also calculate the eccentricity. Note that the orbit is almost a circle with the sun at its center. You may be interested in noting also that we are closer to the sun in winter than in summer. Not so with the South Americans.

4. THE HYPERBOLA

Let there be given two positive numbers a and c with $c > a$. Suppose F_1 and F_2 are two fixed points in the plane whose distance apart $\overline{F_1F_2}$ is $2c$. The set of all points P such that

$$\text{either} \quad PF_1 - PF_2 = 2a \quad \text{or} \quad PF_2 - PF_1 = 2a \tag{1}$$

is called a *hyperbola*. Let us find an equation for the hyperbola.

SOLUTION: Choose axes as shown in Figure IV.12.

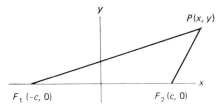

Figure IV.12

Write (1) in the form

$$\sqrt{(x + c)^2 + y^2} - \sqrt{(x - c)^2 + y^2} = \pm 2a. \tag{2}$$

Transpose, square, simplify, square, and simplify as was done for the ellipse. The principal steps follow:

$$\sqrt{(x + c)^2 + y^2} = \pm 2a + \sqrt{(x - c)^2 + y^2};$$
$$x^2 + 2cx + c^2 + y^2 = 4a^2 \pm 4a\sqrt{(x - c)^2 + y^2} + x^2 - 2cx + c^2 + y^2;$$
$$cx - a^2 = \pm a\sqrt{(x - c)^2 + y^2};$$
$$c^2x^2 - 2a^2cx + a^4 = a^2x^2 - 2a^2cx + a^2c^2 + a^2y^2;$$
$$(c^2 - a^2)x^2 - a^2y^2 = a^2(c^2 - a^2);$$

$$\frac{x^2}{a^2} - \frac{y^2}{c^2 - a^2} = 1. \tag{3}$$

It can be shown that if (x, y) satisfies (3), then it satisfies (2). The steps here are not identical with those for the ellipse (see Exercise 6).

Since $c > a$, $c^2 - a^2 > 0$. Thus it is possible to find $b > 0$ such that $b^2 = c^2 - a^2$. Equation (3) then takes the form

$$\frac{x^2}{a^2} - \frac{y^2}{b^2} = 1. \tag{4}$$

The number a is called the *semitransverse axis*. The number b is called the *semiconjugate axis*. The number c is called the *focal distance*. As before the points F_1 and F_2 are *foci* of the hyperbola. (See Figure IV.13.)

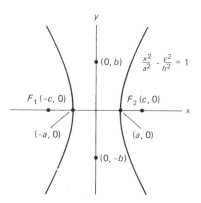

Figure IV.13

If the center of the hyperbola is at the point (h, k) and if the foci lie on the line $y = k$, the equation of the hyperbola is (see Exercise 7)

$$\frac{(x - h)^2}{a^2} - \frac{(y - k)^2}{b^2} = 1. \tag{5}$$

It should be noted that the ellipses and hyperbolas treated so far had their foci on a line parallel to the x-axis or the y-axis. If the foci are given an arbitrary position the equation obtained will be somewhat more complicated.

Equations (7) and (11) of the ellipse given in the previous section and Equations (4) and (5) of the present section are all of the form

$$Ax^2 + Cy^2 + Dx + Ey + F = 0. \qquad (6)$$

Read this as "something times x square plus something times y square plus something times x plus something times y plus a constant equals zero." For example the hyperbola (4) can be written as $b^2x^2 - a^2y^2 - a^2b^2 = 0$. And this is of the form (6) where

$$A = b^2, \qquad C = -a^2, \qquad D = 0, \qquad E = 0, \qquad F = -a^2b^2.$$

We notice that in all cases $A \neq 0$ and $B \neq 0$. Also A and B have the same sign for ellipses and have opposite signs for hyperbolas.

It can be shown that any Equation (6) with $A \neq 0$ and $C \neq 0$ is the equation of an ellipse or a hyperbola. This is shown just as for the case of a circle by completing squares. [See Section 2, formulas (10), (11), and (12).] There is a mild restriction on the value of F that we shall not write down (see Exercise 8).

EXAMPLE: Graph the curve

$$9x^2 - 4y^2 - 54x - 8y + 41 = 0. \qquad (7)$$

SOLUTION: Simple calculations show that

$9x^2 - 54x - 4y^2 - 8y + 41$
$$= 9(x^2 - 6x + 9) - 4(y^2 + 2y + 1) - 81 + 4 + 41$$
$$= 9(x - 3)^2 - 4(y + 1)^2 - 36.$$

Thus the original equation becomes

$$9(x - 3)^2 - 4(y + 1)^2 = 36$$

or

$$\frac{(x - 3)^2}{4} - \frac{(y + 1)^2}{9} = 1. \qquad (8)$$

This is a hyperbola with center $(h, k) = (3, -1)$, $a = 2, b = 3, c = \sqrt{4 + 9} = \sqrt{13}$. The graph is given in Figure IV.14.

Consider now the following problem: Find the equation of a hyperbola whose foci are located at the points $(\sqrt{2}, \sqrt{2})$ and $(-\sqrt{2}, -\sqrt{2})$ and for which $a = \sqrt{2}$.

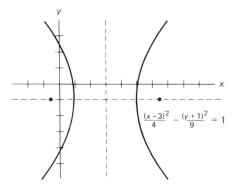

Figure IV.14

In attempting to solve this problem we note right away that the foci are not in standard position. Thus no formula worked out so far is of any help. The desired equation must be derived directly from the definition in (1). Therefore, for a point (x, y) on the hyperbola,

$$\sqrt{(x + \sqrt{2})^2 + (y + \sqrt{2})^2} - \sqrt{(x - \sqrt{2})^2 + (y - \sqrt{2})^2} = \pm 2\sqrt{2}. \quad \textbf{(9)}$$

If we perform the by now customary operations on this equation we arrive finally at the remarkably simple equation

$$xy = 1. \quad \textbf{(10)}$$

This equation is an old friend (see Figure II.12). Its graph is repeated in Figure IV.15.

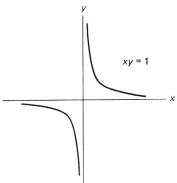

Figure IV.15

As is already known this hyperbola has two asymptotes (the x-axis and the y-axis). All hyperbolas have two asymptotes. See Exercise 9 where hints of the proof are given. (Asymptotes are discussed in Chapter II, Section 10.)

We close this section with a brief discussion of the parabola. One definition of the parabola is the following:

Let F be a fixed point and let d be a fixed line not passing through F. Consider the set of all points P such that

$$\overline{PF} = \text{distance of } P \text{ to } d. \qquad (11)$$

This set of points is called a *parabola*.

To find an equation for the curve, choose coordinate axes as indicated in Figure IV.16. Note that the distance of F to d is p. The coordinates of F are $(p/2, 0)$ and the equation of d is $x = -p/2$. The foot A of the perpendicular from P to d has coordinates $(-p/2, y)$. Equation (11) gives

$$\sqrt{\left(x - \frac{p}{2}\right)^2 + (y - 0)^2} = \sqrt{\left(x + \frac{p}{2}\right)^2 + (y - y)^2}. \qquad (12)$$

Squaring and simplifying gives

$$y^2 - 2px = 0. \qquad (13)$$

This is an equation we have met and studied in detail in Chapter II. There, it appeared in a slightly altered form: $y = ax^2$.

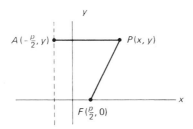

$A\left(-\frac{p}{2}, y\right)$ $P(x, y)$

$F\left(\frac{p}{2}, 0\right)$

Figure IV.16

Although the definition of the parabola given above seems to have little in common with that of the ellipse or hyperbola, the three curves are all very closely related. In fact the parabola is a limiting case of both of the other two curves.

The general equation of the second degree is the equation

$$Ax^2 + Bxy + Cy^2 + Dx + Ey + F = 0. \qquad (14)$$

We have seen that the parabola, ellipse, and hyperbola all have equations of the second degree. The hyperbola (10) is interesting in that for the first time in our experience in finding equations for curves we have come upon a case in which the coefficient of B is not 0. [Note that for (10), $A = 0$, $B = 1$, $C = 0$, $D = 0$, $E = 0$, $F = -1$.] It can be proved that all equations of type (14) give rise to parabolas, ellipses, or hyperbolas. It should be quite apparent why the standard equations obtained so far have had such simple form. It is because the (x, y) axes have been chosen so as to achieve that purpose. If the axes are chosen in "the general position" then the equation for the three curves is of type (14) with all coefficients present. The proof of these various statements could be carried through in reasonable time after the study of Chapter VI, Section 5.

Exercises IV.4.a

1. Find the equation of a hyperbola having its center at the origin and its foci on the y-axis.

2. Graph the hyperbolas whose equations are given below.

(a) $\dfrac{x^2}{9} - \dfrac{y^2}{4} = 1$;   (b) $\dfrac{y^2}{9} - \dfrac{x^2}{4} = 1$;

(c) $\dfrac{x^2}{4} - \dfrac{y^2}{9} = 1$;   (d) $\dfrac{y^2}{4} - \dfrac{x^2}{9} = 1$;

(e) $4x^2 - 9y^2 - 16x - 54y - 101 = 0$;
(f) $7x^2 - 2y^2 + 14x - 16y - 10 = 0$;
(g) $36x^2 - 9y^2 - 108x - 6y + 44 = 0$;
(h) $6x^2 - 4y^2 + 12x + 16y + 110 = 0$.

3. Graph the hyperbolas whose equations are given below.

(a) $(x - 4)(y + 2) = 1$;   (b) $(x + 3)(y - 2) = 2$;
(c) $xy - 2x + y - 1 = 0$;   (d) $xy - 3x - 2y + 5 = 0$;

(e) $y = \dfrac{1}{x - 3} + 1$.

4. Find an equation for the hyperbola with foci at $(1, 1)$, $(-1, -1)$, and with $a = 1$.

5. Find an equation for the hyperbola with foci at $(2, -2)$ and $(-2, 2)$ and with $a = 1$.

6. Show that if (x, y) satisfies (3), it satisfies (2). [*Hint*: Running back up the equations before (3) is easy up to the last step. Now suppose $x > 0$. Then (3) implies that $x \geq a$. Also $2cx > 2a^2$. Thus $(x + c)^2 > 4a^2$ or $\sqrt{(x + c)^2 + y^2} - 2a > 0$. This shows how to choose signs in taking the square root. Similarly if $x < 0$.]

7. Carry out the computation of (5).

8. Show that the equation $Ax^2 + Cy^2 + Dx + Ey + F = 0$ with $A > 0$, $C > 0$ represents an ellipse providing that $D^2/A + E^2/C - 4F > 0$. If $A > 0, C < 0$, it represents a hyperbola providing that $D^2/A + E^2/C - 4F \neq 0$.

9. Show that the lines $y = \pm(b/a)x$ are asymptotes of the hyperbola (4). [*Hint*: Consider the line $y = (b/a)x$. Then for a given $x > 0$, $(b/a)x - (b/a)\sqrt{x^2 - a^2} = ab/(x + \sqrt{x^2 - a^2})$. This quantity is small if x is large. This shows that $y = (b/a)x$ is an asymptote of the curve $y = (b/a)\sqrt{x^2 - a^2}$ for x positive.]

10. Graph the following parabolas.

   (a) $y^2 = 4x$;   (b) $x^2 = 4y$;
   (c) $y^2 = -4x$;   (d) $x^2 = -4y$;
   (e) $y^2 = 2(x - 3)$;   (f) $(y - 1)^2 = 2x$;
   (g) $4(y - 1)^2 = (x + 2)$;   (h) $(y - k)^2 = 2p(x - h)$.

11. Prove that the equation $Ax^2 + Cy^2 + Dx + Ey + F = 0$ represents a parabola in case $A = 0$, $C \neq 0$, and $D \neq 0$. Also in case $C = 0$, $A \neq 0$, $E \neq 0$.

12. A parabola has as its focus the point $(1, 1)$ and as directrix the line $x + y = 0$. (The directrix is the fixed line d given in the definition of a parabola.) In order to obtain an equation for the parabola what new formula or piece of information is needed that we do not have as yet?

5. ALGEBRAIC FUNCTIONS

As has been mentioned earlier, an implicit function is a function that is defined by setting an expression in x and y equal to 0. Upon solving for y in terms of x one or more functions are obtained. For example, if the equation $y^2 - x = 0$ is solved for y, one obtains $y = \sqrt{x}$ and $y = -\sqrt{x}$. Similarly, if the equation $x^2/a^2 - y^2/b^2 = 1$ is solved for y, one obtains $y = (b/a)\sqrt{x^2 - a^2}$ and $y = -(b/a)\sqrt{x^2 - a^2}$. These functions are examples of *algebraic functions*.

We define an algebraic function in general. Let $F(x, y)$ represent a polynomial in x and y, that is, a sum of terms of the form $cx^r y^s$ where c is a real number and r and s are integers ≥ 0. The equation

$$F(x, y) = 0 \tag{1}$$

defines (implicitly) one or more *algebraic functions*. Notice that polynomial functions and rational functions are all algebraic. In the forthcoming chapters we shall meet functions that are not algebraic.

Consider the equation

$$y^2 = x^3. \tag{2}$$

Note that we must have $x \geq 0$ so that $y^2 \geq 0$. For every $x \geq 0$ there are two values of y satisfying (2), namely, $y = \sqrt{x^3}$ and $y = -\sqrt{x^3}$. We can also write $y = \pm x^{3/2}$. The graph is given in Figure IV.17.

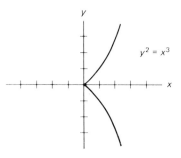

Figure IV.17

Consider now the equation

$$y^2 = x^3 + x = x^2(x + 1). \tag{3}$$

Solving for y gives $y = \pm x\sqrt{x + 1}$. Thus, for one thing, the graph is symmetric about the x-axis. Next, in order to obtain real values for y, it is necessary that $x + 1 \geq 0$, that is, $x \geq -1$. The graph crosses the x-axis at $x = -1$ and at $x = 0$ (twice). To sketch the curve fairly accurately, it remains to calculate a few points. The results are shown in Table IV.1 and Figure IV.18.

Table IV.1

x	-1	$-\frac{1}{2}$	0	$\frac{1}{2}$	1	2	
y	0	$\pm\frac{1}{4}\sqrt{2}$	0	$\pm\frac{1}{4}\sqrt{6}$	$\pm\sqrt{2}$	$\pm2\sqrt{3}$	

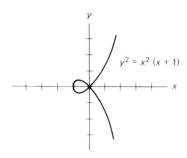

Figure IV.18

Finally consider the equation

$$y^2 = x^3 - x = x^2(x - 1). \tag{4}$$

Clearly, if $x = 0$ or $x = 1$, then $y = 0$. If x does not have these two values, then we must have $x > 1$ in order for y to have real values. Thus the point $(0, 0)$ is an isolated point of the graph! Calculating a few points in Table IV.2 helps us to graph the curve in Figure IV.19.

Table IV.2

x	0	1	$\frac{5}{4}$	$\frac{3}{2}$	2	
y	0	0	$\pm\frac{5}{8}$	$\pm\frac{3}{4}\sqrt{2}$	± 2	

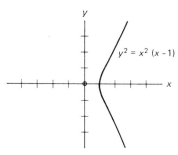

Figure IV.19

Table IV.3

PLANET	DISTANCE FROM SUN	PERIOD	ECCENTRICITY
Mercury	36	0.24	0.20
Venus	67	0.61	0.007
Earth	93	1.00	0.02
Mars	141	1.9	0.09
Jupiter	483	11.9	0.05
Saturn	886	29.4	0.06
Uranus	1782	84.0	0.05
Neptune	2793	164.8	0.009

Exercises IV.5.a

1. Obtain the graph defined by the equations below.

(a) $y^3 = -x^2$;
(c) $y^2 = x^3 + 1$;
(e) $y^2 = x(x^2 - 1)$;
(g) $x^3 + y^3 = 1$;

(b) $y^2 = x^2$;
(d) $y^2 = x(x - 1)^2$;
(f) $xy^2 - x^2 - 2x - 1 = 0$;
(h) $x^4 + y^4 = 1$.

2. Solve for y each of the equations in Exercise 1 giving all appropriate signs to the radicals.

3. The third law of Kepler for planetary motion states that the square of the period of a planet (number of years required for one revolution about the sun) is proportional to the cube of the semimajor axes of the ellipse describing the path of the planet about the sun. In other words, if p is the period in years and a is the semimajor axis in millions of miles, then

$$p^2 = ka^3,$$

where k is a constant. Find the value of k and check Kepler's law.

A table of periods and orbit sizes for the seven principal planets is given in Table IV.3. Because of its interest, the eccentricity is also given. The units in the table are distances in millions of miles and periods in years. Note that when the eccentricity is small, the distance from the sun is very close to the length of the semimajor axis.

ON THE EXISTENCE OF SQUARE ROOTS

The problem is to show that if $a > 0$, there exists a number b such that

$$b^2 = a, \quad \text{that is,} \quad b = \sqrt{a}. \tag{1}$$

This will be done by applying the least upper bound principle and using the "principle of trichotomy": If c and d are real numbers, then one and only one of the following holds: $c = d$, $c > d$, $c < d$.

Let x be any positive number such that $x^2 \leq a$. Consider the set S of all such x. This set is bounded from above. In fact, since $(a + 1)^2 = a^2 + 2a + 1 > a$ then $x < a + 1$. By the least upper bound principle, the set S has a least upper bound. Call it b. We assert that $b^2 = a$.

There are three possibilities:

$$b^2 = a; \quad b^2 < a; \quad b^2 > a. \tag{2}$$

It will be shown that the last two lead to a contradiction. Hence the only possibility is $b^2 = a$ and the problem is solved.

Suppose first that $b^2 < a$. Then $a - b^2 > 0$. For convenience, write

$$a - b^2 = \varepsilon \quad \text{(Greek epsilon).} \tag{3}$$

Then $\varepsilon > 0$.

Note above that $b > 0$. This can be seen as follows. By the Archimedean principle, there exists a natural number n such that $a > 1/n$. Thus since $1 > 1/n$, we have $1/n > 1/n^2$ and $(1/n)^2 < a$. Hence $1/n$ belongs to S and $b \geq 1/n$ by the definition of least upper bound.

Now take any number δ (Greek delta) such that

$$\delta > 0; \quad \delta < 1; \quad \delta < \frac{\varepsilon}{4b}; \quad \delta < \frac{\varepsilon}{2}. \tag{4}$$

Then using the fact that $\delta^2 < \delta$,

$$(b + \delta)^2 = b^2 + 2b\delta + \delta^2 < b^2 + 2b\frac{\varepsilon}{4b} + \delta \tag{5}$$

$$< b^2 + \frac{\varepsilon}{2} + \frac{\varepsilon}{2} = b^2 + \varepsilon = a.$$

Thus $(b + \delta)^2 < a$ and $b + \delta$ is in S. Since (definition of l.u.b.) b is at least as large as any number in S, we obtain $b + \delta \leq b$ or $\delta \leq 0$. This contradicts the fact that $\delta > 0$. Thus the case $b^2 < a$ is impossible.

Now assume that $b^2 > a$. Write

$$b^2 - a = \varepsilon. \tag{6}$$

Define δ again as in (4). Then using the fact that $-\delta^2 > -\delta$, $-\delta > -\varepsilon/4b$, $-\delta > -\varepsilon/2$, one obtains

$$(b - \delta)^2 = b^2 - 2b\delta + \delta^2 > b^2 - \frac{\varepsilon}{2} + \delta^2$$

$$> b^2 - \frac{\varepsilon}{2} - \delta^2 > b^2 - \frac{\varepsilon}{2} - \delta \tag{7}$$

$$> b^2 - \frac{\varepsilon}{2} - \frac{\varepsilon}{2} = b^2 - \varepsilon = a.$$

It is easy to see that in this problem, if $x < b$ then x is in the set S; hence $x^2 \leq a$. Thus since $\delta > 0, (b - \delta)^2 \leq a$. However (7) asserts that $(b - \delta)^2 > a$. This is a contradiction; therefore, $b^2 > a$ is false.

This proof should be reconstructed so as to obtain the result that for any natural number $n > 2$, the number a has an nth root. It will be noticed that the proof given above is rough and ready. It has been our intention in writing it to put it down just as it flowed out of the pencil. This makes it possible to follow some of the thoughts. Normally, proofs are subject to much rewriting, polishing, streamlining. The shortest proofs frequently take the longest to write.

Chapter V

EXPONENTIAL AND LOGARITHMIC FUNCTIONS

1. INTEGRAL EXPONENTS

We have been familiar with exponential notation in its simplest case for some time. The simplest case referred to is the case of the natural numbers. Thus suppose a is any real number. One writes

$$a \cdot a = a^2, \quad a \cdot a \cdot a = a^3, \quad a \cdot a \cdot a \cdot a = a^4,$$

and so on. We can also write, if we wish, $a = a^1$. Finally the symbol a^0 is introduced and its definition is $a^0 = 1$. All this will be set down in a formal definition in just a moment. If $a = 3$, the positive integral powers obtained are successively $3^0, 3^1, 3^2, 3^3, 3^4, \cdots$ and these are equal respectively to $1, 3, 9, 27, 81, \cdots$.

The *laws of exponents* are properties that exponents have. For example, it is clear that $a^2 \cdot a^3 = (a \cdot a) \cdot (a \cdot a \cdot a) = a^5$. Thus $a^2 \cdot a^3 = a^{2+3}$. In general, if n and m are any natural numbers, $a^n \cdot a^m = a^{n+m}$. That this is so can be seen by a direct counting argument. The above law, namely that $a^n \cdot a^m = a^{n+m}$, is the most important law of exponents. Another law is illustrated by the following example: $(a^2)^3 = (a \cdot a) \cdot (a \cdot a) \cdot (a \cdot a) = a^6$. Since $6 = 2 \cdot 3$, this gives $(a^2)^3 = a^{2 \cdot 3} = a^6$. In general $(a^n)^m = a^{nm}$. This can be seen once more by an easy argument:

$$(a^n)^m = (a \cdots a)(a \cdots a) \cdots (a \cdots a) = a^{nm}.$$

Here each parenthesis $(a \cdots a)$ contains n terms and there are m parentheses.

Furthermore, it is clear that for two real numbers a and b, $(a \cdot b)^n = (a \cdot b) \cdots (a \cdot b) = a^n b^n$. For instance,

$$(2 \cdot 7)^3 = (2 \cdot 7)(2 \cdot 7)(2 \cdot 7) = (2 \cdot 2 \cdot 2)(7 \cdot 7 \cdot 7) = 2^3 \cdot 7^3.$$

Now, in addition to natural number exponents, integral exponents, rational exponents, and real exponents can be introduced. These also satisfy the above laws of exponents. It will be noted that the introduction of exponents follows precisely the unfolding of topics in Chapter I. Thus we study the expression a^n and its properties for the four successive cases: n belongs to $\mathbf{N}$, $\mathbf{Z}$, $\mathbf{Q}$, and $\mathbf{R}$.

As mentioned before, all of us have had experience with natural number exponents for some time. The proofs of the laws for this case are essentially trivial. The case of integral exponents is slightly more sophisticated. The proofs here are just a bit more demanding. But all that is required here is a bit of good housekeeping—call it good mind keeping, if you prefer. The case of rational exponents is more complicated. Most readers will have had some experience with rational exponents but will not have seen really clean proofs of the laws of exponents for this case. Such proofs are presented below. Finally there is the case of arbitrary real exponents. It will be our assumption that the reader has had no training in this direction. A great deal of attention is given to this case in the present chapter. The proofs are not easy. They require new material.

We turn to the case of integral exponents. The work will be a little more formal. There is first a formal definition and then a formally stated theorem with its proof. To make the situation as clear as possible, little reference is made to the previous discussion. It will be assumed in this section that $a \neq 0$. Starting with Section 2, it will be assumed that $a > 0$. The case $a = 1$ is interesting, easy, and sometimes excluded. This is because "1 raised to any exponent is 1" and hence the powers of 1 don't generate new numbers. Check that $1^0 = 1$, $1^1 = 1$, $1^2 = 1$, $1^3 = 1$, and so on.

V–1 Definition

If $a \neq 0$ and n is an integer, then
(a) *if $n = 0$, $a^n = 1$. Thus $a^0 = 1$;*
(b) *if $n > 0$, $a^n = \underbrace{a \cdot a \cdots a}_{n \text{ times}}$. In particular $a^1 = a$;*
(c) *if $n < 0$, say $n = -m$, then $a^n = a^{-m} = 1/a^m$. In particular $a^{-1} = 1/a$.*

The following identities, called the *laws of exponents*, may immediately be proved.

V–2 Theorem

If a and b are numbers not zero and n and m are any integers, then

$$a^n \cdot a^m = a^{n+m}; \tag{1}$$

$$(a^n)^m = a^{nm}; \tag{2}$$

$$(a \cdot b)^n = a^n \cdot b^n. \tag{3}$$

The proof of these statements is simple. The way to proceed, say in proving (1), is to consider the various possibilities for n and m. Referring to the definition, we see that there are 3 possibilities for n and 3 possibilities for m. Hence there are $3 \cdot 3 = 9$ possible choices of m and n. The first possibility handled will be the case $n > 0$ and $m > 0$. Then

$$a^n = \underbrace{a \cdot a \cdots a}_{n \text{ times}} \qquad a^m = \underbrace{a \cdot a \cdots a}_{m \text{ times}} \tag{4}$$

and

$$a^{n+m} = \underbrace{a \cdot a \cdots a.}_{n+m \text{ times}} \tag{5}$$

Thus obviously in this case, $a^n \cdot a^m = a^{n+m}$.

If $n > 0$ and $m = 0$, then $n + m = n$ and

$$a^{n+m} = a^n = a^n \cdot 1 = a^n \cdot a^0 = a^n \cdot a^m.$$

If $n > 0$ and $m < 0$, then

$$a^n \cdot a^m = \underbrace{a \cdot a \cdots a}_{n \text{ times}} \times \frac{1}{\underbrace{a \cdot a \cdots a}_{-m \text{ times}}} = a^{n-(-m)} = a^{n+m}. \tag{6}$$

In this way, we may prove (1), (2), (3) for all possible cases (Exercises 7 and 8).

The number a is called the base and n is called the exponent. The expression a^n is read "a raised to the power n," or "a exponent n," or "a to the n."

Exponents are used in scientific questions that involve very large or very small numbers. The base used in discussing these questions is of course 10. Thus for example the number of molecules in a standard volume of gas is 6.02×10^{23} (Avogadro's number). And the wavelength of the yellow line in sodium vapor (throw some table salt into a gas flame) is 5890 Angstrom units where 1 Angstrom is 10^{-10} meters. Similarly, the mass of an electron is 9.1×10^{-28} grams.

Let us make the meaning of the above a bit clearer. Many numbers that are met in scientific work are very large; many are very small. For example, in a short time the population of the world will reach 4,000,000,000. This is quite a few zeros, but even more people. Now $4,000,000,000 = 4 \times 1,000,000,000$. And using exponential notation for the latter, $1,000,000,000 = 10^9$. Thus the population will shortly reach 4×10^9. Similarly, instead of saying that the wavelength of sodium vapor is 0.0000005890 meters, it seems easier to write that it is 5890×10^{-10} meters; it may also be written as 5.890×10^{-7} meters. Writing out the mass of an electron longhand would take close to a whole line!

Keep in mind that 10^{-7} means $(1/10)^7$; hence, it can be expressed as 1 divided by 1 followed by 7 zeros. Another way of looking at it is that multiplication by 10^{-7} means shifting the decimal point to the left 7 places. Multiplying by 10^7 means shifting the decimal point to the right 7 places.

Exercises V.1.a

1. Simplify the following expressions.

   (a) $3^8 \cdot 3^4$; (b) $6^7 \cdot 6^{-12}$; (c) $10^{20}/10^{15}$;
   (d) $a^4 \cdot a^7$; (e) $(x^3)^{-4}$; (f) a^5/a^8;
   (g) $(3^5 x)^0$; (h) $(-2)^3 \times 8^2$; (i) $2^2 \times 6^3 \times 9^4$.

2. Simplify the following expressions.

   (a) $(-3)^4$; (b) $(3^5 \times 7^{-4})^{-4}$;

   (c) $(2^2 \times 3^3 \times 6^4)^5$; (d) $\left(\dfrac{a^8}{a^5}\right)^4$;

   (e) $[(-2a)^4(2b)^{-3}]^2$; (f) $[a^5(ab^2)^3]^5$;

   (g) $[(2x)(3y)^2(4z)^3]^{-1}$; (h) $\left[\dfrac{(abc^2)^3}{2a^2b^3}\right]^0$.

3. Write the following numbers in scientific notation (the numbers include speed of light in miles per second and in meters per second, the annual U.S. budget in dollars, the angle in degrees subtended by a human hair at a distance of 1 mile).

   (a) 186,000; (b) 300,000,000;
   (c) 225,000,000,000; (d) 0.00001.

4. Write the following numbers in scientific notation.

   (a) 0.000015; (b) 150,000;
   (c) 365; (d) 29,700,000;
   (e) 0.000000012; (f) 4.

5. Perform the following operations.

   (a) $(4 \times 10^8)(1.2 \times 10^{-6})$;
   (b) $(3 \times 10^{14})^3(2.5 \times 10^7)^2$;
   (c) $(6.02 \times 10^{23})(2.5 \times 10^5)$ (number of molecules in the U.S. Senate chamber);
   (d) $(2.4 \times 10^5)(5.28 \times 10^3)(1.2 \times 10)(2.54 \times 10^8)$ (distance to moon in Angstroms).

6. Perform the following operations.

(a) $(2 \times 10^4)^3$;

(b) $(3 \times 10^6) \times (5 \times 10^{-1})$;

(c) $\dfrac{6 \times 10^4}{2 \times 10^9}$;

(d) $\dfrac{2.8 \times 10^{-2}}{7 \times 10^{-3}}$;

(e) $\dfrac{(6 \times 10^7)(2.5 \times 10^{-2})}{5 \times 10^3}$;

(f) $(2 \times 10^{-3}) \times (6 \times 10^9)$.

7. Write down the proof of (2) for at least 3 out of the 9 cases.

8. Write down the proof of (3) for all 3 cases.

9. Assuming that the population of the world will double every 60 years, find out in how many years the population will be 64 times as large as it is now.

2. RATIONAL EXPONENTS

In the present section we shall consider rational exponents. That is, we shall define the meaning of a^r where r is a rational number. *From now on, $a > 0$.* We shall see that Theorem V–2 holds for rational exponents.

Interestingly enough, the results of the present section will not be used in the later development. Later we shall define arbitrary exponents (rational or irrational) and prove the validity of Theorem V–2 for them. The principal purpose of going through the present discussion on rational exponents is to make us feel more at home with exponents; to make us feel more comfortable when using them. This will get us ready for the decisive development starting in the next section.

Let r be a rational number and write

$$r = \frac{p}{q},$$

where p and q are integers, $q \neq 0$. Then we define $a^{p/q}$ by

$$a^{p/q} = (\sqrt[q]{a})^p. \tag{1}$$

We remind ourselves that the qth root of a is unique and that we write for it either $\sqrt[q]{a}$ or $a^{1/q}$ (Chapter IV, Section 1). Thus by definition

$$a^{p/q} = (a^{1/q})^p.$$

Let us show that

$$(a^{1/q})^p = (a^p)^{1/q}. \tag{2}$$

EXAMPLE: $(8^{1/3})^2 = 2^2 = 4$. And $(8^2)^{1/3} = (64)^{1/3} = 4$.

Suppose that $a^{1/q} = b$. Then $(a^{1/q})^p = b^p$. Next, since $a = b^q$, $a^p = (b^q)^p = b^{qp}$ by one of the laws of exponents which are known to be valid for *integral* exponents. Furthermore, $(a^p)^{1/q} = (b^{qp})^{1/q} = b^p$ directly from the definition of a qth root. Hence (2) is valid.

Next we show that

$$\text{if} \quad \frac{p}{q} = \frac{p'}{q'} \quad \text{then} \quad a^{p/q} = a^{p'}/q'. \tag{3}$$

For example, $\frac{2}{3} = \frac{4}{6}$. Now $64^{2/3} = (64^{1/3})^2 = 4^2 = 16$, while $64^{4/6} = (64^{1/6})^4 = 2^4 = 16$.

In proving (3), it may be supposed that the expression p/q is in lowest terms (why?) and hence $p' = kp$ and $q' = kq$ for some integer k. Now, suppose $a^{1/q'} = b$; then $a = b^{q'} = b^{kq} = (b^k)^q$. This is true by one of the laws of exponents for *integers*. Since the qth root of a number is unique, this equation tells us that $a^{1/q} = b^k$. Finally,

$$a^{p/q} = (a^{1/q})^p = (b^k)^p = b^{kp} = b^{p'} = (a^{1/q'})^{p'} = a^{p'/q'}. \tag{4}$$

The reader should be relaxed as he reads this string of equalities and should be sure to verify each one. There are six equality signs and hence six things to verify. They are: The first equality comes from the definition. The second uses the fact that $a^{1/q} = b^k$. The third uses Equation (2) of Section 1. The fourth uses the equation $p' = kp$. The fifth substitutes for b its value. The sixth uses the definition.

We are now ready to prove Theorem V–2 for rational exponents. Consider the first law of exponents: $a^n \cdot a^m = a^{n+m}$ where now n and m are rational numbers. Because of what was proved just above, it may be assumed that m and n are expressed with the same denominator. That is,

$$m = \frac{p}{q}, \quad n = \frac{r}{q}, \quad m + n = \frac{p+r}{q}. \tag{5}$$

Then

$$\begin{aligned} a^m \cdot a^n &= a^{p/q} \cdot a^{r/q} = (a^{1/q})^p \cdot (a^{1/q})^r = (a^{1/q})^{p+r} \\ &= a^{(p+r)/q} = a^{n+m}. \end{aligned} \tag{6}$$

The third equality sign is valid because p and r are integers.

The law $(a^m)^n = a^{mn}$ can be proved for rational exponents $m = p/q$ and $n = r/s$ by using (among other results) the fact that if $b = a^{1/q}$, then $(b^p)^{1/s} = (b^{1/s})^p$. The details will not be set down here (see Exercise 6).

Finally, the law $(a \cdot b)^{p/q} = a^{p/q} \cdot b^{p/q}$ is established by verifying the following equalities:

$$\begin{aligned} (a \cdot b)^{p/q} &= [(a \cdot b)^{1/q}]^p = (a^{1/q} \cdot b^{1/q})^p = (a^{1/q})^p (b^{1/q})^p \\ &= a^{p/q} \cdot b^{p/q}. \end{aligned} \tag{7}$$

Here the first equality comes from the definition. The second comes from the fact that $[(ab)^{1/q}]^q = ab$ and $(a^{1/q} \cdot b^{1/q})^q = a \cdot b$ since q is an integer; then uniqueness of qth roots is applied. The third equality comes from applying (3) in Section 1. The last equality stems from the definition.

EXAMPLE 1: Suppose we are asked to solve for x an equation of the form $2^x = 4 \cdot \sqrt{2}$. A possible procedure is this:

$$4 \times \sqrt{2} = 2^2 \cdot 2^{1/2} = 2^{5/2}.$$

Thus

$$2^x = 2^{5/2} \quad \text{or} \quad x = \frac{5}{2}.$$

EXAMPLE 2: Find y such that $y^8 = 4^3 \times 27^5$.

SOLUTION: Since $4^3 \times 27^5 = (2^2)^3 \cdot (3^3)^5 = 2^6 \cdot 3^{15}$, this gives

$$y^8 = 2^6 \times 3^{15}$$

or

$$y = (2^6 \cdot 3^{15})^{1/8} = 2^{6/8} \cdot 3^{15/8} = 2^{3/4} \cdot 3^{15/8}.$$

PROBLEM: A savings bank advertises that money deposited with it will double every 14 years. Obtain a formula for the value of an account with an initial deposit of $100 after n years.

SOLUTION: A one dollar deposit grows after n years to $2^{n/14}$ dollars (check this for $n = 14, 28, 42$). Thus the desired amount A is given by

$$A = 100 \cdot 2^{n/14}.$$

If we are interested in $n = 20$ we must know the numerical value of $2^{20/14} = 2^{10/7}$. We shall learn how to compute this later. There will be more such problems at that time.

Exercises V.2.a

1. Write without exponents.

(a) $32^{3/5}$;
(c) $27^{4/3}$;

(b) $64^{3/2}$;
(d) $(625)^{-1/4}$;

(e) $(100)^{-3/2}$;

(f) $\left(\dfrac{8}{27}\right)^{-4/3}$;

(g) $(\sqrt{2})^{-6}$;
(i) $\sqrt{81} \cdot (81)^{3/4}$;
(k) $36^{2/4}$;

(h) $(\sqrt{3})^4 \cdot (49)^{3/2}$;
(j) $8^{5/3}$;
(l) $16^{-3/2}$.

2. Simplify the following expressions.

(a) $(a^3 \cdot a^{-1/2})^4$;

(b) $(a^2 \cdot a^{-3})^{1/3}$;

(c) $(a^3b^{-2}c^{4/3})^{1/2}$;

(d) $\left(\dfrac{a^2 \cdot a^{-3}}{a^{1/2}}\right)^{2/3}$;

(e) $(a^2 \cdot b^3c^{1/2})^4 \cdot \left(\dfrac{a}{b^2}\right)^3$;

(f) $(2^5x^4)^{3/2}(2^{1/2}y^{-2})^{-1}$;

(g) $(a^{1/3} \cdot a^{-4/3})^2$;

(h) $(6a^4b^5)^{3/5}$;

(i) $(36a^4)^{1/2} \cdot (27b^2)^{-1}$.

3. Solve the following equations for x, y.

(a) $128\sqrt[3]{2} = 2^x$;

(b) $\left(\dfrac{4}{25}\right)^x = \dfrac{16}{625}$;

(c) $x^{3/2} = 5$;

(d) $y^2 = 27\sqrt[3]{2}$;

(e) $(5^{3/2})^x = 625$;

(f) $x^{10} = 10^5$;

(g) $x^{10} = 10^x$.

4. Using Table I, find the approximate value for $x = 7,\ 20,\ 41$ of the following.

(a) $\sqrt{x}$;

(b) $\sqrt[3]{x}$;

(c) $x\sqrt{x} + \sqrt[3]{x}$;

(d) $\dfrac{\sqrt{x}}{\sqrt[3]{x}} = \sqrt[6]{x}$.

5. If at present there are 5000 research articles in mathematics published each year and the number of articles published doubles every 10 years, how many articles will be published 15 years from now?

6. Prove that if m and n are rational numbers then $(a^m)^n = a^{m \cdot n}$.

7. Prove Equation (2) by raising both sides to the qth power. Using (2), prove (4) by raising both sides to a suitable power.

3. PROPERTIES OF THE EXPONENTIAL FUNCTION

Suppose we choose a number $a > 0$ and hold it fixed. We have seen in the preceding sections how to construct a function defined on the rational numbers which associates to each such number x a number a^x. In other words, we have a correspondence

$$x \mapsto a^x, \qquad x \text{ rational.} \tag{1}$$

This function has many interesting properties. Among others we have
(a) For all x, $a^x > 0$.
(b) If $a > 1$, the function is monotone increasing. It takes on large values if x is positive and large. If $a < 1$, the function is monotone decreasing. It takes on large values if x is negative and $|x|$ is large.
(c) The function satisfies all the laws of exponents (Theorem V–2).

PROOF: (a) is obvious. Property (c) was proved in the preceding section. As for (b), see Exercises 6 and 7, where the proof is sketched.

In constructing the function $x \mapsto a^x$ we started first with integral values of x and then extended the function so as to be defined for rational numbers. We now desire to extend this function still further so that it will be defined for *all* real numbers, rational and irrational. It is desirable to carry out this extension in such a way that the new function will have all the properties of the old one listed above. If we succeed, then the value of the function for an irrational number x, no matter how we obtain it, will be called the result of raising a to the power x. For example, if $a = 3$ and $x = \sqrt{2}$, we shall use the expression: raise 3 to the power $\sqrt{2}$. If someone tells us that $3^{\sqrt{2}} = 4.727$ correct to three decimal places, it will not enter our heads to check this by multiplying 3 by itself $\sqrt{2}$ times; nor by some scheme involving the taking of qth roots of 3 and raising them to the pth powers. The extension will be made possible by an argument which is very powerful and completely new: And being new, there will be some mystery in the process. It will be seen when the extension is finally made that the extended function has all the properties listed above and many others that cannot be imagined now.

There is another fact that will come to light. So far, there seems to be a very large number of equally important exponential functions: 2^x, 10^x, π^x, and so on. This is an illusion. There is only *one* exponential function (certainly not 10^x!) and the others are trivial variations of it. There is one star. The rest of the actors are a very mediocre supporting cast whose existence depends exclusively on the star.

The fundamental theorem from which everything else concerning exponentials follows will now be stated.

V–3 Existence Theorem for the Exponential Function

There exists a real-valued function, called exp, *defined for all the real numbers*

$$\exp: R \to R \tag{2}$$

having the properties:
(a) *for every* x, $\exp(x) > 0$;
(b) *the function* exp *is monotone increasing;*
(c) *the function* exp *takes on all positive values. That is, given* $y > 0$, *there exists an* x *such that* $y = \exp(x)$;
(d) *if* x_1 *and* x_2 *are real numbers, then*

$$\exp(x_1 + x_2) = \exp(x_1) \cdot \exp(x_2). \tag{3}$$

Equation (3) is the functional equation of the function exp. Note that it is precisely Equation (1) of Theorem V–2 written in a different notation. We have already touched upon this functional equation in Chapter II, Section 8. The proof of Theorem V–3 will be given in the next section.

Let us say a few words here about the statement of the theorem. It states that a particular function exp to be defined later has properties (a) through (d).

Now many functions have properties (a) through (d). Then what is the point of the theorem? The point is that although many functions have properties (a) through (d), it is impossible to put a hand on a single one until we have a hold of the function exp. The function exp not only has properties (a) through (d) but some additional ones that cannot be described until later when we construct it. In other words, exp is the nerve center through which the entire theory of exponentials and logarithms flows. Looking forward to the moment that the function has been defined, its value at any point a may be considered. In particular, consider the number exp(1). This number is very famous in mathematics. It is denoted by the letter e. But more about it in a moment.

Let us obtain some of the further properties of the function. In the first place

$$\exp(0) = 1. \tag{4}$$

This follows by using in (3) the trivial fact that $0 = 0 + 0$. Thus, $\exp(0) = \exp(0 + 0) = \exp(0) \cdot \exp(0)$. Dividing through by $\exp(0)$ gives $\exp(0) = 1$. The division is allowable because of (a).

Next, set $x = 1$. Then $\exp(1)$ is some number that is greater than 1 since by (b), $1 > 0$ and hence $\exp(1) > \exp(0) = 1$. Writing e for the value of $\exp(1)$,

$$\exp(1) = e. \tag{5}$$

Next it is seen that $\exp(2) = \exp(1 + 1) = \exp(1) \cdot \exp(1) = e \cdot e = e^2$. In general, for any integer n, $\exp(n) = e^n$. In fact,

$$\exp(x) = e^x \qquad \text{if } x \text{ is rational.} \tag{6}$$

The proof of this is easy now. It is based exclusively on the functional equation (3). For details of the proof, refer to Chapter II, Section 8.

Thus the function exp whose existence is asserted in our theorem is identical with the power function of a certain number e whenever that power is a rational number.

We derive some further consequences from Theorem V–3. The theorem states that there exists one particular function exp with a collection of many desirable properties. It will be seen that with the help of that one function exp we can extend to irrational values of x any single one of the power functions that was treated before: 2^x, 10^x, π^x, and so on.

Let it be required to extend to irrational x the power of some number a, where $a > 0$. By (c) of the Existence Theorem, there is some real number, call it u, such that $\exp(u) = a$. Now, consider the function defined for all real x by

$$x \mapsto \exp(ux). \tag{7}$$

Notice that for the values $x = 0, 1, 2, 3, \cdots$, we have $\exp(ux) = 1$, $a, a^2, a^3, \cdots$. In fact, if x is any rational number, we have $\exp(ux) = a^x$ (Exercise 9).

Thus the function defined in (7) for all real x is the extension desired for the function previously defined only for rational x:

$$x \mapsto a^x. \tag{8}$$

Let us show that the function so defined satisfies the laws of exponents in Theorem V–2. The law (1) follows from

$$a^n \cdot a^m = \exp(un) \cdot \exp(um) = \exp(un + um) = \exp[u(n + m)] = a^{n+m}. \tag{9}$$

The law (2) follows from

$$(a^n)^m = [(\exp u)^n]^m = (\exp un)^m = \exp(unm) = a^{nm}. \tag{10}$$

Let us look at law (3). If $a = \exp u$ and $b = \exp v$, then $a \cdot b = \exp u \cdot \exp v = \exp(u + v)$. Thus

$$(a \cdot b)^n = [\exp(u + v)]^n = \exp[(u + v)n] = \exp(un + vn)$$
$$= \exp(un) \cdot \exp(vn) = a^n \cdot b^n. \tag{11}$$

Thus it is apparent that the entire theory of exponents depends on the existence of *one* function with the properties stated in Theorem V–3.

In (6), it is shown that for all rational x, $\exp(x) = e^x$. Now the number e can be used as a base for real exponents, not merely rational ones. Our definition given above of irrational powers of a applies in particular to ir-rational powers of e. It can be seen that

$$\exp(x) = e^x \qquad \text{if } x \text{ is real.} \tag{12}$$

Another way of asserting (7) is to say that for the special case of $a = e, u = 1$.

This function is calculated for various values of x in Table II. For example, we find there that $e^1 = 2.7183$, $e^{-1} = 0.3679$. It should be checked mentally that the product of these two numbers seems to equal 1.

The same table allows us to solve the problem: Find u so that $e^u = 10$. We obtain $u = 2.30$ (approximately). This number allows us to express powers to the base 10 in terms of powers to the base e. In fact, the previous discussion indicates that for all x

$$10^x = e^{2.30x}.$$

Thus, to obtain 10 to any power, say $x = \sqrt{2}$, calculate $2.30 \times \sqrt{2} = 3.24$. The table then gives $e^{3.24} = 25.79$ approximately. Thus $10^{\sqrt{2}} \approx 25.79$. This method of finding powers of 10 is completely effective but entails multiplication by 2.30. It is possible to set up tables of powers of 10 directly where this multiplication is built into the tables. We shall study this later in the section on logarithms. The point to remember is that given a table of the function exp, we are in a position to construct a table of powers to any base whatever. As elsewhere in the book, the symbol "$\approx$" is used to emphasize the fact that approximate equality holds. Thus $\sqrt{3} \approx 1.732$.

Exercises V.3.a

1. Calculate the numbers below. Do this by direct multiplication using $e \approx 2.72$ and check by referring to Table II.

(a) e^2; (b) e^3;
(c) e^4; (d) e^{-1};
(e) e^{-2}; (f) e^{-3}.

2. Using Table II, find the values of

(a) e^5; (b) $e^{1.55}$;
(c) $e^{-4.15}$; (d) $e^{2.30}$;
(e) $10^{\sqrt{3}}$; (f) $2^{\sqrt{2}}$;
(g) $2^{\sqrt{8}}$; (h) $3^{\sqrt[3]{2}}$.

3. Calculate for $x = 2, 3$ the values of

(a) xe^x; (b) $x^2 e^x$;
(c) $x + e^x$; (d) xe^{-x^2};
(e) e^{2x}; (f) $e^{\sqrt{2x}}$.

4. Check from the entries in Table II that all evidence there indicates that

(a) e^x is a monotone increasing function of x;
(b) $e^x \cdot e^{-x} = 1$;
(c) e^x is large when x is positive and large.

5. Find u such that $e^u = 2$. Write the expression $1 + 2 + 2^2 + 2^3 + 2^4$ in terms of powers of e.

6. Given that x_1 and x_2 are rational prove that if $x_1 < x_2$ and $a > 1$ then $a^{x_1} < a^{x_2}$. [*Hint:* Write $x_2 = x_1 + k$ where $k > 0$. Thus $a^{x_2} = a^{x_1+k} = a^{x_1} \cdot a^k$. Then, show that $a^k > 1$. Now if $k = r/s$, then $a^{1/s} > 1$ since $a > 1$. See Chapter IV, Section 1. Finally $(a^{1/s})^r > 1$. Note that since $k > 0$, it follows that $r > 0$, $s > 0$.]

7. Prove that if $a < 1$, the function a^x where x is rational is monotone decreasing.

8. Show that if $a > 1$ then for x positive and large, a^x is positive and large; for x negative and $|x|$ large, a^x is close to 0.

9. Given two real numbers u and a such that $\exp(u) = a$, prove that $\exp(ux) = a^x$ for

(a) natural numbers x;
(b) integers x;
(c) positive rational numbers x;
(d) negative rational numbers x.

4. ON THE EXISTENCE OF THE EXPONENTIAL FUNCTION

In this section we shall define the function exp and indicate the proof of its properties listed in Theorem V–3. The proof will be based on the examination of a special infinite series. It is advisable to touch only the highlights of the section in the first reading.

Although at this stage a methodical study of infinite sequences and series has not been made, we are familiar with the problem of taking limits in special cases. In all cases, these are the limits of increasing sequences. For example, the definition of $\sqrt{2}$ is: $\sqrt{2}$ is the limit of a particular sequence of rational numbers, namely,

$$1, \quad 1.4, \quad 1.41, \quad 1.414, \quad 1.4142, \cdots .$$

In Chapter IV, Section 1, it was shown how to find the nth root of any positive number a with any degree of accuracy. What we did there was to show how to write down a sequence whose limit was the nth root of a. This will indicate that the reader has had some previous experience with sequences and limits.

We remind ourselves as to what a sequence is. It is an array of the form

$$(s_0, s_1, s_2, s_3, \cdots). \tag{1}$$

One usually writes s_n for the number in the nth place. Sequences can then be written in the form (s_n). Note that the number s_0 which starts off the sequence is in zeroth place.

Consider a particular sequence of great importance in mathematics. Choose a number r such that $0 < r < 1$. The terms of the sequence are

$$s_0 = 1, \quad s_1 = 1 + r, \quad s_2 = 1 + r + r^2, \quad \cdots, \quad s_n = 1 + r + r^2 + \cdots + r^n. \tag{2}$$

It is obvious that $s_0 < s_1, s_1 < s_2, s_2 < s_3$, and so on. Thus we have here an *increasing* sequence. Since

$$(1 - r)(1 + r + r^2 + \cdots + r^n) = 1 - r^{n+1}, \tag{3}$$

we see by dividing by $1 - r$ and transposing, that

$$\frac{1}{1 - r} - (1 + r + r^2 + \cdots + r^n) = \frac{r^{n+1}}{1 - r} .$$

Since $0 < r < 1$, as n becomes large, r^{n+1} becomes small (close to zero). Hence $r^{n+1}/(1 - r)$ becomes small. Thus for large values of n, $1 + r + \cdots + r^n$ is close to $1/(1 - r)$. This fact is written as follows:

$$1 + r + r^2 + \cdots + r^n + \cdots = \frac{1}{1 - r} . \tag{4}$$

Note the three dots after r^n.

For example, with $r = \frac{1}{2}$,

$$1 + \frac{1}{2} + \frac{1}{4} + \cdots + \frac{1}{2^n} + \cdots = \frac{1}{1 - \frac{1}{2}} = 2.$$

Check that $s_4 = 1 + \frac{1}{2} + \frac{1}{4} + \frac{1}{8} + \frac{1}{16} = 1.9275$, which is already pretty close to 2. Note that $s_8 \approx 1.9961$.

We were fortunate with the sequence (s_n) given in (2) because we were able to show not only that s_n is close to something when n is large, but we were able to pinpoint what it was close to, namely, $1/(1 - r)$. In the next sequence to be studied it *will* be possible to show that the number in nth place is close to something when n is large but it will not be possible to recognize *what* it is close to.

Now let us proceed to the definition of the function exp. Suppose that $x \geq 0$. Consider the sequence (s_n) where

$$s_n = 1 + x + \frac{x^2}{2!} + \frac{x^3}{3!} + \cdots + \frac{x^n}{n!}. \tag{5}$$

If $x > 0$, then $s_0 < s_1, s_1 < s_2, s_2 < s_3$, and so on. It will be shown that the sequence (s_n) is bounded.

A note about reading proofs. The first thing to understand is the strategy. Then one can go into the details of the tactics. The special tactic of proving boundedness takes about a page. At first reading, skip forward to the phrase "So much for boundedness." Return later.

Let us start with some fixed $x > 0$ (for example, $x = 135.2$). Find a natural number m such that $2x < m$ (for example, $m = 1000$). Note that $x/m < 1/2$. Thus $x/(m + 1) < 1/2$, $x/(m + 2) < 1/2$, and so on. Next remember that $(m + 1)! = (m + 1) \cdot m!$; $(m + 2)! = (m + 2)(m + 1) \cdot m!$, and so on. Thus

$$\frac{x}{(m + 1)!} = \frac{x}{(m + 1)} \frac{1}{m!} < \frac{1}{2} \frac{1}{m!},$$

$$\frac{x^2}{(m + 2)!} = \frac{x}{m + 2} \cdot \frac{x}{m + 1} \cdot \frac{1}{m!} < \frac{1}{2} \cdot \frac{1}{2} \cdot \frac{1}{m!},$$

and so on. Hence [refer to Equation (5) to see why we are interested in this quantity]

$$\frac{x^{m+1}}{(m + 1)!} = \frac{x}{m + 1} \cdot \frac{x^m}{m!} < \frac{1}{2} \cdot \frac{x^m}{m!},$$

$$\frac{x^{m+2}}{(m + 2)!} = \frac{x}{m + 2} \cdot \frac{x}{m + 1} \cdot \frac{x^m}{m!} < \frac{1}{2} \cdot \frac{1}{2} \cdot \frac{x^m}{m!}, \tag{6}$$

and so on. Now let r be any natural number (for example, $r = 10^{10}$). Then

$$\frac{x^{m+1}}{(m+1)!} + \frac{x^{m+2}}{(m+2)!} + \cdots + \frac{x^{m+r}}{(m+r)!} < \frac{x^m}{m!}\left(\frac{1}{2} + \frac{1}{4} + \cdots + \frac{1}{2^r}\right) < \frac{x^m}{m!}$$

since $(\frac{1}{2} + \frac{1}{4} + \cdots + 1/2^r) < 1$. This gives

$$1 + x + \cdots + \frac{x^m}{m!} + \frac{x^{m+1}}{(m+1)!} + \cdots + \frac{x^{m+r}}{(m+r)!}$$
$$< 1 + x + \cdots + \frac{x^m}{m!} + \frac{x^m}{m!}. \tag{7}$$

The left-hand side is s_{m+r}. The right-hand side represents some number k. Since r is an arbitrary natural number, then $s_n < k$ for all $n > m$. Since (s_n) is an increasing sequence, $s_n < k$ for all n. Thus the sequence (s_n) is bounded.

To understand the proof of boundedness, it is important to keep straight the order in which the quantities are selected. First comes x. Then comes m ($m > 2x$). At this stage it is possible to compute k in (7). Then no matter what r is, $s_n < k$. So much for boundedness.

We now apply the least upper bound principle (which is valid in **R**). Since the sequence (s_n) is bounded by k, there exists a least upper bound which will be denoted by l. This means that the difference between l and s_n is very small if n is large (See Chapter I, Section 4). This number l to which s_n in (5) is close when n is large depends on x (obviously). In other words, it is a function of x. We have not met this function before and we shall introduce a symbol for it. That symbol is "exp." The definition that follows allows us to compute exp for any real number.

V–4 Definition
If $x \geq 0$,

$$\exp(x) = 1 + x + \frac{x^2}{2!} + \frac{x^3}{3!} + \cdots + \frac{x^n}{n!} + \cdots \tag{8}$$

and

$$\exp(-x) = \frac{1}{\exp(x)}. \tag{9}$$

The definition reveals many properties of exp.
(a) $\exp(0) = 1$.
(b) When x is large, $\exp(x)$ is large.
(c) If x_1 is close to x_2, then $\exp(x_1)$ is close to $\exp(x_2)$. That is, if $|x_1 - x_2|$ is small, then $|\exp(x_1) - \exp(x_2)|$ is small.
(d) The function exp is monotone increasing, that is, if $x_1 < x_2$, then $\exp(x_1) < \exp(x_2)$.
(e) The function exp assumes all positive values exactly once. That is, if $y > 0$ there is one and only one number x such that

$$y = \exp(x). \tag{10}$$

Let us discuss the proof of these statements. Before starting, note that s_n in (5) depends on x. Therefore we write $s_n(x)$ from now on instead of s_n. (a) is obvious. (b) is easy to see: For $x > 0$, $s_n(x) > x$. Thus if x is large, $s_n(x)$ is large and $\exp(x)$ is even larger. (c) is more delicate but we feel reasonably comfortable about it. First let $x_1 > 0$, $x_2 > 0$. If we compute the values $s_n(x_1)$ and $s_n(x_2)$ these values will be close to each other if x_1 and x_2 are close to each other. This is true because s_n is a polynomial. Going from s_n to exp requires an additional tactical step in the argument. The step is this: For large n, $\exp(x_1)$ is close to $s_n(x_1)$; $s_n(x_1)$ is close to $s_n(x_2)$; $s_n(x_2)$ is close to $\exp(x_2)$. Thus $\exp(x_1)$ is close to $\exp(x_2)$. Also it follows that $1/\exp(x_1)$ is close to $1/\exp(x_2)$ and this takes care of negative values of x.

We look at statement (d). First let $x_1 > 0$. Then since $x_2 > x_1$, $s_n(x_2) > s_n(x_1)$ because $x_2^2 > x_1^2$, $x_2^3 > x_1^3$, and so on; hence $\exp(x_2) > \exp(x_1)$. We have also $-x_2 < -x_1$ and

$$\exp(-x_2) = \frac{1}{\exp(x_2)} < \frac{1}{\exp(x_1)} = \exp(-x_1). \tag{11}$$

This takes care of negative values of x. See also Exercise 5.

Finally, let us look at (e). It is clear that for a given y there cannot be two distinct numbers x_1 and x_2 such that $y = \exp(x_1)$ and $y = \exp(x_2)$. Because if x_1 and x_2 are distinct, we have (say) $x_1 < x_2$. Then by (d) $\exp(x_1) < \exp(x_2)$, thus, these two expressions cannot both equal y. The proof that there is a value of x such that $y = \exp x$ starts off like this. By (b) there is a number $t > 0$ such that $\exp(t)$ is very large. We can choose it so that (can you fill in the tactics?)

$$\exp(-t) = \frac{1}{\exp(t)} < y < \exp(t). \tag{12}$$

Now, as x "runs over" the values from $-t$ to t, $\exp(x)$ goes through all values from $\exp(-t)$ to $\exp(t)$. This includes the value y. The reason for this is that the real number system is connected (has no "gaps") and that the function exp is continuous [Property (c)]. We used the same argument in Chapter III, Section 5, where it was stated that a polynomial of odd degree had at least one root.

If we refer to the Existence Theorem V–3 we see that everything has been proved except the functional equation (3). We shall do this now. The tactic is to do it by brute force.

For $u \geq 0$ and $v \geq 0$,

$$\exp(u) = 1 + u + \frac{u^2}{2!} + \frac{u^3}{3!} + \cdots, \tag{13}$$

$$\exp(v) = 1 + v + \frac{v^2}{2!} + \frac{v^3}{3!} + \cdots. \tag{14}$$

We multiply these two expressions together as if they were polynomials in u and v. We carry out the multiplication in such a way as to herd together all expressions of the form $u^n v^m$ having the same degree $n + m = r$. This gives

$$\left(1 + u + \frac{u^2}{2!} + \frac{u^3}{3!} + \cdots\right)\left(1 + v + \frac{v^2}{2!} + \frac{v^3}{3!} + \cdots\right)$$

$$= 1 \cdot 1 + u \cdot 1 + 1 \cdot v + \frac{u^2}{2!} \cdot 1 + u \cdot v + 1 \cdot \frac{v^2}{2!}$$

$$+ \frac{u^3}{3!} \cdot 1 + \frac{u^2}{2!} v + u \frac{v^2}{2!} + 1 \cdot \frac{u^3}{3!} + \cdots \tag{15}$$

$$= 1 + (u + v) + \frac{(u + v)^2}{2!} + \frac{(u + v)^3}{3!} + \cdots .$$

Thus

$$\exp(u) \cdot \exp(v) = \exp(u + v). \tag{16}$$

The justification of the multiplication procedure is based on the fact that the terms in (13) and (14) are all positive. Thus the functional equation has been established for $u > 0$ and $v > 0$. A further argument shows it to be valid in the case where u and v are both negative or in the case where u is positive and v is negative (Exercise 4).

Thus the discussion of the proof of the existence theorem for exp is complete. It is most important to state that the above discussion does not constitute a rigorous proof. It does constitute an honest attempt at a proof. It is a correct rapid sketch of the rigorous proof.

[*Note:* When ready to reread the material on the function exp, start just before Equation (5) and continue on to this point.]

The preceding discussion leads to the introduction of one of the most remarkable numbers of all of mathematics, the number e. This number was defined before as $e = \exp(1)$. It is now possible to compute it.

$$e = \exp(1) = 1 + 1 + \frac{1}{2} + \frac{1}{6} + \frac{1}{24} + \frac{1}{120} + \frac{1}{720} + \cdots . \tag{17}$$

This gives for e, correct to a reasonable number of decimals,

$$e = 2.7182818284 \cdots . \tag{18}$$

As was seen earlier using the functional equation, $\exp(x) = e^x$ for rational x. Thus the expression $\exp(x)$ and e^x are interchangeable. The number e is called the *natural base* for exponentiation. It is the gift of God to man. All other bases are poor imitations. Since human beings have 10 fingers on our hands, the decimal base 10 is useful. Electric machinery which can only detect whether a current is on or off prefers the binary base 2. However, mathematics recognizes only one base: e.

To obtain the graph of $\exp(x)$ one makes a chart, computing $\exp(2)$, $\exp(3)$, and so on. For example,

$$\exp(2) = 1 + 2 + \frac{4}{2} + \frac{8}{6} + \frac{16}{24} + \frac{32}{120} + \frac{64}{720} + \cdots. \tag{19}$$

This gives $\exp(2) = 7.355$ at least. Squaring 2.718 gives 7.3875, which is a little more accurate. Similarly (it takes a bit of time), $\exp(3) = 20.07$, $\exp(-1) = 0.368$, $\exp(-2) = 0.135$.

The graph of exp is given in Figure V.1.

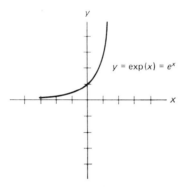

y = exp(x) = e^x

Figure V.1

The function exp is of a completely new type. It is not a polynomial function, since for any polynomial function p, $|p(x)|$ is large when $|x|$ is large. Instead, if $|x|$ is large, exp x is large when $x > 0$, and exp x is close to 0 when $x < 0$. It is not a rational function because it can be shown that for a rational function r, either $|r(x)|$ is large when $|x|$ is large or $|r(x)|$ is close to a constant for $|x|$ large (Exercise 7 in III.6.a). It can be shown that it is not an algebraic function (defined in Chapter IV, Section 5).

The number e is not the root of any polynomial with integral coefficients. Such numbers are called *transcendental*. The transcendency of e was proved in 1873 by the French mathematician Charles Hermite (1822–1901). The transcendency of π was proved in 1882 by the German mathematician C. Lindemann (1852–1939).

One last fact concerning e will be mentioned here. Suppose that we compute

$$t_n = \left(1 + \frac{1}{n}\right)^n, \qquad n = 1, 2, 3, \cdots. \tag{21}$$

This gives a sequence whose first few terms can be written down.

$$t_1 = 1 + 1 = 2,$$

$$t_2 = \left(1 + \frac{1}{2}\right)^2 = 1 + 1 + \frac{1}{4} = 2.25,$$

$$t_3 = \left(1 + \frac{1}{3}\right)^3 = 1 + 3 \times \frac{1}{3} + 3 \times \frac{1}{9} + \frac{1}{27} = 2.369.$$

It can be shown that for large values of n, $t^n \approx e$. Here the symbol "$\approx$" means "is approximately equal." This fact will be examined in greater detail in Chapter VII when the binomial expansion is obtained. In the applications that follow, use will be made of the approximation $(1 + 1/n)^n \approx e$ as well as the approximation $(1 + 1/n)^{nt} \approx e^t$. These questions are discussed in Exercises VII.3.a.

Some remarks about the exercises that follow. Having given the graph of e^x (Figure V.1) it is rather trivial to construct that of e^{-x}. The graph of e^{x^2} can be found by using Table II; if it is preferred Figure V.1 can be substituted for Table II (a graph is equivalent to a table). The graph of e^{-x^2} is highly interesting. It is essentially what is known as "the curve." Teachers are frequently asked "Do you grade on the curve?" Well, this *is* the curve, except for a constant factor. The complete equation of "the curve" is $y = (1/\sqrt{\pi})e^{-x^2}$. This gives one of the many relations involving π and e.

To find the graph of 10^x, we can proceed in two ways, each of which should be tried. The first is by direct computation of 10^x for $x = 0, \pm1, \pm2, \pm\frac{1}{2}$, and so on. The second is to remember that $10 = \exp(2.30) = e^{2.30}$ approximately (see the end of Section 3) and hence $10^x = e^{2.30x}$. Thus, given x, multiply by 2.30 and use Table II.

Exercises V.4.a

1. Graph each of the following functions (use Table II).

(a) e^{-x};   (b) e^{2x};
(c) e^{x^2};   (d) e^{-x^2};
(e) $e^x + e^{-x}$;   (f) $e^x - e^{-x}$.

2. Graph each of the following functions.

(a) 10^x;   (b) 2^x;
(c) $(\frac{1}{2})^x$;   (d) 3^{-x};
(e) $2^{x/2}$.

3. Prove that

$$\left(\frac{e^x + e^{-x}}{2}\right)^2 - \left(\frac{e^x - e^{-x}}{2}\right)^2 = 1.$$

4. Prove the functional equation of exp in the case $u < 0$ and $v < 0$; in the case $u < 0$ and $v > 0$. [*Hint*: If $u < 0, v < 0$, use Equation (9) and apply (15), which is valid for positive values. Now suppose $u < 0, v > 0$, and $u + v > 0$. Then $v = (u + v) + (-u)$; hence, by (15) and (9) $\exp(v) = \exp(u + v)\exp(-u) = \exp(u + v)1/(\exp u)$.]

5. Show that if $x_2 > 0$ and $x_1 < 0$, $\exp x_2 > \exp x_1$.

5. APPLICATIONS OF THE EXPONENTIAL FUNCTION

The exponential function plays a fundamental role in a very large number of important phenomena in physics, chemistry, biology, engineering, psychology, economics, and so on. The list is long and the role is stellar. We cannot hope to consider here any except the simplest applications.

To organize our thinking let us consider the problem of the growth of money deposited in a savings bank. Suppose that we find out what happens to a dollars deposited at 5 percent compounded annually. At the end of 1 year, there are $a + 0.05a = a(1 + 0.05)$ on the account. At the end of 2 years there are $a(1 + 0.05) + a(1 + 0.05)0.05 = a(1 + 0.05)^2$ on the account. Similarly, at the end of t years, the amount of money on the account is $a(1 + 0.05)^t$.

Suppose now the bank compounds its interest twice a year. Then at the end of $\frac{1}{2}$ year the amount on the account is $a(1 + 0.05/2)$, at the end of 1 year it is $a(1 + 0.05/2)^2$, at the end of t years, it is $a(1 + 0.05/2)^{2t}$. Note that the amount at the end of t years depends on t. If we assume the bank compounds interest n times during the year we have at the end of t years,

$$a(t) = a(0)\left(1 + \frac{0.05}{n}\right)^{nt}. \tag{1}$$

For the most part, savings banks use formula (1) for the case $n = 4$. We shall use the formula for large values of n. This leads to the notion of continuous compounding and gives us a fundamental type of equation for growth.

We shall use the result discussed earlier that for large values of u,

$$\left(1 + \frac{1}{u}\right)^u \approx e. \tag{2}$$

Here, as usual, $a \approx b$ means "a is close to b."

Therefore, for large values of n,

$$\left(1 + \frac{0.05}{n}\right)^{nt} = \left[\left(1 + \frac{0.05}{n}\right)^{n/0.05}\right]^{0.05t} \approx e^{0.05t}. \tag{3}$$

Thus the formula for interest compounded *continuously* at 5 percent is

$$a(t) = a(0)e^{0.05t}. \tag{4}$$

EXAMPLE 1:   Let us find in how many years money deposited at 5 percent compounded continuously will double. We have $a(t) = 2a(0)$; hence,

$$2 = e^{0.05t}.$$

Looking up Table II we find that $e^{0.70} \approx 2$; hence,

$$0.05t = 0.70 \quad \text{or} \quad t = 14.$$

Keep in mind that without compounding, the principal will double in 20 years. This compares unfavorably with the 14 years needed for compounding. It explains why no savings bank could stay in business if it did not pay compound interest.

EXAMPLE 2:   Find at what rate of interest money must be deposited so as to double in 10 years if compounded continuously.

SOLUTION: Let the rate be r. Then the amount of money after t years is $a(t) = a(0)e^{rt}$. In the present instance $e^{10r} = 2$ because $a(10) = 2a(0)$. Since $e^{0.70} = 2$ this gives $10r = 0.70$ or $r = 0.07$. Note that we are using the tables in an approximate fashion. In order to obtain more accurate results interpolation must be used. This will be done later.

The previous discussion can be generalized as follows: There is a function $a(t)$ representing the amount of substance present at time t. The amount of this substance is either continuously growing (getting larger) or continuously decreasing (getting smaller) as t increases. The *rate* of increase or decrease is proportional to the amount present at any instant. Then the amount $a(t)$ is given by a formula

$$a(t) = a(0)e^{kt}, \tag{5}$$

where k is a constant. If $k > 0$, there is *growth*. If $k < 0$, there is *decay*.

EXAMPLE 3:   The element radium decays at a constant rate because of its radioactivity. A given mass of radium decreases by the emission of alpha particles, electrons, and gamma rays. The *half-life* of radium means that length of time t_0 such that a given quantity of radium will be reduced to one half of that quantity after t_0 years. Physicists tell us that for radium $t_0 = 1620$ years. A hospital owns 1 gram of radium. Find out how much radium it will have in 100 years.

SOLUTION: We use formula (5) with $a(0) = 1$ and $a(1620) = \frac{1}{2}$. Substitution in (5) gives

$$\frac{1}{2} = e^{1620k}.$$

Table II in the Appendix gives $e^{-0.70} = \frac{1}{2}$. Hence

$$1620k = -0.70 \quad \text{or} \quad k = -0.00043.$$

Thus

$$a(t) = e^{-0.00043t}.$$

Setting $t = 100$,

$$a(100) = e^{-0.043} = 0.95.$$

In other words, radium loses one twentieth of its mass every century.

EXAMPLE 4:   Under certain circumstances various living organisms increase in number at a rate proportional to the number present at any instant. This is true of bacteria in the proper medium, rabbits when first introduced in Australia, and in many other cases. Thus the equation for the number present at time t, namely $N(t)$, is given by

$$N(t) = N(0)e^{kt}, \quad k > 0.$$

If k is large, the growth is rapid. For slow growth k must be small. Suppose that for a given colony of bacteria we estimate that $N(1) = 10^4$ and $N(3) = 3 \times 10^7$. Here t is given in hours. Find the value of k, the value of $N(0)$, and the number of bacteria present when $t = 10$.

SOLUTION: We have

$$10^4 = N(0)e^k \quad \text{and} \quad 3 \times 10^7 = N(0)e^{3k}.$$

Thus, by division,

$$3 \times 10^3 = \frac{3 \times 10^7}{10^4} = \frac{N(0)e^{3k}}{N(0)e^k} = e^{3k-k} = e^{2k}.$$

Since Table II gives $e^8 = 2981$, we may write

$$2k = 8 \quad \text{or} \quad k = 4.$$

To compute $N(0)$, set $t = 1$ in the equation for $N(t)$. Thus

$$10^4 = N(0)e^4 \quad \text{or} \quad 10^4 = 54N(0).$$

Hence

$$N(0) = \frac{10^4}{54} = 185.$$

Finally, for $N(10)$,

$$N(10) = 185e^{40}.$$

This number is approximately 4×10^{15}! It is interesting to compare this problem with Example 1 on compound interest. One of the ways of telling a savings bank from a lot of bacteria is to remember the value of $k: 0.05$ as against 4!

Exercises V.5.a

1. In the absence of hunters, the deer population in North American forests doubles every s years. Assuming that $s = 7$, find the size of a herd of 200 deer after 25 years. In how many years will the herd number 1000?

2. In a certain part of Africa, hunters are killing off one third of the hippopotamuses each year. If the carnage goes on at this same rate, how many years will it take for a herd of 500 animals to be reduced to 10?

3. In an atomic explosion a certain radioactive substance is created which has a half-life of 1 second. How long will it take before the amount present of this substance is $1/10,000$ of what it was?

4. Tennis player A is 4 times as good as tennis player B. A's playing ability is doubling every 3 months, whereas B's is tripling every 3 months. After how many months will the players be evenly matched?

5. Assume that the intensity of sound of a note on the piano t seconds after being struck is given by $I(t) = I(0)e^{-kt}$. Supposing that for a given make of piano the intensity dies down to one half after 2 seconds, find out in how many seconds the intensity will be $1/20$ of the initial intensity.

6. If a warm body at temperature T is immersed in surroundings of temperature T_0, $T > T_0$, then

$$x = Ae^{-kt},$$

where $x = T - T_0$, t is the time in hours, A and k are constants. In a house heated by electricity to $70°$ Fahrenheit, there is a power failure while the outside temperature is $10°$. Assuming that for that particular house $k = 0.10$, after how many hours will the temperature be down to $32°$? [*Note*: The purpose of insulating a house is to reduce the magnitude of k.]

7. If a professional mathematician works intensively at his researches, he doubles his mathematical worth every 10 years. If he takes up full-time administrative duties, he loses one half of his worth every 2 years. Find out how much of a sacrifice a professor of mathematics makes by accepting a 3-year term as chairman of the department.

6. THE LOGARITHMIC FUNCTION

If f is a function, it is said to be one-to-one providing that if $x_1 \neq x_2$, then $f(x_1) \neq f(x_2)$. For example, if $f(x) = 3x + 4$, then f is one-to-one. On the other hand, if $f(x) = x^2$ where x is any real number, then f is not one-to-one since $f(x) = f(-x)$. However, if x is restricted to be positive, then $f(x) = x^2$ is one-to-one.

Suppose $y = f(x)$ where f is one-to-one. Then we can "solve" for x obtaining $x = g(y)$. For example, if $y = 3x + 4$, then $x = (y - 4)/3$. If $y = x^2$ where $x \geq 0$, then $x = \sqrt{y}$ where $y \geq 0$. The function so obtained is called the *inverse* of the given function.

Consider now the function exp defined in the preceding pages. It was seen that exp is defined for all real numbers, has positive values, and is one-to-one. Thus the equation $y = \exp(x)$ can be solved for x in terms of y. The solution is written

$$x = \ln(y). \tag{1}$$

This is read "x is the natural logarithm of y." Notice that by Theorem V–3(b) and (c), the function ln is defined for all values > 0; it assumes all real values. Thus the equations $y = \exp(x)$ and $x = \ln(y)$ mean exactly the same. Whenever one is true for two numbers x and y, the other one is also true for those numbers. For reasons of convenience we interchange the letters x and y. Then the equations

$$y = \ln(x) \quad \text{and} \quad x = \exp(y) \tag{2}$$

state exactly the same thing. The graph of (2) is given in Figure V.2. Compare Figure V.2 with Figure V.1. Evidently one graph is obtained from the other by reflection in the line $y = x$. The reason for this is as follows: The graphs of $y = \exp(x)$ and of $x = \ln(y)$ are identical. The graph of $y = \ln(x)$ is obtained from the graph of $x = \ln(y)$ by interchanging the roles of x and y, that is, by reflection in the line $y = x$. This relation between graphs always holds for a function and its inverse.

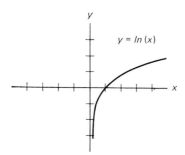

Figure V.2

Let us list some properties of the function ln.

(a) ln is defined for each $x > 0$;
(b) ln is monotone increasing;
(c) ln assumes every real value. That is, given any real number y, there is a number $x > 0$ such that $y = \ln x$;
(d) if x_1 and x_2 are two positive numbers, then

$$\ln(x_1 x_2) = \ln(x_1) + \ln(x_2). \tag{3}$$

These properties are merely paraphrases of the properties listed for exp in Theorem V–3. Let us look at the proof of Equation (3). This is known as the functional equation for ln.

If

$$y_1 = \ln(x_1) \quad \text{and} \quad y_2 = \ln(x_2),$$

then

$$x_1 = \exp(y_1) \quad \text{and} \quad x_2 = \exp(y_2),$$

and

$$x_1 \cdot x_2 = \exp(y_1) \cdot \exp(y_2) = \exp(y_1 + y_2).$$

This states that

$$\ln(x_1 x_2) = y_1 + y_2 = \ln(x_1) + \ln(x_2).$$

Note that from our definitions,

$$\exp[\ln(x)] = x \quad \text{and} \quad \ln[\exp(x)] = x. \tag{4}$$

Remark on functional notation: We have used parentheses in our functional notation up to this point. Thus we have written $\exp(x)$ and $\ln(x)$. It is customary to drop the parentheses for ln. We may drop them also for exp if we wish. In the coming sections the functions log, $\log_a$, sin, cos, and so on will be used without parentheses. Naturally, parentheses are used on $\exp(x_1 + x_2)$ and $\ln(x_1 x_2)$ in order to distinguish these from $(\exp x_1) + x_2$ and $(\ln x_1)x_2$.

The two following corollaries to the functional equation (3) are important. Since $x \cdot 1/x = 1$, we obtain from (3) that

$$0 = \ln 1 = \ln\left(x \cdot \frac{1}{x}\right) = \ln x + \ln \frac{1}{x}. \tag{5}$$

This gives

$$\ln \frac{1}{x} = -\ln x. \tag{6}$$

For example, $\ln \frac{1}{2} = -\ln 2(\approx -0.70)$.

Apply (6) to the problem of division. Since $x_1/x_2 = x_1 \cdot 1/x_2$, $\ln(x_1/x_2) = \ln(x_1 \cdot 1/x_2) = \ln x_1 + \ln(1/x_2) = \ln x_1 - \ln x_2$. We display this below:

$$\ln \frac{x_1}{x_2} = \ln x_1 - \ln x_2. \tag{7}$$

Finally, if $y = \ln x$, then $x = e^y$. Raising both sides to the t power gives $x^t = (e^y)^t = e^{ty}$. The last equality comes from a property of the exponential function. If this equation is translated into logarithmic language we obtain $\ln x^t = ty$, that is,

$$\ln x^t = t \ln x. \tag{8}$$

Exercises V.6.a

1. Write a statement equivalent to each of the following using logarithmic notation.

(a) $\exp(0) = 1$;

(b) $\exp(1) = e$;

(c) $\exp(3) = \exp(2) \cdot \exp(1)$;

(d) $\exp(2.302) = 10$;

(e) $\exp(s) = 3$;

(f) $\exp(t) > 1$;

(g) $e^{3x+2} = e^{3x} \cdot e^2$;

(h) $e^{tx} = (e^x)^t$;

(i) $e^{0.70} = 2$;

(j) $\exp(t)$ is defined for all t;

(k) for all t, $\exp(t) > 0$.

2. Write a statement equivalent to each of the following using exponential notation.

(a) $\ln 10 = 2.302$;

(b) $\ln 10 = \ln 2 + \ln 5$;

(c) $\ln e = 1$;

(d) $\ln 1 = 0$;

(e) $\ln x$ is defined for $x > 0$;

(f) $\ln x$ assumes all values;

(g) $\ln t > 0$;

(h) $\ln v > 2$.

3. Given that $\ln 2 = 0.6931$, $\ln 3 = 1.0986$, $\ln 5 = 1.6094$, compute the following.

(a) $\ln 6$;

(b) $\ln 10$;

(c) $\ln \dfrac{1}{3}$;

(d) $\ln 125$;

(e) $\ln (8 \cdot 81)$;

(f) $\ln 0.02$;

(g) $\ln 100$;

(h) $\ln \sqrt{6}$;

(i) $\ln 0.64$;

(j) $\ln \dfrac{25}{81}$.

4. Find x in the equations below.

(a) $x = e^{\ln 7}$;

(b) $x = \ln e^{-3}$;

(c) $e^{\ln x} = 5$;

(d) $\ln \dfrac{1}{x} = -2$;

(e) $\ln x = 1 + \ln 3$;

(f) $e^{4\ln x} = 16$.

We have introduced above the function ln which is inverse to the function exp. The function ln can also be written $\log_e$ (read: log to the base e) or just log. We now introduce $\log_a$ for any $a > 0$, $a \neq 1$. The expression $\log_a x$ is read "log of x to the base a."

The function defined by $y = a^x$ where $a > 0$, $a \neq 1$, is defined for each x; it assumes all positive values precisely once; if $a > 1$ it is monotone increasing; if $a < 1$ it is monotone decreasing. All this was discussed in Section 3.

Thus we may solve for x. The solution is written in the form $x = \log_a y$. For reasons of convenience, the letters x and y are interchanged. This gives

$$y = \log_a x, \quad \text{that is,} \quad x = a^y. \tag{9}$$

For each value of a, the function $\log_a$ has the properties (a) and (c) given above for the function ln and satisfies the functional equation (3). If $a > 1$, $\log_a$ is monotone increasing; if $a < 1$, $\log_a$ is monotone decreasing.

As before, the graph of $y = \log_a x$ can be obtained from the graph of $y = a^x$ by reflection in the line $y = x$. See Figure V.3 for the cases $a = 2$ and $a = \frac{1}{2}$.

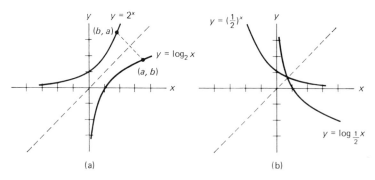

Figure V.3

In view of the fact that we use the decimal system for expressing numbers, the function $\log_{10}$ plays a special role among logarithm functions. We show why this role is special by considering some examples. Suppose we wish to find $\log_{10} 347$. We write $347 = 10^2 \times 3.47$. Then

$$\log_{10} 347 = \log_{10}(10^2 \times 3.47) = \log_{10} 10^2 + \log_{10} 3.47 = 2 + \log_{10} 3.47.$$

This shows that in order to find the logarithm to the base 10 of any number, it is necessary to know only the logs of numbers between 1 and 10. Thus a table of logs base 10 will contain only the logs of numbers from 1 to 10. This is precisely the reason for using the base 10 when making computations. If we wrote our numbers in the base 2 we would use logs to the base 2 and a table of logs would contain only the logs of numbers between 1 and 2. Logarithms to the base 10 are called *common logarithms*.

For purposes of computation, the following device is useful. Start with the fact that

$$\ln 10 = 2.302.$$

Now if y is given and we desire $\ln y$ we write

$$y = 10^x = (e^{2.302})^x = e^{2.302x} \qquad \text{and} \qquad \ln y = 2.302x = 2.302 \log_{10} y.$$

Thus we see how to construct one table of logarithms from another. A specific example follows.

PROBLEM: Find $\log_5 7$.

SOLUTION: Write $\log_5 7 = x$. Hence $5^x = 7$. Since $\log_{10} 5 = 0.6990$, $5 = 10^{0.6990}$. Hence $5^x = 10^{0.6990x}$. This means that $7 = 10^{0.6990x}$. Hence (use Table IV), $0.6990x = \log_{10} 7 = 0.8451$. Thus finally $x = 0.8451/0.6990$. It will be seen in the next section how to make this division in a methodical way using logarithms.

Exercises V.6.b

1. Using Table IV, verify the following.

(a) $\log_{10} 2 = 0.3010$;   (b) $\log_{10} 3.35 = 0.5250$;
(c) $\log_{10} 347 = 2.5403$;   (d) $\log_{10} 9980 = 3.9991$;
(e) $\log_{10} 0.04 = 0.6021 - 2$;   (f) $\log_{10} 0.863 = 0.9360 - 1$;
(g) $\log_{10} (5.02 \times 10^{-10}) = 0.7007 - 10$;
(h) $\log_{10} (6.06 \times 10^{24}) = 0.7825 + 24$.

2. Find, using Table IV, the value of the following.

(a) $\log_{10} 5.81$;   (b) $\log_{10} 31.6$;
(c) $\log_{10} 0.000327$;   (d) $\log_{10} (1.86 \times 10^6)$;
(e) $\log_{10} e$;   (f) $\log_{10} e^2$;
(g) $\log_{10} (1.23)^{1/2}$;   (h) $\log_{10} (0.00412)^{2/3}$;
(i) $\log_{10} (0.006)^{3/4}$.

3. Check, using Table IV, that

(a) $\log_{10} 6 = \log_{10} 2 + \log_{10} 3$;
(b) $\log_{10} 10 = \log_{10} 2 + \log_{10} 5$;
(c) $\log_{10} 81 = 4 \log_{10} 3$;
(d) $\log_{10} 24 = \log_{10} 72 - \log_{10} 3$.

4. Find the values of the following logarithms. Use no tables.

(a) $\log_2 16$;   (b) $\log_{\sqrt{2}} 512$;

(c) $\log_{1/3} 81$;   (d) $\log_5 \sqrt{125}$;

(e) $\log_3 \dfrac{72 \times 6}{16}$; (f) $\log_{16} 2$;

(g) $\log_3 27\sqrt{3}$;   (h) $\log_{\sqrt{7}} 343$;

(i) $(\log_5 125)^2$.

5. Using tables calculate approximate values of the following.

(a) $\log_7 6$;

(b) $\log_\pi e$;

(c) $\log_{13} \dfrac{169}{100}$;

(d) $\log_2 6.06$.

6. Using the fact that $\ln 10 = 2.302$ and using Table IV of logarithms to the base 10, compute the following. Check the results in Table III.

(a) $\ln 2$;

(b) $\ln 3$;

(c) $\ln 5.20$;

(d) $\ln 6.79$.

7. Using Table IV, find the logarithms below. Do not carry out multiplications or divisions in the answer.

(a) $\log_3 8$;

(b) $\log_{641} 257$;

(c) $\log_\pi e$;

(d) $\log_\pi 10$;

(e) $\log_{\sqrt{2}} \sqrt{3}$;

(f) $\log_7 11$.

8. Prove that $\log_a b \cdot \log_b a = 1$.

9. Prove, using Table IV, that $\sqrt{10} > \pi$. What percentage error is made in writing $\sqrt{10} = \pi$?

7. APPLICATIONS

A principal application of the theory of exponents and logarithms is to the theory of computation. This application is less important now that there are electronic and mechanical means (computers) available for carrying out laborious multiplications. The fundamental idea is simple. With the help of logarithms multiplication can be changed into addition. And since it is at least 5 times as easy to add two numbers each with 5 digits than to multiply them, we have the key to the success of logarithms.

Since numerical quantities are expressed decimally, the logs used below are principally to the base 10. A short collection of the logarithms of numbers from 1 to 10 is given in the back of the book (Table IV).

We start by learning to use the tables. Let us find log 317.8. In the first place, $317.8 = 100 \times 3.178$. Thus (since $\log_{10} 100 = \log_{10} 10^2 = 2$)

$$\log_{10} 317.8 = \log_{10} 100 + \log_{10} 3.178 = 2 + \log_{10} 3.178.$$

Table IV gives $\log_{10} x$, $1 \le x \le 10$. Here x is given to 3 digits. Thus

$$\log_{10} 3.17 = 0.5011,$$
$$\log_{10} 3.18 = 0.5024.$$

Now 3.178 is $\frac{8}{10}$ of the way between 3.17 and 3.18 and so log 3.178 will be $\frac{8}{10}$ of the way between 0.5011 and 0.5024. Since $0.5024 - 0.5011 = 0.0013$, one calculates $\frac{8}{10} \times 13 = 10$. Hence

$$\log 3.178 = 0.5011 + 0.0010 = 0.5021.$$

In order to save time and avoid errors, the work is tabulated as follows (note that the first and third lines are written first; then comes the middle line):

$$\left.\begin{array}{l} \log_{10} 3.170 = 0.5011 \\ \log_{10} 3.178 = 0.5021 \\ \log_{10} 3.180 = 0.5024 \end{array}\right\} \! \begin{array}{l} 10 \\ \end{array} \! \left.\vphantom{\begin{array}{l} 1\\1\\1 \end{array}}\right\} 13.$$

Hence the desired answer is: $\log 317.8 = 2.5021$.

The procedure used above is called *linear interpolation*. It rests on the assumption that if two points on a graph are close together, then the line segment joining the two points is a good approximation to the graph. See Figure V.4, which shows a good place for linear approximation (on the right) and a bad one (on the left).

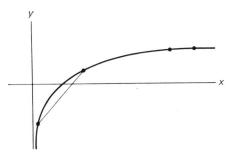

Figure V.4

The use of linear interpolation to approximate to the value of a function is rather similar to the use of tangent lines (Chapter IX). In linear interpolation, a curve is replaced by the line passing through two points on the curve. In tangential approximation, the curve is replaced by the tangent line. One says suggestively but erroneously that the tangent line is the line through two consecutive points.

Suppose we now have the problem of finding the number x such that $\log_{10} x = 0.2167 - 3$. The "-3" means that we have to find the number whose log is 0.2167, and then divide by $10^3 = 1000$ to get the desired answer. Thus the effect of the "-3" is to move the decimal point three places to the left.

Examination of the table gives

$$\left.\begin{array}{l} \log_{10} 1.640 = 0.2148 \\ \log_{10} x \quad\;\; = 0.2167 \\ \log_{10} 1.650 = 0.2175 \end{array}\right\} \! \begin{array}{l} 19 \\ \end{array} \! \left.\vphantom{\begin{array}{l} 1\\1\\1 \end{array}}\right\} 27.$$

Since $19/27 = 0.7$, this gives $x = 1.647$. Thus the desired answer is $1.647 \times 10^{-3} (= 0.001647)$.

Consider now a new type of problem, that of multiplication. Let us compute

$$x = 317.8 \times 21.35 \times 4038.$$

The functional equation for the logarithm gives

$$\log_{10} x = \log_{10} 317.8 + \log_{10} 21.35 + \log_{10} 4038.$$

The table gives

$$\log_{10} 317.8 = 2.5021$$
$$\log_{10} 21.35 = 1.3294$$
$$\log_{10} 4038 = 3.6062$$

Hence

$$\log_{10} x = 7.4377$$
$$x = 2.739 \times 10^7.$$

The above example shows how logarithms are helpful in computing expressions involving multiplication and division. For division use Equation (7) of Section 6. If the expression involves sums and differences as well as multiplications and divisions the time-saving feature of logarithms is much smaller.

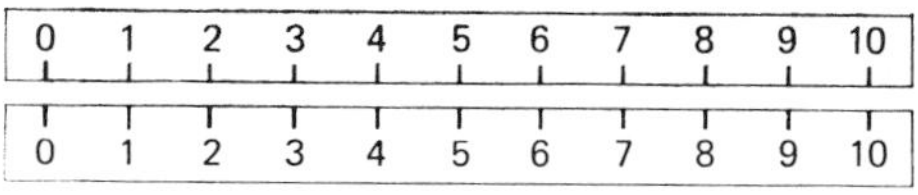

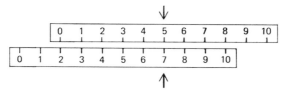

Figure V.5

The slide rule is a device for multiplying and dividing, whose success is due to the properties of logarithms. It uses the fact that with the help of two graduated rules, addition is trivial. Consider two such rules (Figure V.5), one sliding above the other. To perform the operation $2 + 5$, slide the top rule above the bottom one as shown in Figure V.6 and read off the answer: $2 + 5 = 7$.

Figure V.6

Suppose now we wish to perform the operation 2×3. This will be accomplished by logs. We have

$$\log_{10} (2 \times 3) = \log_{10} 2 + \log_{10} 3 = 0.301 + 0.477.$$

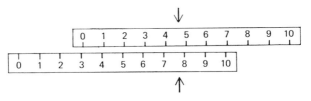

Figure V.7

Now perform the addition

$$0.301 + 0.477 = 0.778$$

on the two sliding rules. This is shown in Figure V.7. To make a slide rule it is merely necessary to mark on the scale the numbers

$$\log_{10} 1 = 0.000, \log_{10} 2 = 0.301, \log_{10} 3 = 0.477, \log_{10} 4 = 0.602,$$

$$\log_{10} 5 = 0.699, \log_{10} 6 = 0.778, \log_{10} 7 = 0.845,$$

$$\log_{10} 8 = 0.903, \log_{10} 9 = 0.954, \log_{10} 10 = 1.000.$$

At the same time we erase the original numbers. Finally instead of labeling 0.301 as "$\log_{10} 2$," we label it "2." The result is shown in Figure V.8.

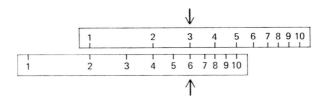

Figure V.8

In other words, the slide rule does not really say $2 \times 3 = 6$. It states that $\log_{10} 2 + \log_{10} 3 = \log_{10} 6$.

The following is a word exercise leading to the use of logarithms to the base 10.

The owner of a hardware store notices that every year his income from his business increases by 12 percent. How long will it take him to quadruple his income?

Let his income after t years be $I(t)$. Then $I(1) = I(0)(1 + 0.12)$. Also, $I(2) = I(1)(1 + 0.12) = I(0)(1 + 0.12)^2$. In general,

$$I(t) = I(0)(1 + 0.12)^t.$$

We are interested in the value of t such that $(1 + 0.12)^t = 4$. This gives $t \log_{10} 1.12 = \log_{10} 4$. Hence by Table IV,

$$0.0492t = 0.6021.$$

Hence

$$t = \frac{0.6021}{0.0492}.$$

The answer is approximately $t = 12$. Don't use logs to figure it out more precisely. It isn't worth it.

Exercises V.7.a

1. Find the values of the indicated logarithms. Use interpolation if necessary.

(a) $\log_{10} 3.46$;

(b) $\log_{10} 571.5$;

(c) $\log_{10} 0.00374$;

(d) $\log_{10} 0.002643$;

(e) $\log_{10} (3.792)^2$.

2. Solve for x in the equations below. Use interpolation if necessary.

(a) $\log_{10} x = 0.7796$;

(b) $\log_{10} x = 0.9547 - 2$;

(c) $\log_{10} x = 5.6590$;

(d) $\log_{10} x = 0.3172$;

(e) $\log_{10} x = 0.6100 - 1$;

(f) $\log_{10} x = 4.8782$;

(g) $\log_{10} x = \frac{1}{2} \times 3.9621$;

(h) $\log_{10} x^3 = 0.3118$.

3. Using logarithms compute the following without using interpolation and also with interpolation.

(a) $\dfrac{317}{1063}$;

(b) 2^{64};

(c) 0.00162×43.84;

(d) $\sqrt[3]{1001}$;

(e) $4\pi^2$;

(f) $\dfrac{39.6 \times 289.1}{487.2}$;

(g) $\dfrac{163.1}{0.00214 \times (5.11)^2}$;

(h) $(31.62 \times 272) + \left(\dfrac{4.152}{0.0379}\right)^2$.

4. A sum of $100 is deposited in each of two savings banks. They each pay interest at the rate of 6 percent per annum; the first compounds the interest annually, the second quarterly. Find the amount in each bank after 10 years.

5. A table tennis ball loses $\frac{1}{9}$th of its height every time it bounces. How many times should it bounce so that it will have lost approximately $\frac{1}{2}$ of its height?

6. A certain prizefighter loses $\frac{1}{30}$ of his energy every time he is hit. When his energy falls to 40 percent of maximum his opponent is told to try for – a knockout blow. How many times must he be hit before this point is reached?

7. A rent-a-car agency discovers that on the average after renting out a given car 40 times, its value has declined by a factor of 30 percent which they consider the point of replacement. Assuming that each trip out of the garage reduces the value of the car by the same fraction, find out what this "wear factor" is.

The company decides to lower the replacement level from 30 percent to 40 percent loss of value. How many more trips will they now be able to make with the cars?

8. A businessman X places a man Y in a position of trust but discovers too late that Y is dishonest. X estimates that Y's credibility is decreased by 1/7 every time he is caught in a lie and X decides that he will get rid of him when the credibility rating goes down to 0.6 of its starting value. After how many lies does Y get bounced?

9. Make a slide rule as follows: Obtain a box in the form of a circular cylinder with a top. For example, an empty box for face powder. Buy one sheet of logarithm graph paper at the local book store. Cut off two strips of the paper and glue them to the box and top along the edge separating them. Label the divisions 1, 2, 3, etc., and you have an excellent slide rule.

Chapter VI

THE CIRCULAR FUNCTIONS

1. THE WINDING NUMBER

In this chapter we introduce the functions sin, cos, tan, and so on. These are called circular functions because they are closely related to the circle of radius 1 whose equation is $u^2 + v^2 = 1$. We shall prove later that precisely this relation holds for the functions sin and cos; in other words, $\sin^2 x + \cos^2 x = 1$. These functions are also called trigonometric functions. Trigonometry is the science of triangles and it turns out that these functions are needed to calculate the lengths of the sides and the size of the angles of a triangle. However, the value of these functions goes far beyond their use for calculating sides and angles of triangles. The title "circular functions" underlines this fact. These functions are fundamental to all of mathematics and its applications.

We are familiar with the notion of winding. We start with a plane and pick a fixed point O in it. Let us consider some other point P_0 which will be considered the starting point. We then begin to "wind around" O starting at P_0 and ending at P_1. It is clear in Figure VI.1 that the indicated path winds around P_0 $1\frac{1}{3}$ times. The number $1\frac{1}{3}$ is called the *winding number* of the path. Figure VI.2 shows two paths with winding numbers 2 and $4\frac{1}{4}$. Arrows have been placed on the paths to indicate the direction of the winding.

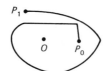

Figure VI.1

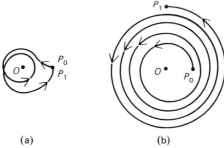

(a)   (b)

Figure VI.2

It will be noticed that there are two directions for winding. These are illustrated in Figure VI.3. It is customary to call one of these directions the positive direction and the other direction the negative direction. Thus the winding number of the path in Figure VI.3(a) is $\frac{3}{4}$ while that in Figure VI.3(b) is $-\frac{5}{4}$. The positive direction is opposite to that of a clock, that is, it is *counterclockwise*. The negative direction is the same as that of a clock, that is, it is *clockwise*. Note that as we wind counterclockwise, we keep the point O on the left. In winding clockwise, the point O is on the right.

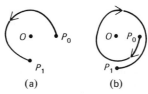

(a)   (b)

Figure VI.3

Let us introduce coordinate systems with the origin at O and with P_0 on the positive x-axis. This will help us to visualize the winding a little better. We notice several facts:

(a) The winding number of a path is a real number, positive or negative, or zero.

(b) Given any real number, there exists a path about O whose winding number is that number.

(c) The winding number for any circle with the center at the origin and described counterclockwise from the point P_0 until the return to the starting point is 1.

A winding number 1 corresponds to one *revolution*. Thus the winding number is equal to the number of revolutions. In other words, the winding number measures the amount of winding and the unit used in measuring it is the revolution.

Now, the amount of winding may be measured by other units. For example, it may be measured in right angles. Since 4 right angles are equivalent to one revolution, the amount of winding in right angles is equal to 4 times the winding number. Or, the amount of winding may be measured in degrees. Since

$$1 \text{ revolution } = 360°, \tag{1}$$

the amount of winding in degrees is obtained by multiplying the winding number by 360. Thus in Figure VI.3(a), the winding in right angles is 3 right angles; and in Figure VI.3(b) there are -5 right angles. The winding in degrees is $270°$ in (a) and $-450°$ in (b).

Many equivalent paths determine the same amount of winding. If two paths starting from points P_0 and Q_0 on the positive x-axis and terminating at P_1 and Q_1 determine the same amount of winding, then the ray (half-line) starting at O and going through P_1 will go through Q_1. However the ray OP_1 may contain Q_1 without the amount of winding being the same. These two possibilities are illustrated in Figures VI.4(a) and (b).

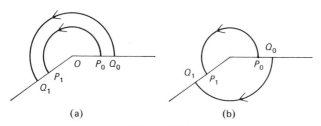

(a)   (b)

Figure VI.4

The above observation leads us to recognize that the quantity of winding can be considered as generated by a ray which starts on the positive x-axis and winds to some terminal position. A mechanism which realizes winding is the hand of a clock (either one). When the clock is running the winding takes place in the negative direction (clockwise). When we set the clock we "sweep" the hands around either clockwise or counterclockwise.

We can now give the definition of an angle.

VI–1 Definition

An angle is a figure consisting of a ray OP_0 called the initial ray and a ray OP_1 called the terminal ray along with an amount of winding from the position OP_0 to the position OP_1.

The measure of an angle is the number which indicates the quantity of winding. This quantity is given in terms of some unit. So far, we have mentioned three types of units: revolutions, right angles, and degrees. The situation here is somewhat similar to that of exponents and logarithms. We had many bases: 2, 3, 10, and so on. However, there is one base for exponents that outshines all the others, namely e. With angles also there is one unit of angle measure that is "correct" while the others are secondary. This special unit of angle measure is called the radian. We introduce its definition in a moment.

A convenient way to indicate the amount of winding is to consider that the path which winds around O starting at P_0 and finishing at P_1 does its winding along the circle of radius 1 and center at O. Then the amount of winding is completely determined by the length of that path. In Figure VI.5 we show a path that winds $1\frac{1}{3}$ times around O. We then unwind the path and lay it out straight. Its length is a measure of the amount of winding, that is, its length is a measure of the angle P_0OP_1.

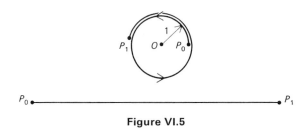

Figure VI.5

Recall that the circumference (length) of a circle of radius r is $2\pi r$. In the present case, the radius is 1. Thus the circumference of the circle is 2π. Hence the length of the path P_0P_1 is $1\frac{1}{3} \times 2\pi = \frac{8}{3}\pi = 8.378$. The number $\frac{8}{3}\pi$ or 8.378 is thus the measure of the angle P_0OP_1 using that unit which makes 1 revolution have measure 2π. This unit is called the *radian*. Therefore,

$$2\pi \text{ radians } = 1 \text{ revolution.} \tag{2}$$

Since 1 revolution $= 360°$,

$$2\pi \text{ radians } = 360°,$$

and thus 1 radian $= 360/2\pi° = 360/7.2832$ or (with more precision than we shall ever need)

$$1 \text{ radian } = 57.296° = 57°17'45''. \tag{3}$$

On the other hand, $1° = \pi/180$ radians. This gives

$$1° = 0.017453 \text{ radians.} \tag{4}$$

For example, an angle of 3 radians has as its degree measure $3 \times 57.3 = 171.9$. An angle of $10\frac{1}{6}$ revolutions has $10\frac{1}{6} \times 360° = 3660°$. An angle of 100 revolutions has $100 \times 2\pi$ radians $= 200\pi$ radians $= 628.32$ radians. The same angle of 100 revolutions has 100×4 right angles $= 400$ right angles and it has 100×360 degrees $= 36,000$ degrees.

The notion of radian measure for angles may be made clear as follows. Take a spool of thread and pull out a quantity l of thread. Mark carefully on the edge of the spool the point P_0 where the taut thread leaves the spool. Now wind the thread on the spool and mark on the spool the point P_1 where the end of the thread makes contact with the spool. This gives the angle $P_0 O P_1$ (Figure VI.6). If the radius of the spool is 1, the radian measure of the angle is l radians. Notice that the steps in Figure VI.6 correspond to those in Figure VI.5 in reverse order.

Figure VI.6

The various measures of some familiar angles are listed in Table VI.1.

Table VI.1

REVOLUTIONS	DEGREES	RIGHT ANGLES	RADIANS
0	0	0	0
$\frac{1}{12}$	30	$\frac{1}{3}$	$\pi/6$
$\frac{1}{8}$	45	$\frac{1}{2}$	$\pi/4$
$\frac{1}{6}$	60	$\frac{2}{3}$	$\pi/3$
$\frac{1}{4}$	90	1	$\pi/2$
$\frac{1}{2}$	180	2	π
1	360	4	2π

Exercises VI.1.a

1. Draw the indicated angle.

(a) $\frac{1}{3}$ revolution;

(b) 2 right angles;

(c) $-240°$;

(d) $\dfrac{\pi}{6}$ radians;

(e) $-2\frac{1}{4}$ revolutions;

(f) $760°$;

(g) 30 radians;

(h) $6\pi°$;

(i) $-10,000°$;

(j) $\dfrac{1}{2\pi}$ revolutions;

(k) π right angles;

(l) 10^4 revolutions;

(m) $7\tfrac{1}{2}°$;

(n) $-\tfrac{1}{3}$ radian.

2. A spool of thread contains 300 yards of thread. If the spool has a radius of 1 inch, find out through what angle the spool is turned at the factory to wind the thread on it. Assume that the thread has no thickness (hence radius of spool does not change as the winding proceeds). Give the answer in radians, degrees, revolutions (1 yard = 36 inches).

3. Telephone wire is wound on drums 2 yards in diameter. Assuming that at the factory the drums were turned through 450 revolutions to wind them, find out how many yards of wire are on a drum. Assume thickness of wire to be negligible.

4. A roll-up windowshade is wound on a roller of $\tfrac{1}{2}$-inch diameter. Find out through what angle the roller turns when the shade is pulled down to cover a window 6 feet high. Give the answer in radians, degrees, and revolutions.

5. A grandfather clock works by a weight pulling on a drum $1\tfrac{1}{2}$ inches in diameter which is 6 feet above the floor. To wind the clock the drum is turned and the weight is raised 5 feet. Find out through what angle the drum has to be turned in order to wind the clock. Assuming that one winding makes the clock run for $5\tfrac{1}{2}$ days, find out through what angle the drum turns during 1 hour.

6. Calculate the number of revolutions made by the wheels of a diesel locomotive that is going from New York to Chicago (800 miles) assuming the diameter of each wheel is 3 feet (1 mile equals 5280 feet).

   If you prefer, the same problem for a French locomotive going from Paris to Marseille (800 kilometers) given that the diameter of the wheel is 1 meter (1 kilometer = 1000 meters).

7. In order to start a gasoline-powered hand tractor, the starting cord is pulled through a distance of 3 feet to turn the motor $2\tfrac{1}{2}$ revolutions. Find the radius of the drum on which the starting cord is wound.

8. Three Russian cosmonauts established a world record in June–July 1971 for number of days spent in outer space: 24. Assuming that each revolution about the earth of their Soyuz 11 module took 88 minutes, find the number of revolutions they made.

9. Let x be a real number with the property that an angle α of x radians and an angle β of x degrees have the same initial side and the same terminal side. What can you say about the number x?

2. THE DEFINITION OF THE CIRCULAR FUNCTIONS

We shall define the six circular functions. They are the sine, the cosine, the tangent, the cotangent, the secant, and the cosecant. The symbols for these functions are given below:

NAME OF FUNCTION	SYMBOL OF FUNCTION
sine	sin
cosine	cos
tangent	tan
cotangent	cot
secant	sec
cosecant	csc

These functions are defined for real numbers. The first two are defined for all real numbers. The domain of definition of the remaining four will become apparent shortly.

We proceed to define the functions

$$\sin : R \to R \qquad \text{and} \qquad \cos : R \to R. \tag{1}$$

Let x be any real number. Consider in the (u, v) plane the circle of radius 1, center the origin. Its equation is $u^2 + v^2 = 1$. On the circumference of this circle, starting at the point P_0 (1, 0), lay off an arc of length $|x|$, counterclockwise if $x > 0$ and clockwise if $x < 0$. This gives a terminal point P_1 (u, v) on the circle. Then, by definition,

$$\sin x = v, \qquad \cos x = u. \tag{2}$$

That is, we start with x, and locate the point P_1. We calculate the coordinates u and v of P_1 and then set down the definition for sin and cos given in (2). Clearly, for every value of x, sin x and cos x are unambiguously defined.

Figure VI.7(b) shows an x-axis and marked on it are the points 0, 1, and x. There is also a (u, v) plane [Figure VI.7(a)] with the given unit circle. The arc on the circle from P_0 to P_1 has length x.

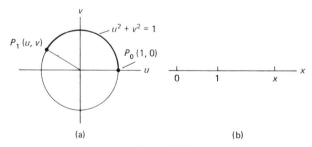

Figure VI.7

It will be noted immediately that the measure in radians of angle $P_0 \, O \, P_1$ is x. An alternative way of finding the point P_1 is to take that unique point on the circle such that the measure of the angle $P_0 \, O \, P_1$ is x.

Two facts are made clear:

(a) The functions sin and cos are defined for real numbers (not for angles).
(b) In the process of defining the functions for the real numbers x it is convenient to construct an angle whose measure is x radians. That is, given an angle of x radians it is immediately possible to determine the values of sin x and cos x. When we consider a real number x we sometimes represent it as a line segment (whose length is $|x|$). In the same way, when we calculate sin x or cos x we may represent x as an angle (whose radian measure is x).

Let us compute the sine and cosine of a few numbers. Let $x = \pi/2$. Then the point P_1 is the point $(0, 1)$ on the v-axis. See Figure VI.8. Thus,

$$\sin \frac{\pi}{2} = 1 \qquad \cos \frac{\pi}{2} = 0. \tag{3}$$

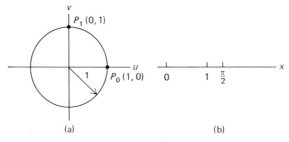

(a)   (b)

Figure VI.8

The reader will note that writing out the decimal approximation of $\pi/2 \, (\pi/2) = 1.57079$) is of no help. It is in fact a waste of time.

Now compute the sine and cosine for the number $x = \tfrac{3}{4}\pi$. See Figure VI.9. It is not difficult to see that the coordinates of P_1 are $u = -1/\sqrt{2}$, $v = 1/\sqrt{2}$. This can be seen more easily by considering the measure of the

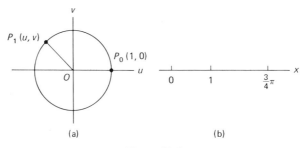

(a)   (b)

Figure VI.9

angle $P_0 \, O \, P_1$ in degrees instead of in radians. Here

$$\frac{3}{4} \pi \text{ radians} = 135°.$$

Thus the segment $O \, P_1$ lies on the bisector of the second quadrant and hence for the coordinates of P_1, we have $|u| = |v|$. Since $u^2 + v^2 = 1$, we have $2u^2 = 1$ or $u^2 = \frac{1}{2}$. Since $u < 0$ this gives $u = -1/\sqrt{2}$. Also $v^2 = \frac{1}{2}$, and since $v > 0$, $v = 1/\sqrt{2}$. Hence

$$\sin \frac{3}{4} \pi = \frac{1}{\sqrt{2}}, \qquad \cos \frac{3}{4} \pi = -\frac{1}{\sqrt{2}}. \tag{4}$$

We have had success so far in computing the value of the sine and cosine of $\pi/2$ and $\frac{3}{4}\pi$. However, the class of real numbers for which the value of these functions can be determined easily is very limited. Suppose we wish to compute them for $x = 1$ (see Figure VI.10). We have no information from plane geometry to help us as before. At this stage the only reasonable thing to do is to make a very careful diagram and read off the values. This gives approximately

$$\sin 1 = 0.84, \qquad \cos 1 = 0.54.$$

For those who need them, tables have been computed giving the functions of any number with incredible accuracy. We shall be satisfied with modest tables which are given in the rear of the book (Table V).

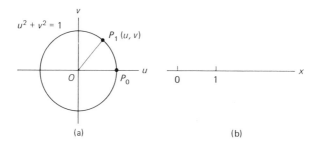

Figure VI.10

For the purpose of refreshing our memory, we set in the form of diagrams (Figure VI.11) the relations found in plane geometry concerning certain right triangles: those having an acute angle of 30°, 45°, and 60°. These relations will be useful in computing the values of the coordinates (u, v) of P_1 in special cases.

Using Figure VI.11, it is not difficult to see that $\sin \pi/6 = \frac{1}{2}$ and $\cos \pi/6 = \sqrt{3}/2$. [Use Figure VI.11(a) and set $a = \frac{1}{2}$.] This shows how the above diagrams enable us to construct a small table of values (Table VI.2) of the functions sin and cos for a few well-mannered angles.

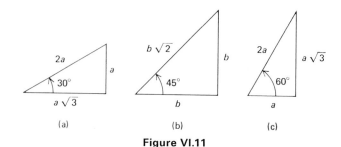

Figure VI.11

Table VI.2

x	0	$\pi/6$	$\pi/4$	$\pi/3$	$\pi/2$	$\frac{2}{3}\pi$	$\frac{3}{4}\pi$	$\frac{5}{6}\pi$
$\sin x$	0	$\frac{1}{2}$	$\frac{1}{2}\sqrt{2}$	$\frac{1}{2}\sqrt{3}$	1	$\frac{1}{2}\sqrt{3}$	$\frac{1}{2}\sqrt{2}$	$\frac{1}{2}$
$\cos x$	1	$\frac{1}{2}\sqrt{3}$	$\frac{1}{2}\sqrt{2}$	$\frac{1}{2}$	0	$-\frac{1}{2}$	$-\frac{1}{2}\sqrt{2}$	$-\frac{1}{2}\sqrt{3}$

DEGREE MEASURE	0	30	45	60	90	120	135	150

x	π	$\frac{3}{2}\pi$	2π	$2\pi + \pi/6$	$2\pi + \pi/4$	$2\pi + \pi/2$	3π	4π
$\sin x$	0	-1	0	$\frac{1}{2}$	$\frac{1}{2}\sqrt{2}$	1	0	0
$\cos x$	-1	0	1	$\frac{1}{2}\sqrt{3}$	$\frac{1}{2}\sqrt{2}$	0	-1	1

DEGREE MEASURE	180	270	360	390	405	450	540	720

The values may be read off from Figure VI.12 where the positions of P_1 on the circle $u^2 + v^2 = 1$ are given and where the coordinates are computed using the information in Figure VI.11.

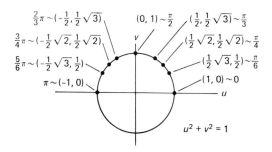

Figure VI.12

The definition of the sine and cosine make certain facts immediately apparent. For one thing, the point P_1 is on the circle $u^2 + v^2 = 1$ and hence

u satisfies $-1 \leq u \leq 1$, and v also satisfies $-1 \leq v \leq 1$. Thus (since $u = \cos x$, $v = \sin x$),

$$-1 \leq \sin x \leq 1,$$
$$-1 \leq \cos x \leq 1.$$
(5)

Note that the sine and the cosine take on *all* values between -1 and 1. This is apparent from the definition (see Figure VI.7).

Next it is seen that for any number x

$$(\sin x)^2 + (\cos x)^2 = 1.$$

It is customary to write $\sin^2 x$ instead of $(\sin x)^2$ and thus the above equation becomes

$$\sin^2 x + \cos^2 x = 1.$$
(6)

The above equation is an *identity* because it is valid for all numbers x. We have already met some algebraic identities [for example, $x^2 - 1 = (x - 1)(x + 1)$] but this is the first trigonometric identity. The algebraic identities are not very deep. In a certain sense, there are only trivial algebraic identities. If two polynomial functions p and q are equal for all values of x, then by the unique representation theorem for polynomials the coefficients of p and q are the same and therefore the identity $p(x) = q(x)$ for all x is not startling. However the identity (6) is startling. Nothing can be done to make it look trivial. This is the first of a long series of similar identities. Another example of a nontrivial identity is the functional equation for exp: $\exp(x + y) = \exp(x) \cdot \exp(y)$. This is an identity in two variables.

Another very important fact that will be mentioned here concerning the sine and cosine is that these functions are periodic. Periodic functions were defined in Chapter II, Section 9. Recall that f is periodic if there exists a number $p \neq 0$ such that for all x,

$$f(x + p) = f(x).$$
(7)

As for the sine and the cosine, it is quite apparent that

$$\sin (x + 2\pi) = \sin x,$$
$$\cos (x + 2\pi) = \cos x.$$
(8)

Thus, the number 2π is a period of sin and cos. It has been seen that if p is a period of a function f, so are $2p$, $3p$, and so on. Thus $2 \times 2\pi$ or 4π, 6π, and so on are all periods of these functions. The full set of periods is $n \times 2\pi$ where n is any integer, positive or negative.

Let us go back to Equations (8) and give two words of proof. Take a number x. It corresponds by the winding process about the unit circle to a point P_1. Given this point P_1, if we continue to wind for one more revolution, we fall again on P_1. But one revolution along the circle of radius 1 has length 2π. Hence the numbers x and $x + 2\pi$ give exactly the same point $P_1(u, v)$. Thus x and $x + 2\pi$ have the same sine and cosine.

Not only are the sine and cosine periodic but they are in a certain sense the most important of the periodic functions: Every periodic function $f(x)$ of period 2π can be approximated by sums made up of sines and cosines and their speed-up versions (see Section 3, Historical Note): $\sin 2x$, $\sin 3x$, $\cos 2x$, $\cos 3x$, and so on. The study of this approximation procedure is called *harmonic analysis*.

Let us now graph the two functions. We start with cos. As usual, consider a collection of values of x and calculate $\cos x$. The most convenient values to use are $x = 0, \pi/6, \pi/4, \pi/3, \pi/2$, and so on. To find out where these values fall on the x-axis, it is necessary to calculate them decimally. Since $\pi = 3.14$,

$$\frac{\pi}{6} = 0.52, \qquad \frac{\pi}{4} = 0.78, \qquad \frac{\pi}{3} = 1.05, \qquad \frac{\pi}{2} = 1.57.$$

An alternative procedure is to locate $\pi = 3.14$ on the x-axis and then to obtain $\pi/2$ by bisection (by eye) and $\pi/3$ by trisection, and so on. For these values of x, Table VI.2 gives the values of $\sin x$. The corresponding points of the graph are plotted in Figure VI.13. We underline the fact that we use the

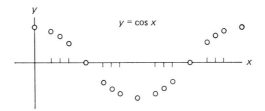

Figure VI.13

same scale on the x- and y-axes. Next note that cos is an even function, that is,

$$\cos(-x) = \cos x. \tag{9}$$

This fact is apparent from the definition. If the number x in Figure VI.7 gives rise to the point (u, v) on the circle, the number $-x$ gives rise to the point $(u, -v)$. Thus $\cos(-x) = u = \cos x$. This argument shows also that $\sin(-x) = -v = -\sin x$; in other words, sin is an odd function. We state this formally:

$$\sin(-x) = -\sin x. \tag{10}$$

Since cos is even, the graph for negative x is obtained by reflection through the y-axis. Since cos has period 2π, the curve repeats itself beyond $x = 2\pi$. The complete graph is given in Figure VI.14.

The graph of sin is found in a similar way. That is, we plot the points on the graph corresponding to $x = 0, \pi/6, \pi/4, \pi/3, \pi/2$, and so on, up to 2π. Then we use periodicity plus the fact that sin is an odd function. The result is shown in Figure VI.15.

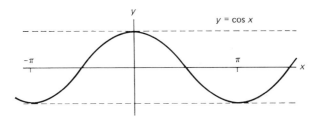

Figure VI.14

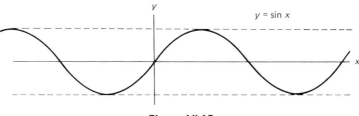

Figure VI.15

It has already been noted that sin and cos take on all values between -1 and 1 and take on no other values. To underline this fact, Figures VI.14 and VI.15 also show the lines $y = 1$ and $y = -1$.

The values of the circular functions have been computed. The results are to be found in tables such as Table V. For example, let us find sin 0.1745. Examination of the table shows that the argument x is to be found in the second column while sin x is in the third. Thus sin 0.1745 = 0.1736. The table is given for values of x over the range $0 \le x \le \pi/4 = 0.7854$. The third column gives cos x over the same range.

The degree and minute equivalent of x radians is given in the first column.

Due to the existence of certain identities to be proved later, tables need not be constructed beyond $x = \pi/4$. Over the range $\pi/4 \le x \le \pi/2$, we read the value of x in the next to last column on the right. The functions are now indicated on the bottom. Thus cos 1.1606 = 0.3987 while sin 1.1606 = 0.9171. Interpolation may be used here if one is interested in high accuracy. Thus cos 0.1789 = 0.9841.

Exercises VI.2.a

1. Compute the value of the following.

(a) $\cos\left(-\dfrac{\pi}{6}\right)$;

(b) $\sin\left(\dfrac{5}{6}\pi\right)$;

(c) $\cos 4\pi$;

(d) $\cos\dfrac{\pi}{4} \times \sin\dfrac{\pi}{4}$;

(e) $(\cos \pi)^3$;

(f) $\sin 5\pi + \cos 5\pi$;

(g) $\sin^2 \dfrac{\pi}{4} + \cos^2 \dfrac{\pi}{4}$;

(h) $\dfrac{\sin \pi}{\cos \pi}$;

(i) $\cos^2 \dfrac{\pi}{3} - \sin^2 \dfrac{\pi}{3}$;

(j) $\sin \dfrac{2}{3}\pi \times \cos \dfrac{2}{3}\pi$;

(k) $\dfrac{\cos \pi/2}{\sin \pi/2}$;

(l) $\dfrac{1}{\sin(-\pi/4)}$.

2. With the help of Table V, find

   (a) $\sin 0.2443$;

   (b) $\cos 1.2915$;

   (c) $\sin 1$;

   (d) $\cos \frac{1}{2}$;

   (e) $\sin 0.5236$;

   (f) $\cos 1.500$.

3. Find all x, $0 \le x < 2\pi$, for which

   (a) $\sin x = \frac{1}{2}$;

   (b) $\cos x = \dfrac{\sqrt{3}}{2}$;

   (c) $\cos x = -\dfrac{\sqrt{2}}{2}$;

   (d) $\sin 2x = 1$;

   (e) $\cos \frac{1}{2}x = \frac{1}{2}$;

   (f) $\sin^2 x = 1$;

   (g) $\dfrac{\sin x}{\cos x} = 0$;

   (h) $(\sin x)(\cos x) = 0$;

   (i) $\sin^2 x = \sin x$.

4. Graph the following functions.

   (a) $\sin 2x$;

   (b) $\sin 3x$;

   (c) $\cos 2x$;

   (d) $2 \cos x$;

   (e) $\frac{1}{2} \sin x$;

   (f) $\cos x + 1$;

   (g) $\sin^2 x$;

   (h) $\sin x + \cos x$;

   (i) $\cos^2 x$;

   (j) $\sin \frac{1}{2}x$.

We now define the tangent, the cotangent, the secant, and the cosecant. The definitions are

$$\tan x = \frac{\sin x}{\cos x};$$
        (11)

$$\cot x = \frac{\cos x}{\sin x};$$
        (12)

$$\sec x = \frac{1}{\cos x};$$
        (13)

$$\csc x = \frac{1}{\sin x}.$$
        (14)

It is understood that the domain of definition of each of these functions is the largest possible. This means that each function is defined for all values of x, except those values that give a zero denominator. It can be seen therefore that tan x is defined for all x except those x for which cos $x = 0$. Since the cosine is 0 for $x = \pm\frac{1}{2}\pi, \pm\frac{3}{2}\pi, \pm\frac{5}{2}\pi, \cdots$, we may state that tan is defined for all x except

$$x = \frac{1}{2}\pi + n\pi, \qquad n = 0, \pm1, \pm2, \cdots. \tag{15}$$

The domain of definition of the secant is the same.

The functions cot and csc are defined everywhere except for those x such that sin $x = 0$. Since sin $x = 0$ for $x = 0, \pm\pi, \pm2\pi, \pm3\pi, \cdots$, we see that cot and csc are defined for all x except

$$x = n\pi, \qquad n = 0, \pm1, \pm2, \cdots. \tag{16}$$

When preparing to graph these functions, it is wise to examine their behavior for values of x close to the excluded values. Let us look at the cotangent. If x is close to 0, π, or $-\pi$, then sin x is close to 0. This means that $|\cot x|$ is large when x is close to the above values. In other words, the vertical lines $x = 0$, $x = \pi$, and $x = -\pi$, are asymptotes of the graph. The asymptotes are spaced π units apart. These same lines are asymptotes of the graph of the csc. The vertical lines $x = \frac{1}{2}\pi + n\pi$, $n = 0, \pm1, \pm2, \cdots$, are asymptotes of the graphs of the functions tan and sec.

Making use of the fact that $\sin(-x) = -\sin x$ and $\cos(-x) = \cos x$, it may be seen immediately that

$$
\begin{aligned}
\tan(-x) &= -\tan x; \\
\cot(-x) &= -\cot x; \\
\sec(-x) &= \sec x; \\
\csc(-x) &= -\csc x.
\end{aligned}
\tag{17}
$$

Thus these four functions are: odd, odd, even, and odd, respectively.

These functions obviously are periodic and 2π is the smallest period of sec and csc since the same is true of sin and cos. However, 2π is not the smallest period of tan and cot. It will be shown that

$$
\begin{aligned}
\tan(x + \pi) &= \tan x; \\
\cot(x + \pi) &= \cot x.
\end{aligned}
\tag{18}
$$

Let us return to the fundamental diagram defining sin and cos. If the number x corresponds to the point $P_1(u, v)$ on the circle $u^2 + v^2 = 1$, then $x + \pi$ corresponds to the point $P_2(-u, -v)$ (see Figure VI.16). Thus

$$
\begin{aligned}
\sin(x + \pi) &= -\sin x; \\
\cos(x + \pi) &= -\cos x.
\end{aligned}
\tag{19}
$$

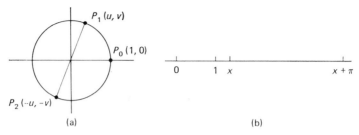

Figure VI.16

Hence

$$\tan(x + \pi) = \frac{\sin(x + \pi)}{\cos(x + \pi)} = \frac{-\sin x}{-\cos x} = \tan x; \qquad \textbf{(20)}$$

and similarly

$$\cot(x + \pi) = \cot x. \qquad \textbf{(21)}$$

To find the graph of the tangent, we shall first find a few points on the graph. At this point, refer to the diagrams in Figure VI.11.

Remembering that $\sqrt{3} = 1.732$, we obtain $\sqrt{3}/3 = 0.566$. Thus using the fact that $\tan(-x) = -\tan x$, we obtain the points in Figure VI.17.

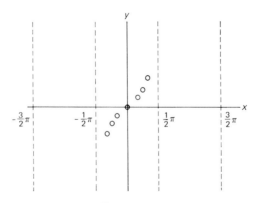

Figure VI.17

We fill in the missing points and use periodicity to obtain the full graph. See Figure VI.18.

The three remaining graphs are shown in Figures VI.19, VI.20, and VI.21. It is left as an exercise to verify their correctness (Exercise 4).

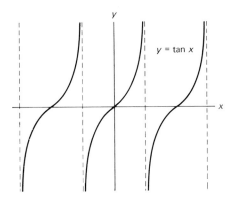

Figure VI.18

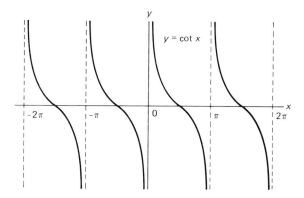

Figure VI.19

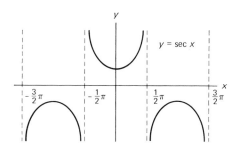

Figure VI.20

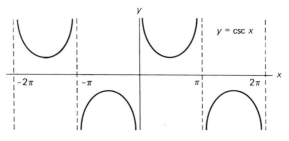

Figure VI.21

We add two identities to the ones already obtained, namely,

$$\tan^2 x + 1 = \sec^2 x, \tag{22}$$

and

$$\cot^2 x + 1 = \csc^2 x. \tag{23}$$

To obtain the first, start with $\sin^2 x + \cos^2 x = 1$. Divide throughout by $\cos^2 x$. This gives

$$\frac{\sin^2 x}{\cos^2 x} + 1 = \frac{1}{\cos^2 x}.$$

Written slightly differently, this gives

$$\left(\frac{\sin x}{\cos x}\right)^2 + 1 = \left(\frac{1}{\cos x}\right)^2.$$

This is precisely (22). To obtain (23), start with $\sin^2 x + \cos^2 x = 1$ and divide by $\sin^2 x$.

Exercises VI.2.b

1. Find the number below using the tables.

  (a) tan 0.2094;   (b) cot 0.4043;
  (c) tan 1.2915;   (d) cot 0.8358;
  (e) tan 0.5236;   (f) cot 1.0472.

2. Calculate

  (a) $\sin(-0.6632)$;   (b) $\cos(-0.7359)$;
  (c) $\sin(\pi + 0.6632)$;   (d) $\cos(\pi + 0.7359)$;
  (e) $\tan(-0.7359)$;   (f) $\cot(-0.6632)$;
  (g) $\sin 4$;   (h) $\cos(-4)$;
  (i) $\tan 4$.

3. Table V indicates that when x is small $\sin x$ is approximately equal to x. Find the smallest value of x such that $x - \sin x \geq 0.0001$; $x - \sin x \geq 0.0010$. What conclusion do you draw as to the number $\sin x/x$ when x is small?

4. Graph the functions (obtain several points on each curve).

(a) $\cot x$;   (b) $\sec x$;

(c) $\csc x$.

5. Graph the functions.

(a) $\tan 2x$;   (b) $\tan \frac{1}{2}x$;

(c) $\tan\left(x - \dfrac{\pi}{2}\right)$;   (d) $\cot 3x$;

(e) $\sec \frac{1}{2}x$;   (f) $\tan(x - 1)$;

(g) $3 \tan x$;   (h) $\tan^2 x$;

(i) $\cot^2 x$.

6. By examining Table V, verify that $\sin$ is an increasing function in the interval, $0 < x < \pi/2$; that $\cos$ is a decreasing function in that interval; that $\tan$ is increasing in that interval; that $\cot$ is decreasing in that interval.

3. ILLUSTRATIONS

We consider a few illustrations to indicate the significance of the circular functions. In many problems to be taken up below, the independent variable is the time t. For reasons of convenience we deal with the function $\sin(2\pi t)$ instead of $\sin t$ since the former has period 1. This is clear from

$$\sin[2\pi(t + 1)] = \sin(2\pi t + 2\pi) = \sin 2\pi t. \tag{1}$$

In physics and engineering one frequently meets functions of the type

$$y = k \sin 2\pi\omega t, \tag{2}$$

where k and ω (omega, the last letter of the Greek alphabet) are constants. We sketch in Figure VI.22 two curves showing the effect of these constants on the graph.

The action of the number k is to increase or decrease the height of the graph. For this reason k is called the *amplitude*. The action of ω is to determine the number of complete cycles (or waves) in the unit interval. It is called the *frequency*. For example, in $y = \sin 1000\pi t$, the frequency is 500. Thus there are 500 complete cycles of the curve in the unit interval!

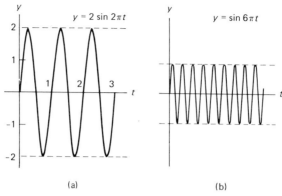

Figure VI.22

ILLUSTRATION 1: The oboe player of a local symphony orchestra gets the orchestra to tune up by playing on his oboe the note middle A, which has a frequency of 440. (When he blows into his instrument he sets up a molecular vibration of the air in which the molecules move back and forth 440 times in 1 second.) Assuming his amplitude is 1, the equation representing the sound is

$$y = \sin(2\pi \times 440t). \tag{3}$$

If a violinist's instrument is "flat" it means that his frequency is < 440. He therefore tightens his A string to raise it to 440. In other words, he gets his value of ω equal to that of the oboe player.

ILLUSTRATION 2: The local power company delivers alternating current at 115 volts and 60 cycles. Thus the voltage at any instant t is given by

$$V = 115 \sin(2\pi \times 60t). \tag{4}$$

Before plugging in an electrical gadget, the user must be sure that it is made for the same amplitude and frequency. If not, the gadget will not work and may be burned out.

ILLUSTRATION 3: Physicists tells us that various rays can be explained in terms of an electromagnetic vibration whose equation is of the form (2). The number k is indicative of the intensity (brightness) of the ray. The frequency determines the quality of the ray. Here follow some typical frequencies:

Power transmission	$\omega = 10^2$;
Local AM radio station	$\omega = 2 \times 10^5$;
Local FM radio station	$\omega = 3 \times 10^6$;
Channel n on television	$\omega = 10^8$;
Radar	$\omega = 10^{10}$;
Red light	$\omega = 4 \times 10^{14}$;
Violet light	$\omega = 8 \times 10^{14}$;
X-rays	$\omega = 10^{18}$;
Cosmic rays	$\omega = 10^{21}$.

ILLUSTRATION 4:   The gasoline engine of a hot-rod car turns over 6000 revolutions per minute at maximum speed. Describe the motion of a piston with a 4-inch stroke assuming that Equation (2) fits this situation.

$$y = 2 \sin(2\pi \times 6000t) \qquad (t \text{ in minutes}).$$

The distance traveled back and forth by the piston in 1 minute is 4 times the amplitude $\times$ 6000 $=$ 48,000 inches or over $\frac{3}{4}$ of a mile.

ILLUSTRATION 5:   The length of daylight in New York City (sunrise to sunset) is 12 hours on March 21 and September 21. At other times it varies from 12 by a number of minutes $2y$ for which we give an approximation below. The maximum value of $2y$ is 174 minutes (2 hours 54 minutes), reached on June 21. The value of y for the tth day after January 1 is

$$y = 87 \sin\left[\frac{2\pi}{365}(t - 80)\right]. \tag{5}$$

Here the figure 80 indicates that March 21 is the 80th day of the year.

The above example is an equation of the type

$$y = k \sin\left[2\pi\omega(t - t_0)\right]. \tag{6}$$

The quantity $2\pi\omega t_0$ is an indication of the "lag" of the sine curve. Instead of "starting" at $t = 0$, it starts at $t = t_0$. In the previous example, the curve starts off from the t-axis on the 80th day of the year, March 21.

ILLUSTRATION 6:   At 5 p.m. of a given day, an electric power company is delivering electricity at 115 volts, 60 cycles. It decides to "cut in" an additional generator to take care of the peak load that comes at 6 p.m. Before being cut in, the new generator has to be tuned up so that its voltage output and frequency are the same as those on the working generators and so that there be no lag between the generators. If there are serious discrepancies in this adjustment process, there will be burned out generators and unpleasant power failures.

ILLUSTRATION 7:   If the note A (above middle C) is struck on the piano, the strings vibrate back and forth 440 times in a second. There is a difference between these vibrations and those of the oboe player in Illustration 1. The sound of the piano string dies down in a few seconds while the oboe sound keeps constant as long as the player has breath in his lungs. The motion of a point on the piano string is given by an equation of the type

$$y = ke^{-ct} \sin(2\pi\omega t), \tag{7}$$

where k, c, and ω are positive constants. In the present instance, $\omega = 440$ and k is small (the maximum value of y will be a few hundredths of an inch). The value of c depends on the quality of the piano, among other things. The motion of the string is said to be *damped*. The graphs in Figure VI.23 indicate

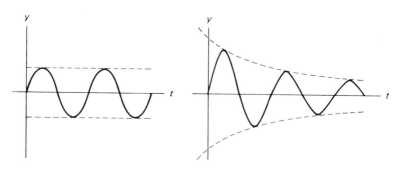

Figure VI.23

the difference between the oboe and the piano (we have selected a scale to suit our convenience). We have graphed the curves $y = \pm ke^{-ct}$ in dotted lines since they form the boundary of our oscillating motion. Note that the principle of damped harmonic motion which we have illustrated here applies also to the motion of a shock absorber on a car. For the latter, c is large and ω is small (fortunately for the passengers).

Equations (2) and (7) are those of simple harmonic motion and damped harmonic motion. Examples of motions of this type are about us on all sides. Going beyond these "pure" cases are those motions which can be described by the equations above without doing too much damage to truth. Some of the problems we have given below may fall into this category. There are also problems whose main purpose is to develop a flexible point of view in the student and to induce him to develop scope in his understanding and the exploratory urge in his approach; also to give him pleasure, satisfaction, and even amusement.

Exercises VI.3.a

1. The phases of the moon (new moon, first, second, and third quarters, full moon) can be measured in terms of the fraction of the angle α which the full moon subtends on the earth. Assuming that the variations in α can be described by Equation (2), write down the equation. Use the fact that $\alpha = 31$ minutes (angle measure) and that the period of the moon is 29 days. The variation should be measured positively and negatively from the starting value $\frac{1}{2}\alpha = \frac{31}{2}$ minutes.

2. Write an equation describing the motion of Donatella's swing in the example of periodicity given in Chapter II, Section 9.

3. Geologists have discovered that there have been alternations on the earth of colder and warmer periods. In particular, a time of maximum cold is called an ice age. Assuming that the process is periodic and that the variations of average temperature (at a given point on the earth) can be given

by Equation (2), write down this variation T in terms of a maximum variation T_0 and the length of time in years n between two successive ice ages. See if you can find information about the value of T_0 and n in an encyclopedia or geology book.

4. A transatlantic liner has the unfortunate habit of constantly rolling as it makes its trips across the ocean. Assuming that the angle of roll is 3° from horizontal and that the period of the roll is 15 seconds, obtain a formula for the angle of roll α in terms of the time. A lady in first class spends the entire trip in her outside cabin, which is situated 35 feet from the axis of rolling. If the trip takes 4 days, find the total vertical distance (up and down) through which her body is transported during the trip.

5. A bright student in a precalculus course is paying no attention to the classroom discussion and watches instead the girl next to him, who has her legs crossed and whose foot is moving back and forth regularly with the pulse of her heart. He assumes that the motion is simple harmonic and calculates the total distance through which her foot moves back and forth during 30 minutes of the lesson, noting that at each pulse beat the foot moves up $\frac{1}{4}$ inch. He obtains the answer: 90 feet. Find the girl's pulse. Was his assumption of simple harmonic motion necessary or would periodicity have been sufficient? Explain your reasoning by drawing one or more diagrams.

6. When the tower of a structure similar to the Empire State Building is struck by a sharp gust of wind, it sways back and forth approximately in damped simple harmonic motion [Equation (7)]. Suppose $c = 1$ and $\omega = 0.4$. Graph the displacement y (in feet) as a function of t (in seconds). The constant k is a constant depending on the intensity of the wind. The time $t = 0$ corresponds to the instant that the gust strikes the building.

7. An Eagle Scout notices that when he releases the needle of any compass, the needle moves back and forth in damped simple harmonic motion until it finally settles on magnetic north. His own high quality compass has a settling time of 30 seconds and a period of 4 seconds. Assuming that settling time means the time necessary for the amplitude of swing to be reduced to $1/20$, find the constants c and ω in the equation $y = ke^{-ct}(\cos 2\pi\omega t)$ for this compass. [Note that for the sake of convenience we have replaced Equation (7) by an analogous one.]

8. A pulsating star is a star in the form of a sphere whose radius alternately becomes bigger and smaller. (This expansion and contraction can be detected because the light emitted by the star changes in color and intensity.) The particular star known as δ-Cephei has a period of perturbation of 5.366 days. It has an average radius of 20 million miles which changes by $\pm 1\frac{1}{4}$ million miles in the course of a pulsation. Assuming that Equation (2) is applicable, write a relation expressing the radius of the star as a function of the time.

Historical Note. It has been shown that the functions $\sin x$, $\cos x$, $\sin 2x$, $\cos 2x$, $\cdots$ are periodic. It was the French mathematician, J. B. J. Fourier (1768–1830), who showed that arbitrary periodic functions can be expressed as sums (infinite series) of the above. Thus all phenomena of periodicity come into the domain of study of the circular functions.

4. ELEMENTARY IDENTITIES AND EQUATIONS

The reader has already met several identities. The fundamental equation $\sin^2 x + \cos^2 x = 1$ and two similar equations [Equations (22) and (23) of Section 2] involving the four other functions are the most striking. Other identities are all the functional equations, such as $\sin x = -\sin(-x)$, $\tan(x + \pi) = \tan x$, and so on. Still others are the definitions, such as $\sec x = 1/\cos x$. These 21 or so identities encountered so far are but a handful out of a collection which is quite large and varied. Such identities will be studied in this section. We shall learn how to determine whether a given equation is an identity or not; and we shall learn how to manufacture new identities. Remember that an identity is a statement of equality that is valid for each value of the variable or variables in the equation. The assertion

$$\sin^2 x + \cos x = 1 \qquad (1)$$

is not an identity. To see this, it is sufficient to show that for one value of x, (1) is false. This value of x can almost be chosen at random. Let us make things easy for ourselves and choose $x = \pi$. Then $\sin \pi = 0$, $\cos \pi = -1$, and $0 + (-1) \neq 1$. And that settles it. If we also try $x = \pi/6$, $\pi/4$, we see again that (1) is not an identity. Do not try $x = 0$ or 2π.

Let us consider now the statement

$$\sin^4 x - \cos^4 x = \sin^2 x - \cos^2 x. \qquad (2)$$

Suppose that we are told that this is an identity and that we are to prove it. A correct proof would be of the following nature.

First of all, for all x,

$$\sin^2 x - \cos^2 x = \sin^2 x - \cos^2 x.$$

Next for all x

$$\sin^2 x + \cos^2 x = 1.$$

Thus by multiplication, one has, for all x,

$$(\sin^2 x + \cos^2 x)(\sin^2 x - \cos^2 x) = 1 \cdot (\sin^2 x - \cos^2 x).$$

Carrying out the necessary algebraic operations gives for all x,

$$\sin^4 x - \cos^4 x = \sin^2 x - \cos^2 x,$$

and this is what we had to prove. Note that we write $\sin^4 x$ for $(\sin x)^4$. Thus $\sin^2 x \cdot \sin^2 x = (\sin x)^2 \cdot (\sin x)^2 = (\sin x)^4 = \sin^4 x$.

Let us try another example. Establish the identity

$$\frac{\cos x - \sin x}{\cos x + \sin x} = \frac{1 - \tan x}{1 + \tan x}. \tag{3}$$

Note that to say that this is an identity means that it is true for all x for which it has meaning. The values of x for which it does not have meaning are those for which $\tan x$ is not defined and those for which $\cos x + \sin x = 0$ and $1 + \tan x = 0$. Let us start.

We have, for all x under consideration,

$$\frac{\cos x - \sin x}{\cos x + \sin x} = \frac{\dfrac{\cos x}{\cos x} - \dfrac{\sin x}{\cos x}}{\dfrac{\cos x}{\cos x} + \dfrac{\sin x}{\cos x}}.$$

Next, for all x under consideration,

$$\frac{\sin x}{\cos x} = \tan x.$$

Thus, for all x under consideration,

$$\frac{\cos x - \sin x}{\cos x + \sin x} = \frac{1 - \tan x}{1 + \tan x}.$$

Let us now consider assertions that are not identities. The problem here is to find all values of the variable for which the given equation is valid.

PROBLEM: Find all values x, such that

$$\sin x = \cos x. \tag{4}$$

SOLUTION: Let x be any value making (4) true. Then dividing both sides by $\cos x$, we obtain

$$\frac{\sin x}{\cos x} = 1,$$

that is,

$$\tan x = 1. \tag{5}$$

Now, if for a given x, one has $0 \le x < \pi$ and $\tan x = 1$, then $x = \pi/4$.

To find all solutions of (4), and hence of the equation $\tan x = 1$, we invoke the fact that tan is periodic with period π. Thus the solutions of (4) are

$$x = \frac{\pi}{4}, \ \pi + \frac{\pi}{4}, \ 2\pi + \frac{\pi}{4}, \cdots \quad \text{or} \quad -\pi + \frac{\pi}{4}, \ -2\pi + \frac{\pi}{4}, \cdots; \tag{6}$$

in other words,

$$x = \frac{\pi}{4} + n\pi, \qquad n = 0, \pm 1, \pm 2, \cdots. \tag{7}$$

Consider now the following.

PROBLEM: Find all values of x such that

$$2 \sin^2 x - 7 \sin x + 3 = 0. \tag{8}$$

SOLUTION: We have, for all x,

$$2 \sin^2 x - 7 \sin x + 3 = (\sin x - 3)(2 \sin x - 1).$$

Thus if x is such that (8) is satisfied, either $\sin x - 3 = 0$ or $2 \sin x - 1 = 0$. Now for any x, $-1 \le \sin x \le 1$, hence we never have $\sin x - 3 = 0$. Thus we have to consider only

$$2 \sin x - 1 = 0,$$

$$\sin x = \frac{1}{2}.$$

The solutions of this equation are obtained by finding first all solutions x such that $0 \le x < 2\pi$ and then invoking the periodicity of sin. This gives

$$x = \frac{\pi}{6} + 2n\pi \qquad \text{or} \qquad \frac{5}{6}\pi + 2n\pi, \qquad n = 0, \pm 1, \pm 2, \cdots. \tag{9}$$

PROBLEM: Find all x such that

$$\sin x + \cos x = 1. \tag{10}$$

SOLUTION: Squaring both sides gives

$$\sin^2 x + 2 \sin x \cos x + \cos^2 x = 1,$$

that is, since $\sin^2 x + \cos^2 x = 1$ for all x,

$$2 \sin x \cos x = 0.$$

Hence either (i): $\sin x = 0$ and hence by (10) $\cos x = 1$. This gives

$$x = 2n\pi, \qquad n = 0, \pm 1, \pm 2, \cdots. \tag{11}$$

Or (ii): $\cos x = 0$ and hence by (10) $\sin x = 1$. This gives

$$x = \frac{\pi}{2} + 2n\pi, \qquad n = 0, \pm 1, \pm 2, \cdots. \tag{12}$$

PROBLEM: Find all values, $0 \le x < 2\pi$, satisfying $\cos x = x$. Use the tables.

SOLUTION: Examine the two appropriate columns in the tables and find out when the entry under $\cos x$ equals the entry under x. Making a rough graph tells us approximately where this is. The tables indicate that there is a value between $x = 0.7330$ ($\cos x = 0.7431$), and $x = 0.7418$ ($\cos x = 0.7373$).

[*Note*: To solve the problem $\cos x = x^2$, prepare 3 columns: one for x, another for x^2, and a third for $\cos x$. A graph indicates the approximate value of x rather easily. It corresponds to the point where the curves $y = x^2$ and $y = \cos x$ intersect.]

Exercises VI.4.a

1. Prove the following identities.

(a) $(\sin t + \cos t)^2 = 1 + 2 \sin t \cos t$;

(b) $\cos^2 x - \sin^2 x = \dfrac{1 - \tan^2 x}{1 + \tan^2 x}$;

(c) $\dfrac{1 + \tan^2 x}{\tan^2 x} = \csc^2 x$;

(d) $\tan u + \cot u = \sec u \csc u$;

(e) $(1 - \sin x)(1 + \sin x) = \dfrac{1}{1 + \tan^2 x}$;

(f) $\sec^2 t + \csc^2 t = \sec^2 t \cdot \csc^2 t$;

(g) $\cos^2 x - \sin^2 x = \dfrac{1 - \tan^2 x}{1 + \tan^2 x}$;

(h) $1 - 2 \sin^2 y = 2 \cos^2 y - 1$;

(i) $\dfrac{1 - \sin x}{\cos x} = \dfrac{\cos x}{1 + \sin x}$;

(j) $\dfrac{1 + \sin t}{\cos t} + \dfrac{\cos t}{1 + \sin t} = 2 \sec t$;

(k) $\dfrac{1 - \tan u}{1 + \tan u} = \dfrac{\cot u - 1}{\cot u + 1}$;

(l) $\dfrac{1}{1 + \sin s} + \dfrac{1}{1 - \sin s} = 2 \sec^2 s$;

(m) $\dfrac{\tan x}{1 - \cot x} + \dfrac{\cot x}{1 - \tan x} = 1 + \tan x + \cot x$.

2. Find the values of the unknown which satisfy the following.

(a) $4 \sin^2 x + 1 = 8 \cos x$;   (b) $\cot 4t = 1$;

(c) $\sin 2x = \frac{1}{2}$;   (d) $\cos 2\pi x = \frac{\sqrt{2}}{2}$;

(e) $\tan \frac{\pi}{2} t = 1$;   (f) $2 \sin^2 x + 9 \sin x - 5 = 0$;

(g) $\tan^3 u + \tan^2 u - 3 \tan u - 3 = 0$;
(h) $\tan x = \cot x$.

3. Find the approximate values of the unknown which satisfy the following relations (make rough graphs and use tables).

(a) $\sin x = \frac{1}{2}x$;   (b) $\sin x = x^2$;

(c) $\sin x > x^2$;   (d) $\cos x > \frac{x}{2}$;

(e) $2 \cos x = e^x$, $x > 0$.

5. THE ADDITION FORMULAS

It was seen in Chapter V that the function exp satisfies a remarkable equation: $\exp(u + v) = \exp(u) \cdot \exp(v)$. This equation could be called an addition formula since it concerns the relations among $\exp(u)$, $\exp(v)$, and $\exp(u + v)$. There exist similar relations for the circular functions. This fact is not surprising since there is a very close relation between the function exp and the functions sin and cos. The relation is indeed very close but it is also very deep and cannot be investigated without a knowledge of complex numbers. The addition formulas are identities involving two variables.

The two fundamental identities for sin and cos are:

$$\sin(x + y) = \sin x \cos y + \sin y \cos x; \tag{1}$$

$$\cos(x + y) = \cos x \cos y - \sin x \sin y. \tag{2}$$

There are also identities for $\tan(x + y)$ and $\cot(x + y)$.

Let us consider the proof of (2). Naturally, these identities are valid for all numbers x and y, positive and negative. We shall give a proof that is not quite as elegant as some others but is quite short. We shall help ourselves in carrying through the proof by drawing a diagram. As usual, when using a diagram, only one special case seems to be handled. It is absolutely essential to write down a proof that is valid for all cases. Thus it is advisable to make several diagrams showing special situations and to letter them in such a way that the written proof applies to each (Exercise 4).

The proof is based on the following fact: Take a circle of radius 1, two points on the circle P_0 and Q_0, and a real number t. Wind around the circle the distance t starting at P_0. This gives a point P_1. Now wind around the circle the distance t starting at Q_0. This gives Q_1. Then the distance from P_0 to P_1 (measured in a straight line) equals the distance from Q_0 to Q_1. In elementary geometry, this fact is stated: *Equal arcs subtend equal chords*. (Make a diagram at this point. If help is needed, Figure VI.24 will provide some.)

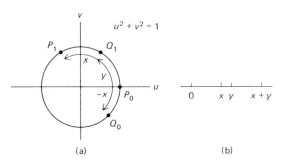

(a)   (b)

Figure VI.24

Consider two numbers x and y. Starting at the point $P_0(1, 0)$ in the (u, v) plane mark off on the circle $u^2 + v^2 = 1$ the three arc distances $-x, y, x + y$. This gives three points Q_0, Q_1, and P_1 (see Figure VI.24). The coordinates of Q_1 are (u, v) where $u = \cos y$ and $v = \sin y$. In other words, the coordinates of Q_1 are $(\cos y, \sin y)$. The coordinates of P_1 are $(\cos(x + y), \sin(x + y))$. The coordinates of Q_0 are $(\cos(-x), \sin(-x))$, that is, they are $(\cos x, -\sin x)$. Thus the four points are

$$P_0(1, 0), \qquad P_1(\cos(x + y), \sin(x + y)),$$
$$Q_0(\cos x, -\sin x), \qquad Q_1(\cos y, \sin y). \tag{3}$$

Since the length $\overline{P_0 P_1}$ equals the length $\overline{Q_0 Q_1}$, we obtain by substitution in the distance formula (Chapter IV, Section 2),

$$\sqrt{[\cos(x + y) - 1]^2 + [\sin(x + y) - 0]^2}$$
$$= \sqrt{(\cos y - \cos x)^2 + (\sin y + \sin x)^2}. \tag{4}$$

Squaring and expanding the brackets gives

$$\cos^2(x + y) - 2\cos(x + y) + 1 + \sin^2(x + y)$$
$$= \cos^2 y - 2\cos x \cos y + \cos^2 x \tag{5}$$
$$+ \sin^2 y + 2\sin x \sin y + \sin^2 x.$$

We now use, three times, the identity

$$\sin^2 t + \cos^2 t = 1,$$

once with $t = x + y$, once with $t = x$, and once with $t = y$. This gives

$$2 - 2\cos(x + y) = 2 - 2\cos x \cos y + 2\sin x \sin y. \qquad (6)$$

Cancellation and division by 2 and changing sign gives

$$\cos(x + y) = \cos x \cos y - \sin x \sin y. \qquad (7)$$

This is the desired identity (2).

Before deriving (1) let us obtain two important identities that can be derived from (7). First set $y = \pi/2$ in (7) obtaining

$$\cos\left(x + \frac{\pi}{2}\right) = \cos x \cos \frac{\pi}{2} - \sin x \sin \frac{\pi}{2}$$
$$= \cos x \cdot 0 - \sin x \cdot 1$$
$$= -\sin x. \qquad (8)$$

Since the last equation is valid for all values of the variable, we may write in (8) $x + \pi/2$ instead of x. This gives

$$\cos\left(x + \frac{\pi}{2} + \frac{\pi}{2}\right) = -\sin\left(x + \frac{\pi}{2}\right). \qquad (9)$$

that is,

$$\sin\left(x + \frac{\pi}{2}\right) = -\cos(x + \pi).$$

But we know that $\cos(x + \pi) = -\cos x$. Thus we have the identity

$$\sin\left(x + \frac{\pi}{2}\right) = \cos x. \qquad (10)$$

We also display the final result of the calculation in (8).

$$\cos\left(x + \frac{\pi}{2}\right) = -\sin x. \qquad (11)$$

Identities (10) and (11) are very important.

We now return to the proof of (1). We have, using first (11), then (7), then (10) and (11),

$$-\sin(x + y) = \cos\left(x + y + \frac{\pi}{2}\right) = \cos\left[x + \left(y + \frac{\pi}{2}\right)\right]$$
$$= \cos x \cos\left(y + \frac{\pi}{2}\right) - \sin x \sin\left(y + \frac{\pi}{2}\right) \qquad (12)$$
$$= \cos x(-\sin y) - \sin x \cos y.$$

Thus

$$\sin(x + y) = \sin x \cos y + \cos x \sin y. \qquad (13)$$

This is the desired identity.

We derive the identity

$$\tan(x + y) = \frac{\tan x + \tan y}{1 - \tan x \tan y}. \tag{14}$$

Using successively the definition of tan and (1) and (2) plus some algebraic manipulations, we obtain

$$\tan(x + y) = \frac{\sin(x + y)}{\cos(x + y)} = \frac{\sin x \cos y + \cos x \sin y}{\cos x \cos y - \sin x \sin y}$$

$$= \frac{\dfrac{\sin x \cos y}{\cos x \cos y} + \dfrac{\cos x \sin y}{\cos x \cos y}}{\dfrac{\cos x \cos y}{\cos x \cos y} - \dfrac{\sin x \sin y}{\cos x \cos y}} \tag{15}$$

$$= \frac{\dfrac{\sin x}{\cos x} + \dfrac{\sin y}{\cos y}}{1 - \dfrac{\sin x \sin y}{\cos x \cos y}} = \frac{\tan x + \tan y}{1 - \tan x \tan y}.$$

A formula can easily be obtained for $\sin(x - y)$. More precisely,

$$\sin(x - y) = \sin[x + (-y)] = \sin x \cos(-y) + \cos x \sin(-y) \tag{16}$$
$$= \sin x \cos y - \cos x \sin y.$$

Similarly, formulas can be derived simply for $\cos(x - y)$, $\tan(x - y)$, $\cot(x + y)$, and $\cot(x - y)$. These are left as exercises.

Exercises VI.5.a

1. Establish the identities below.

(a) $\cos(x - y) = \cos x \cos y + \sin x \sin y$;

(b) $\tan(x - y) = \dfrac{\tan x - \tan y}{1 + \tan x \tan y}$;

(c) $\cot(x + y) = \dfrac{\cot x \cot y - 1}{\cot x + \cot y}$;

(d) $\cot(x - y) = -\dfrac{\cot x \cot y + 1}{\cot x - \cot y}$;

(e) $\sin\left(\dfrac{\pi}{2} - x\right) = \cos x$;

(f) $\cos\left(\dfrac{\pi}{2} - x\right) = \sin x$;

(g) $\sin(\pi - x) = \sin x$;

(h) $\cos(\pi - x) = -\cos x$.

2. Establish the identities.

(a) $\sin(x + y) + \sin(x - y) = 2 \sin x \cos y$;
(b) $\sin(x + y) - \sin(x - y) = 2 \cos x \sin y$;
(c) $\cos(x + y) + \cos(x - y) = 2 \cos x \cos y$;
(d) $\cos(x + y) - \cos(x - y) = -2 \sin x \sin y$.

3. Use the results obtained in Exercise 2 and make the substitution $x + y = u$ and $x - y = v$ to obtain the identities below.

(a) $\sin u + \sin v = 2 \sin \dfrac{u + v}{2} \cos \dfrac{u - v}{2}$;

(b) $\sin u - \sin v = 2 \cos \dfrac{u + v}{2} \sin \dfrac{u - v}{2}$;

(c) $\cos u + \cos v = 2 \cos \dfrac{u + v}{2} \cos \dfrac{u - v}{2}$;

(d) $\cos u - \cos v = -2 \sin \dfrac{u + v}{2} \sin \dfrac{u - v}{2}$.

4. Draw several diagrams for possible values of x, y, $x + y$ in Figure VI.24. Find the coordinates of the points P_1, Q_0, Q_1 in each case. Do the equations in the book apply to your diagram? They should.

5. Establish the identities.

(a) $\sin^2 x - \sin^2 y = \sin(x + y) \sin(x - y)$;
(b) $\cos^2 x - \sin^2 y = \cos(x + y) \cos(x - y)$;
(c) $\cos x = \cos(x + y) \cos y + \sin(x + y) \sin y$;
(d) $\sin x = \sin(x - y) \cos y + \cos(x - y) \sin y$.

6. MULTIPLE ANGLE FORMULAS

If we set $y = x$ in the addition formulas for the sine, cosine, and tangent of $x + y$, we obtain interesting new identities. Starting with the sine, one has

$$\sin(x + x) = \sin x \cos x + \cos x \sin x.$$

Hence

$$\sin 2x = 2 \sin x \cos x. \tag{1}$$

The cosine formula gives

$$\cos(x + x) = \cos x \cos x - \sin x \sin x.$$

Hence

$$\cos 2x = \cos^2 x - \sin^2 x. \tag{2}$$

Setting $\sin^2 x = 1 - \cos^2 x$ and afterwards $\cos^2 x = 1 - \sin^2 x$, two other formulas for $\cos 2x$ are obtained:

$$\cos 2x = 2 \cos^2 x - 1; \tag{3}$$

$$\cos 2x = 1 - 2 \sin^2 x. \tag{4}$$

Making the substitution $x = y$ in the tangent formula (14) of the preceding section gives

$$\tan(x + x) = \frac{\tan x + \tan x}{1 - \tan x \tan x},$$

or

$$\tan 2x = \frac{2 \tan x}{1 - \tan^2 x}. \tag{5}$$

Writing x instead of $2x$ in formula (3) gives

$$\cos x = 2 \cos^2 \frac{x}{2} - 1,$$

hence

$$\cos^2 \frac{x}{2} = \frac{1 + \cos x}{2}.$$

This leads to

$$\cos \frac{x}{2} = \pm \sqrt{\frac{1 + \cos x}{2}}. \tag{6}$$

The sign "$\pm$" in front of the radical means: choose that one of the two signs which is correct. This will depend on the situation at hand. In any given situation one of the two signs has to be chosen but usually not both.

If we start with formula (4) and replace $2x$ by x, we get

$$\sin \frac{x}{2} = \pm \sqrt{\frac{1 - \cos x}{2}}. \tag{7}$$

Formulas (6) and (7) are called the "half-angle formulas." They enable us to calculate the sine and cosine for a very large number of new angles.

EXAMPLE: Compute the sine and cosine of $\pi/8$.

SOLUTION: Using (7) and (6) and noting that the positive sign must obviously be chosen, one obtains

$$\sin \frac{\pi}{8} = \sqrt{\frac{1 - \cos \pi/4}{2}} = \sqrt{\frac{1 - \sqrt{2}/2}{2}} = \frac{1}{2} \sqrt{2 - \sqrt{2}},$$

$$\cos \frac{\pi}{8} = \sqrt{\frac{1 + \cos \pi/4}{2}} = \sqrt{\frac{1 + \sqrt{2}/2}{2}} = \frac{1}{2} \sqrt{2 + \sqrt{2}}. \tag{8}$$

Proceeding as above it is possible to compute the functions of $\pi/16$, $\pi/32$, and so on. In other words, the functions of certain small numbers can be computed. Using the addition formula, we can then calculate the functions for values close to $\pi/6$, $\pi/4$, $\pi/3$, and so on. In this way (with a lot of hard work) we can compute a table of sines and cosines that is as accurate as desired. Tables may not be made by this method, but we now have the satisfaction of knowing that they could be so made if necessary.

The word sine which we use today is of ancient Hindu origin. The first table of sines was given about 1600 years ago and contained 24 entries; that is, the right angle is divided into 24 equal parts, each of $3\frac{3}{4}°$. This corresponds to our dividing $\pi/6$ into 8 parts. Naturally, the Hindu tables were empirically arrived at and hence are only mildly accurate.

Let us calculate $\cos 3x$ using the addition formula. This gives

$$
\begin{aligned}
\cos(2x + x) &= \cos 2x \cos x - \sin 2x \sin x \\
&= (2 \cos^2 x - 1) \cos x - (2 \sin x \cos x) \sin x \\
&= 2 \cos^3 x - \cos x - 2 \cos x(1 - \cos^2 x).
\end{aligned}
$$

Thus

$$
\cos 3x = 4 \cos^3 x - 3 \cos x. \tag{9}
$$

The formula just found shows that $\cos 3x$ is a polynomial in $\cos x$. The polynomial is of degree 3. It was discovered in (3) that $\cos 2x$ is a polynomial of degree 2 in $\cos x$. It can be shown that for any positive integer n, $\cos nx$ is a polynomial of degree n in $\cos x$ (see Exercise 5). These polynomials are highly interesting and are named after the Russian mathematician Tchebycheff (1821–1894). Note that $\sin nx$ is not a polynomial in $\sin x$ for all n. Try, for example, $n = 2$.

Equation (9) plays a role in the solution of a problem of historical interest. If in (9) we set $3x = \frac{2}{3}\pi$ and write $\cos x = y$, then since $\cos \frac{2}{3}\pi = -\frac{1}{2}$ we obtain

$$
8y^3 - 6y + 1 = 0. \tag{10}
$$

It can be shown that this cubic does not have zeros of a specially simple form and this leads to the conclusion that $\frac{2}{3}\pi$ (or $120°$) cannot be trisected by "ruler and compass." This answers negatively a classical problem of the ancient Greeks: that of trisecting an angle by ruler and compass. Another such problem called squaring of the circle by ruler and compass was proved impossible when it was shown that π is transcendental (see Chapter V, Section 4).

The so-called third problem of the Greeks, the duplication of the cube, leads to the equation $x^3 - 2 = 0$. This also cannot be solved by extracting square roots. It should be added that by a ruler and compass construction is meant something highly precise that cannot be defined here. These constructions are of historical interest only. They have no practical significance and their mathematical ramifications are not extensive.

Table VI.3   Principal Identities

(1) $\sin^2 x + \cos^2 x = 1$
(2) $\tan^2 x + 1 = \sec^2 x$
(3) $\cot^2 x + 1 = \csc^2 x$
(4) $\sin(-x) = -\sin x$
(5) $\cos(-x) = \cos x$
(6) $\tan(-x) = -\tan x$
(7) $\sin(x + 2\pi) = \sin x$
(8) $\cos(x + 2\pi) = \cos x$
(9) $\tan(x + \pi) = \tan x$
(10) $\sin(x + \pi) = -\sin x$
(11) $\cos(x + \pi) = -\cos x$

(12) $\sin\left(x + \dfrac{\pi}{2}\right) = \cos x$

(13) $\cos\left(x + \dfrac{\pi}{2}\right) = -\sin x$

(14) $\sin\left(\dfrac{\pi}{2} - x\right) = \cos x$

(15) $\cos\left(\dfrac{\pi}{2} - x\right) = \sin x$

(16) $\sin(x + y) = \sin x \cos y + \cos x \sin y$
(17) $\cos(x + y) = \cos x \cos y - \sin x \sin y$
(18) $\sin(x - y) = \sin x \cos y - \cos x \sin y$
(19) $\cos(x - y) = \cos x \cos y + \sin x \sin y$

(20) $\tan(x + y) = \dfrac{\tan x + \tan y}{1 - \tan x \tan y}$

(21) $\tan(x - y) = \dfrac{\tan x - \tan y}{1 + \tan x \tan y}$

(22) $\sin(2x) = 2 \sin x \cos x$
(23) $\cos(2x) = \cos^2 x - \sin^2 x$
$$= 2\cos^2 x - 1$$
$$= 1 - 2\sin^2 x$$

(24) $\sin^2 \dfrac{1}{2} x = \dfrac{1 - \cos x}{2}$

(25) $\cos^2 \dfrac{1}{2} x = \dfrac{1 + \cos x}{2}$

(26) $\tan \dfrac{1}{2} x = \dfrac{\sin x}{1 + \cos x}$

Exercises VI.6.a

1. Prove the following identities.

(a) $1 - 4 \sin^2 x \cos^2 x = \cos^2 2x$;

(b) $\sec^2 2x - 1 = \dfrac{2 \sin x \cos x}{\cos^2 x - \sin^2 x}$;

(c) $\dfrac{1 - \cos 2x}{\sin 2x} = \tan x$;

(d) $\dfrac{2 \tan x}{1 + \tan^2 x} = \sin 2x$;

(e) $\tan 3x = \dfrac{3 \tan x - \tan^3 x}{1 - 3 \tan^2 x}$;

(f) $\tan \dfrac{x}{2} = \dfrac{1 - \cos x}{\sin x}$;

(g) $\tan \dfrac{x}{2} = \dfrac{\sin x}{1 + \cos x}$;

(h) $\dfrac{\cos x + \cos 3x}{2} = 2 \cos^3 x - \cos x$;

(i) $\dfrac{\sin x + \sin 3x}{4} = \sin x \cos^2 x$;

(j) $\sin 3x = 3 \sin x - 4 \sin^3 x$;
(k) $\sin 4x = 2(\sin x - 2 \sin^3 x) \cos x$.

2. Compute $\sin \pi/12$, $\cos \pi/12$ using the fact that

(a) $\dfrac{\pi}{12} = \dfrac{\pi}{3} - \dfrac{\pi}{4}$;

(b) $\dfrac{\pi}{12} = \dfrac{1}{2} \dfrac{\pi}{6}$.

3. Write down the values of $\sin \pi/16$, $\cos \pi/16$.

4. Given that $\sin x = 3/5$, $0 < x < \pi/2$, calculate

(a) $\sin 2x$;

(b) $\cos 2x$;

(c) $\tan 2x$;

(d) $\sin \dfrac{x}{2}$;

(e) $\cos \dfrac{x}{2}$;

(f) $\tan \dfrac{x}{2}$;

(g) $\sin 3x$;

(h) $\cos 3x$;

(i) $\tan 3x$.

5. Prove that there exists a polynomial $p(t)$ such that $p(\cos x) = \cos 4x$. The same for $\cos 5x$. [Note Exercise 1(k).]

6. Show how to compute the functions of $\pi/10$. [*Hint*: Letting $\pi/10 = x$, then $3x = \pi/2 - 2x$. Hence $\cos 3x = \sin 2x = 2 \sin x \cos x = 2 \cos x \sqrt{1 - \cos^2 x}$. Then use Equation (9). This gives an equation in $\cos x$ which can be solved by radicals.]

7. Establish the identity

$$\frac{\sin x - \sin y}{\cos x + \cos y} = \tan \frac{x - y}{2}.$$

Using this identity, derive the formula $\tan x/2 = (\sin x)/(1 + \cos x)$.

8. Find the values of x which satisfy the following.

(a) $\sin x = \sin 2x$;   (b) $\cos x = \cos 2x$;
(c) $\tan \frac{1}{2}x = \sin x$;   (d) $\cos 3x = \cos x$;
(e) $\sin 3x = \sin x$.

Historical Note. Pafnuti Tchebycheff made outstanding contributions to the analytic theory of numbers. He and Nicolai Lobachevsky (1793–1856), one of the founders of non-Euclidean geometry, were the leading Russian mathematicians of the nineteenth century.

    One of the greatest figures in early mathematics is Ptolemy of Alexandria. He lived during the first part of the second century after Christ. The formulas for $\sin(x \pm y)$ and $\cos(x \pm y)$ are known by his name since he had discovered a theorem in geometry whose modern interpretation gives the addition identities. Similarly, the half-angle formulas were known to Ptolemy. Using these and allied devices, he made the equivalent of our trigonometric tables from $\frac{1}{4}°$ to $90°$, proceeding in steps of $\frac{1}{4}°$. These tables were fundamental to scientific calculations for over a thousand years.

7. THE INVERSE FUNCTIONS

Suppose $F(x, y)$ represents an expression in x and y. For example, $F(x, y) = x^2 - 3xy + y^5$ or $F(x, y) = y^2 - 3 \sin^3 x$. By the graph of $F(x, y) = 0$ is meant the collection of all pairs (x, y) such that

$$F(x, y) = 0. \tag{1}$$

Notice that if for any function f, $F(x, y) = y - f(x)$, then the graph of $F(x, y) = 0$ is precisely the graph of f as previously defined.

    Suppose that there is given an expression $F(x, y)$ and assume that the graph of $F(x, y) = 0$ has been determined. Suppose now that we interchange the roles of x and y and consider $F(y, x)$. Question: How does one obtain the graph of $F(y, x) = 0$? The answer is simple. Just reflect the graph of $F(x, y) = 0$ through the line $y = x$. Thus the point (a, b) is on the graph of $F(x, y) = 0$ if the point (b, a) is on the graph of $F(y, x) = 0$ and only in that case. See Figure VI.25. For example, let $F(x, y) = y - e^x$. Then $F(y, x) = x - e^y$. The two graphs are given in Figure VI.26.

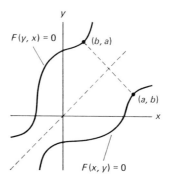

Figure VI.25

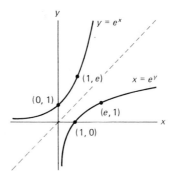

Figure VI.26

It will have been noticed that the equation $x = e^y$ is equivalent to $y = \ln x$. This suggests therefore that if it is possible to solve the equation $y = f(x)$ for x obtaining $x = g(y)$, then the graph of the inverse function $y = g(x)$ is given by the above reflection procedure. Note that the graphs of $y = f(x)$ and $x = g(y)$ are the same. Thus to get the graph of $y = g(x)$, we just look for the graph of $x = f(y)$.

Having said this, it is trivial to find the graph of $x = \sin y$, $x = \cos y$, and so on. Merely reflect the graph of $y = \sin x$, $y = \cos x$ through the line $x = y$. We do this in Figure VI.27 for the case $x = \sin y$. The graph of the curve $y = \sin x$ has been dotted in so that the reflection process may be followed.

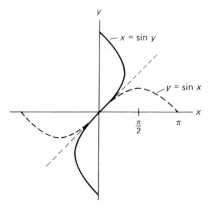

Figure VI.27

Now let us consider the problem of solving $x = \sin y$ for y. In order to solve, it is necessary that the function sin be one-to-one. In other words, it is necessary that distinct values of y give distinct values of x. This is certainly not the case. ($y = 0$, 2π, and 4π all give the value $x = 0$.) Possibly, by restricting the value of y suitably, the function can be made one-to-one. For example, let y be restricted so that $-\pi/2 \leq y < \pi/2$. Then clearly the function *is* one-to-one and we can solve for y. The solution for y of $x = \sin y$ is written $y = \sin^{-1} x$ (read "inverse sine of x"). We have therefore:

The function sin *on the interval* $-\pi/2 \leq x < \pi/2$ *is one-to-one and maps this interval onto an interval* $-1 \leq y < 1$. *It has an inverse* $\sin^{-1}$. *The function* $\sin^{-1}$ *is defined on the interval* $-1 \leq x < 1$ *and maps this interval onto the interval* $-\pi/2 \leq y < \pi/2$.

The notation arcsin is also used to denote $\sin^{-1}$. Thus one may write interchangeably,

$$y = \sin^{-1} x \qquad \text{or} \qquad y = \arcsin x. \tag{2}$$

Both notations are used in the exercises.

To obtain the graph of the function defined by $y = \sin^{-1} x$, all we have to do is to take the graph of the function defined by $y = \sin x$, $-\pi/2 \leq x < \pi/2$, and reflect it in the line $y = x$. This is done in Figure VI.28.

A remark on notation: If a function f has an inverse, it is usual to denote it by f^{-1}. However, this is not done in all cases. For example the inverse function to exp is ln. Note furthermore that we write $\sin^n x$ instead of $(\sin x)^n$ for all integers n—*except* $n = -1$ because $\sin^{-1}$ means the inverse function.

If we wish to solve for y in the equation $x = \cos y$, we find the same difficulty as before. Unless the domain of y is suitably restricted, the function taking y to $\cos y$ is not one-to-one. However, as in the case of the sine, the function can be made one-to-one by restricting the domain of y. The domain to which y is restricted is $0 \leq y < \pi$. (Note that it is not the same as for the

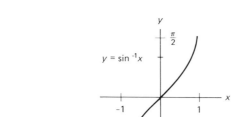

Figure VI.28

sine.) Solving for y, one writes $y = \cos^{-1} x$ (read "inverse cosine of x"). We
have:

   The function cos *on the interval* $0 \le x < \pi$ *is one-to-one and maps this
interval onto the interval* $-1 < y \le 1$. *It has an inverse* $\cos^{-1}$. *The function*
$\cos^{-1}$ *is defined on the interval* $-1 < x \le 1$ *and maps this interval onto the
interval* $0 \le y < \pi$. (See Figure VI.29.)

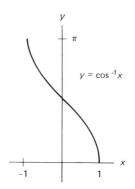

Figure VI.29

For the function $\tan^{-1}$ we decide as follows:
   The function $\tan^{-1}$ *is defined for all real numbers. The range of the map
defined by* $y = \tan^{-1} x$ *is the interval* $-\pi/2 < y < \pi/2$. Its graph is given in
Figure VI.30.

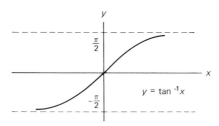

Figure VI.30

The notation arccos is also used to denote $\cos^{-1}$. Similarly, arctan and $\tan^{-1}$ mean the same thing.

It has been noticed before that if the function f is defined by $f(t) = t^2$ where t is any real number, then f^{-1} does not exist. Or put another way, the equation $x = y^2$ does not have a solution for y, it has two of them: $y = \sqrt{x}$ and $y = -\sqrt{x}$. See Figure VI.31.

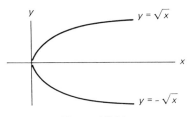

Figure VI.31

Obviously these two functions are Siamese twins and are bound together by the one equation $y^2 - x = 0$. Conceivably, there is something short-sighted about our notion of function that forces us to separate these twins from one another. Is there possibly some more sophisticated way of looking at functions which would allow the lower and upper functions in Figure VI.31 to stay united and form just one function? The answer to this question is "yes" and was developed by the German mathematician G. F. B. Riemann (1826–1866). Riemann restored the one-to-one character of the function by defining it not on a single line (the x-axis), but on a many layered line called a *Riemann surface*.

This device can be used to solder together the infinite number of functions obtained by trying to invert $y = \sin x$ (there is an inverse on the interval $-\pi/2 \le x < \pi/2$ as we have seen; there is an inverse on the interval $\pi/2 \le x < \frac{3}{2}\pi$; there is an inverse on the interval $\frac{3}{2}\pi \le x < \frac{5}{2}\pi$; and so on). From this point of view the graph of $y = \sin^{-1} x$ becomes identical with the graph of $x - \sin y = 0$ instead of being only a part of it.

The student will appreciate the idea of a Riemann surface by considering a little more closely the manner in which we mapped real numbers x onto the circle $u^2 + v^2 = 1$ in discussing winding numbers in Section 1. It was seen there that many numbers x map onto the same point $P_1(u, v)$ of the circle. In fact, x, $x + 2\pi$, $x + 4\pi$, $\cdots$ all map onto the same point. How can the mapping be made one-to-one?

Very easily! But it is necessary to discard the circle and replace it by a curve that rises off the plane as one winds around it; in other words, the circle is replaced by a helix. See Figure VI.32. The best picture for this is a metal spring of "radius" 1 and of infinite length. Note that for this "generalized circle" the map from x to P_1 *is* one-to-one. The above type of construction and the problems it leads to pervade large domains of mathematics. It is studied in detail in the branch of mathematics known as topology.

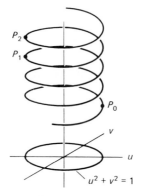

Figure VI.32

Exercises VI.7.a

1. Find a numerical value between 0 and $\pi/2$ inclusive for the following.

(a) $\arcsin \dfrac{1}{\sqrt{2}}$;

(b) $\tan^{-1} 0$;

(c) $\cos^{-1} 1$;

(d) $\arctan 1$;

(e) $\sin^{-1} \frac{1}{2}$;

(f) $\arccos 0$;

(g) $\arctan \sqrt{3}$;

(h) $\cot^{-1} \dfrac{\sqrt{3}}{3}$;

(i) $\sec^{-1} 2$.

2. Using the tables find the numerical value of

(a) $\sin^{-1} 0.2250$;

(b) $\arctan 0.6745$;

(c) $\tan^{-1} 3.867$;

(d) $\cos^{-1} 0.9511$;

(e) $\arcsin 0.7071$;

(f) $\arccos 0.8660$.

3. Calculate the numbers below, keeping in mind that $0 < \sin^{-1} \frac{3}{5} < \pi/2$ and $0 < \cos^{-1} \frac{12}{13} < \pi/2$.

(a) $\sin(\sin^{-1} \frac{3}{5})$;

(b) $\cos(\sin^{-1} \frac{3}{5})$;

(c) $\tan(\cos^{-1} \frac{12}{13})$;

(d) $\sin(2 \sin^{-1} \frac{3}{5})$;

(e) $\cos(\frac{1}{2} \cos^{-1} \frac{12}{13})$;

(f) $\csc(\sin^{-1} \frac{3}{5})$;

(g) $\sin(\sin^{-1} \frac{3}{5} + \cos^{-1} \frac{12}{13})$;

(h) $\tan(\sin^{-1} \frac{3}{5} - \cos^{-1} \frac{12}{13})$.

4. Given that $0 < \arcsin x < \pi/2$, and that $0 < \tan^{-1} x < \pi/2$, prove that

(a) $\cos(\arcsin x) = \sqrt{1 - x^2}$;

(b) $\tan(\arcsin x) = \dfrac{x\sqrt{1 - x^2}}{1 - x^2}$;

(c) $\sin(2 \arcsin x) = 2x\sqrt{1 - x^2}$;

(d) $\sin(\frac{1}{2} \arcsin x) = \sqrt{\dfrac{1 - \sqrt{1 - x^2}}{2}}$;

(e) $\cos(2 \arcsin x) = 1 - 2x^2$;

(f) $\sin(\arccos \sqrt{1 - x^2}) = x$;

(g) $\sin(\tan^{-1} x) = \dfrac{x}{\sqrt{1 + x^2}}$;

(h) $\cos(2 \tan^{-1} x) = \dfrac{1 - x^2}{1 + x^2}$;

(i) $\sin(\csc^{-1} x) = \dfrac{1}{x}$;

(j) $\tan(2 \arctan x) = \dfrac{2x}{1 - x^2}$.

5. Evaluate the following assuming that all inverse functions have values between 0 and $\pi/2$ inclusive.

(a) $\tan(\pi + \arcsin \frac{3}{5})$;

(b) $\sin\left(\dfrac{\pi}{2} - \tan^{-1} \sqrt{3}\right)$;

(c) $\sin(\sin^{-1} \frac{1}{3} + \sin^{-1} \frac{1}{4})$;

(d) $\cos(\sin^{-1} 1 - \sin^{-1} \frac{4}{7})$;

(e) $\tan(\arcsin \frac{2}{3} + \arctan \frac{2}{3})$;

(f) $\tan(\frac{1}{2} \tan^{-1} \frac{5}{12})$;

(g) $\sin(\frac{1}{2} \arccos \frac{1}{8})$;

(h) $\cos(2 \arccos \frac{1}{3})$;

(i) $\sin(2 \cos^{-1} \frac{1}{4}) + \cos(2 \sin^{-1} \frac{1}{4})$;

(j) $\sin^{-1}\left(\sin \dfrac{\pi}{4}\right)$;

(k) $\cos^{-1}\left(\sin \dfrac{\pi}{6}\right)$;

(l) $\tan^{-1}\left(3 \tan \dfrac{\pi}{6}\right)$.

Historical Note. G. F. Bernhard Riemann (1826–1866) in his short life introduced ideas which influenced the development of mathematics in a profound way for a century. Besides his work in complex analysis where the notion of Riemann surface is fundamental, he developed principal concepts in differential geometry and integration.

Chapter VII

MATHEMATICAL INDUCTION

1. THE METHOD OF PROOF

In Section 1 of Chapter I we stated the Principle of Mathematical Induction. We shall study a method of proof which is closely connected with this principle. This method of proof is called: *proof by mathematical induction.* First we restate the principle.

I–1 Principle of Mathematical Induction
Suppose a collection of natural numbers is considered that has the properties:
    (a) *0 is in the collection;*
    (b) *whenever a is in the collection, a + 1 is also in the collection.*
Then this collection contains all natural numbers.

    Stated in a slightly different form, the conclusion above states: Then this collection of natural numbers is the collection of *all* natural numbers. There is no mystery about this principle. It is intuitively obvious since the natural numbers are obtained precisely by starting with 0 and adding 1. Thus the set of natural numbers is the collection consisting of 0, 0 + 1, (0 + 1) + 1, ((0 + 1) + 1) + 1, and so on.

    Notice that both conditions (a) and (b) are essential. Neither can be left out or be substantially changed. Notice also that it is not possible to formulate a similar simple statement which holds for the rational numbers or the real numbers. Only **N** can be described in this way.

In mathematics we frequently meet certain propositions that are of the form:

For all natural numbers n, such and such a statement involving n is true.

Here are three examples of statements of this type:

For all natural numbers n,

$$(1 + n)^2 \geq 1 + n^2. \tag{1}$$

For all natural numbers n,

$$0 + 1 + 2 + \cdots + n = \frac{n(n + 1)}{2}. \tag{2}$$

For all natural numbers n,

$$0^2 + 1^2 + 2^2 + \cdots + n^2 = \frac{n(n + 1)(2n + 1)}{6}. \tag{3}$$

Suppose we try to prove these statements. We are going to discover that the proof of (1) is particularly easy. The proof of (2) can be carried out by a clever person. However, (3) requires more than passing cleverness. Essentially it requires a particular technique of proof called *proof by mathematical induction*.

Before going to the proof of these three statements, let us examine them a little more carefully. Statement (1) is meaningful not merely for natural numbers but also for positive real numbers. Statements (2) and (3) have a meaning only if n is a natural number. Notice that (2) is considerably easier to face than the following variant:

Prove that there exists a polynomial p such that for all natural numbers n,

$$0 + 1 + 2 + \cdots + n = p(n). \tag{4}$$

Find that polynomial.

At least (2) tells you what the answer is.

Let us now prove (1). This is easy. We have

$$(1 + n)^2 = 1 + 2n + n^2 \geq 1 + n^2, \tag{5}$$

since $n \geq 0$.

As for (2), here is a clever proof that works in this special case. Write

$$0 + 1 + 2 + \cdots + (n - 2) + (n - 1) + n = a, \tag{6}$$

and underneath write

$$n + (n - 1) + (n - 2) + \cdots + 2 + 1 + 0 = a. \tag{7}$$

Then add (6) and (7) by columns. This gives

$$n + n + n + \cdots + n + n + n = 2a. \tag{8}$$

Since the number of terms in (8) is $n + 1$,

$$(n + 1)n = 2a, \tag{9}$$

and this gives the proof of (2).

You may wish to prove (3) by sheer cleverness. It is not impossible. We shall give a mechanical proof in just a moment. No cleverness required. Just the ability to drive a bulldozer forward.

To prove (2) means to show that the equation

$$0 + 1 + 2 + \cdots + n = \frac{n(n + 1)}{2} \tag{10}$$

holds for all natural numbers n. Let us try to check this. For $n = 0$, there is just one term on the left in (10), namely 0, and the right-hand side gives $0(0 + 1)/2 = 0$. Thus (10) is correct for $n = 0$.

For $n = 1$, (10) gives $0 + 1 = (1 \times 2)/2$, which is correct. For $n = 2$, (10) gives $0 + 1 + 2 = (2 \times 3)/2$, which again is correct. And so on. We are *convinced* by now that (10) is true for all natural numbers n but we have not yet proved it.

It is here that the Principle of Mathematical Induction steps to the fore. According to this principle, in order to prove (10) for all n, it is sufficient to know that it is true for $n = 0$ (this is proved just above) and that if it is true for the natural number a, it is also true for the natural number $a + 1$.

Assume that (10) holds for the special natural number a. We then have

$$0 + 1 + 2 + \cdots + a = \frac{a(a + 1)}{2}. \tag{11}$$

Add $a + 1$ to both sides of (11). This gives

$$0 + 1 + 2 + \cdots + a + a + 1 = \frac{a(a + 1)}{2} + a + 1. \tag{12}$$

Now,

$$\frac{a(a + 1)}{2} + a + 1 = \frac{a(a + 1) + 2(a + 1)}{2} = \frac{(a + 1)(a + 2)}{2}.$$

Thus

$$0 + 1 + 2 + \cdots + a + a + 1 = \frac{[(a + 1)(a + 1) + 1]}{2}. \tag{13}$$

Looking at (13), we see right away that it states that (10) is correct for $n = a + 1$. In other words, assuming the validity of (10) for the value a, we have shown its validity for $a + 1$. Thus, by the Principle of Mathematical Induction, (10) holds for all natural numbers n.

This is an example of a proof "by the method of mathematical induction."

Let us apply the same method of proof to (3). It is clear that the formula given in (3) is valid for $n = 0$ since the equation $0 = [0 \times (0 + 1)(0 + 1)]/6$ is true. It is also valid for $n = 1$ since $0^2 + 1^2 = (1 \times 2 \times 3)/6$. Writing $n = 2$ in (3) gives $0^2 + 1^2 + 2^2 = (2 \times 3 \times 5)/6$ which is again correct.

Assume that the formula is correct for a particular natural number a. Thus

$$0^2 + 1^2 + \cdots + a^2 = \frac{a(a + 1)(2a + 1)}{6} \tag{14}$$

is a true statement. Adding $(a + 1)^2$ to both sides of (14) gives

$$0^2 + 1^2 + \cdots + a^2 + (a + 1)^2 = \frac{a(a + 1)(2a + 1)}{6} + (a + 1)^2, \tag{15}$$

which is again a true statement. Now it can be seen that

$$\frac{a(a + 1)(2a + 1)}{6} + (a + 1)^2 = \frac{a(a + 1)(2a + 1) + 6(a + 1)^2}{6}$$

$$= \frac{(a + 1)[a(2a + 1) + 6(a + 1)]}{6} \tag{16}$$

$$= \frac{(a + 1)(2a^2 + 7a + 6)}{6}$$

$$= \frac{(a + 1)(a + 2)(2a + 3)}{6}.$$

Thus

$$0^2 + 1^2 + \cdots + a^2 + (a + 1)^2 = \frac{(a + 1)[(a + 1) + 1][2(a + 1) + 1]}{6}.$$

which is the formula given in (3) for $n = a + 1$. Thus assuming (3) to be a true statement for a natural number a, the statement (3) is also true for the natural number $a + 1$. Since (3) is true for the natural number 0, it follows from the Principle of Mathematical Induction that (3) is true for all natural numbers.

In Chapter I we proved that for all natural numbers n, we have $2^n > n$. The proof there given was based on the Well-Ordering Principle. It is essentially equivalent to a proof by induction (see Exercise 8).

A final word about the way we have written our formulas. In (2), the expression $0 + 1 + 2 + \cdots + n$ could equally well have been written $1 + 2 + \cdots + n$. In proving the required formula by induction some of us may feel more comfortable if we actually check it for $n = 0, 1, 2$, and even 3 before embarking on the second and difficult part of the proof.

Furthermore, there are variations that can be given on the induction principle. Suppose we wish to prove a formula for all $n \geq 5$. Then all that is necessary is to show that

(a) the formula holds for $n = 5$;
(b) whenever the formula holds for a number a, it holds for $a + 1$.

Thus in an induction process, we should feel relaxed about starting where we want. If the formula does not seem to have much meaning for $n = 0$, we pass on to $n = 1$.

Exercises VII.1.a

1. Prove that for every natural number $n \geq 1$, the following identities hold. A star is placed in front of problems where a second proof is available to the student.

(a)* $1 + 3 + 5 + \cdots + (2n - 1) = n^2$;

(b)* $2 + 4 + 6 + \cdots + 2n = n(n + 1)$;

(c)* $\dfrac{1}{2} + \dfrac{1}{2^2} + \cdots + \dfrac{1}{2^n} = 1 - \dfrac{1}{2^n}$;

(d) $\dfrac{1}{1 \cdot 2} + \dfrac{1}{2 \cdot 3} + \cdots + \dfrac{1}{n(n + 1)} = \dfrac{n}{n + 1}$;

(e)* $2 + 2^2 + 2^3 + \cdots + 2^n = 2^{n+1} - 2$;

(f)* $1 + r + r^2 + \cdots + r^n = \dfrac{1 - r^{n+1}}{1 - r}$, $r \neq 1$;

(g) $1^3 + 2^3 + \cdots + n^3 = (1 + 2 + \cdots + n)^2$;

(h) $1 \cdot 3 + 2 \cdot 4 + \cdots + n(n + 2) = \dfrac{n(n + 1)(2n + 7)}{6}$;

(i) $1^3 + 2^3 + 3^3 + \cdots + n^3 = \dfrac{n^2(n + 1)^2}{4}$;

(j) $\left(1 - \dfrac{1}{4}\right)\left(1 - \dfrac{1}{9}\right)\cdots\left(1 - \dfrac{1}{n^2}\right) = \dfrac{n + 1}{2n}$, $(n \geq 2)$;

(k) $\dfrac{1}{3} + \dfrac{1}{15} + \cdots + \dfrac{1}{4n^2 - 1} = \dfrac{n}{2n + 1}$.

2. Prove that for every natural number $n \geq 1$,

(a) $n(n + 1)(n + 2)$ is divisible by 6;

(b) $(1 + t)^n \geq 1 + nt$, t real, $t > -1$;

(c) $2^{n-1} \leq 1 \cdot 2 \cdot 3 \cdots n$;

(d) $\sin t + \sin 2t + \cdots + \sin nt = \dfrac{\sin \frac{1}{2}(n + 1)t \sin \frac{1}{2}nt}{\sin \frac{1}{2}t}$;

(e) $\cos t + \cos 2t + \cdots + \cos nt = \dfrac{\cos \frac{1}{2}(n + 1)t \sin \frac{1}{2}nt}{\sin \frac{1}{2}t}$;

(f) $u^n - v^n$ is divisible by $u - v$;

(g) $0 < a < b$ implies $a^n < b^n$;

(h) $|a_1 + a_2 + \cdots + a_n| \leq |a_1| + |a_2| + \cdots + |a_n|$;

(i) $(1 - a_1)(1 - a_2) \cdots (1 - a_n) > 1 - a_1 - \cdots - a_n$, where $0 < a_1 < 1, \cdots, 0 < a_n < 1, n \geq 2$.

3. Give an example of a formula involving n which is valid for $n = 0$ but for which it is impossible to pass from n to $n + 1$. (In other words, the first part of the induction proof goes through but the second does not.)

4. Give an example of a formula involving n which is false for $n = 0$ but for which the second part of the induction procedure can be carried out.

5. Describe four distinct sets of natural numbers such that 0 is in the set and if a is in the set, so is $a + 2$. How many such sets are there?

6. Describe all sets of natural numbers such that 5 is in the set and such that if a is in the set, so is $a + 1$.

7. What is the smallest set of natural numbers such that 0 and 1 are in the set, and such that if a is in the set, so is $5a$? What is the largest set with that property?

8. Prove by mathematical induction that for each natural number n, $2^n > n$. Refer to the proof using the Well-Ordering Principle given in Chapter I, Section 1. Compare the two proofs.

9. Consider the formula: $1 - 1 + 1 - 1 \cdots = 0$ where there are n terms on the left. Prove that the formula is valid for $n = 0$. Prove that if the formula holds for $n = k$, it holds for $n = k + 2$ but is false for $n = k + 1$.

10. Prove that the polynomial $n(n - 1)(n - 2)$ equals 0 for $n = 0, 1, 2$ but $\neq 0$ for any other values. Thus given any natural number k, find a polynomial in n, $p(n)$, such that $p(n) = 0$ for $n = 0, 1, 2, \cdots, k$ but $p(n) \neq 0$ for any other value of k. How does this help us to understand induction processes?

11. A puzzle handed down with many variations from antiquity goes as follows. Suppose you have a choice of receiving one of the following: (a) 1,000,000 tons of wheat; (b) a checkerboard holding 2 grains of wheat on the first square, 4 grains on the second square, 8 on the third, and so on. Which should you take so as to become wheat rich? Assume that there are 10,000 grains of wheat in a pound. There are 2000 pounds in a ton and 64 squares in a checkerboard. Use formula 1(e) and use logs to get an idea of the relative sizes of your numbers.

2. THE BINOMIAL THEOREM

The Binomial Theorem is concerned with the expression

$$(x + y)^n, \tag{1}$$

where n is a natural number. Let us calculate the value of $(x + y)^n$ for a few values of n.

$$(x + y)^0 = 1;$$
$$(x + y)^1 = x + y;$$
$$(x + y)^2 = x^2 + 2xy + y^2;$$
$$(x + y)^3 = x^3 + 3x^2y + 3xy^2 + y^3;$$
$$(x + y)^4 = x^4 + 4x^3y + 6x^2y^2 + 4xy^3 + y^4.$$

For example, for the case $n = 4$,

$$(x + y)^4 = (x + y)(x + y)(x + y)(x + y).$$

In multiplying this out, terms in x^4, x^3y, x^2y^2, xy^3, and y^4 are obtained. To find out the coefficient of xy^3 above, it is necessary to count the number of times it occurs. This number is clearly 4 because in the multiplication the term x can be selected from a parenthesis just once and then only the term y must be selected in the other parentheses. This choice of parenthesis for x can be made in four ways. This gives 4 for the coefficient of xy^3. The coefficients of x^4 and of y^4 are obviously 1. The coefficient of x^2y^2 is not so immediately found.

If instead of $(x + y)^4$, we had considered $(x + y)^9$, the situation would have been much more complicated. Obviously there are terms x^4y^5 in the expansion of $(x + y)^9$. But how many are there?

The Binomial Theorem gives a formula for the expanded form of $(x + y)^n$ in the general case and establishes that formula. Since

$$(x + y)^n = (x + y)(x + y) \cdots (x + y) \quad (n \text{ factors}), \tag{2}$$

it is clear how to go about getting the product expansion. Select from each parenthesis either an x or a y. Then multiply them. If y is selected r times and x is selected $n - r$ times, this gives the term

$$x^{n-r}y^r, \quad 0 \leq r \leq n. \tag{3}$$

Since these choices for y and therefore also the choices for x can be made in many ways, the number of terms (3) that can be so obtained has to be counted. It is clear that the coefficient of $x^{n-r}y^r$ after the counting operation has taken place will be a natural number. It is the purpose of the Binomial Theorem to state precisely what the coefficient is.

VII–1 Binomial Theorem
For all real numbers x and y and for each natural number n,

$$(x + y)^n = x^n + nx^{n-1}y + \frac{n(n - 1)}{2} x^{n-2}y^2 + \cdots$$
$$+ \frac{n!}{r!\,(n - r)!} x^{n-r}y^r + \cdots + nxy^{n-1} + y^n. \tag{4}$$

Note that the intent of the theorem is to state that for all r, $0 \leq r \leq n$, the coefficient of $x^{n-r}y^r$ is

$$\frac{n!}{r!\,(n-r)!}.\tag{5}$$

Here, as will be remembered, for any natural number $m \geq 1$, the symbol $m!$ (m factorial) is defined by

$$m! = 1 \cdot 2 \cdot 3 \cdots (m-1)m.\tag{6}$$

For $r = 1$, formula (5) gives n as indicated in (4). For $r = n - 1$, formula (5) again gives n as desired.

For $r = 0$ and $r = n$ the expression in (5) is somewhat puzzling because it contains the factor $0!$. We shall see in a moment that for this case the coefficient (5) is 1 as a result of a definition; thus once more, this agrees with what appears in (4).

For reasons of convenience (in fact, of great convenience) we define

$$0! = 1.\tag{7}$$

Thus $n!$ is defined for all natural numbers n. We repeat that formula (5) now gives the value 1 for $r = 0$ and $r = n$, and that this agrees with what appears in (4).

Now we proceed to prove the theorem. This will be done by mathematical induction. Note first of all that there are $n + 1$ terms in the right-hand side of (4). Start the induction with the value $n = 1$ (leave aside $n = 0$, which is a bit slippery and not illuminating). The left-hand side of the equation in (4) is $(x + y)$. The right-hand side has $n + 1$ terms in it, that is, two terms: the first one x and the last one y [be sure to substitute the value $r = 0$ and 1 in (5)].

In order to get the real flavor of the formula, try $n = 2$. The left-hand side of the equation in (4) gives $(x + y)^2$. The right-hand side has the three terms

$$\frac{2!}{0!\,2!}\,x^2 + \frac{2!}{1!\,1!}\,xy + \frac{2!}{2!\,0!}\,y^2.\tag{8}$$

This reduces to $x^2 + 2xy + y^2$, the correct answer. As a good exercise in handling factorials, try the cases $n = 3, 4$, and 5. This takes care of the first part of the induction proof. In fact it takes care of it very well.

We now consider the second part of the induction proof. We assume that formula (4) is correct for $n = k$. We shall then prove it correct for $n = k + 1$.

By hypothesis, Equation (4) is assumed correct for $n = k$. We take this correct equation and multiply both sides by $(x + y)$. This gives $(x + y)^{k+1}$ on the left-hand side. On the right-hand side, it gives a seemingly complicated expression from which we have to pull out the quantities that interest us.

What interests us is the coefficient of $x^{k+1-r}y^r$. What has to be proved is that this coefficient is the one given in (5) with n replaced by $k + 1$. In other words, it must be shown that

$$\text{the coefficient of } x^{k+1-r}y^r \text{ is } \frac{(k+1)!}{r!\,(k+1-r)!}. \tag{9}$$

Now there are two ways of obtaining a term of the form $x^{k+1-r}y^r$ when multiplying $(x+y)^k$ by $(x+y)$. One is to multiply the term $x^{k-r}y^r$ by x. The other is to multiply the term $x^{k+1-r}y^{r-1}$ by y. Therefore, the correct coefficient for our proof is the sum of the two coefficients in question. We write these out.

$$\text{The coefficient of } x^{k-r}y^r \text{ is } \frac{k!}{r!\,(k-r)!}; \tag{10}$$

$$\text{the coefficient of } x^{k+1-r}y^{r-1} \text{ is } \frac{k!}{(r-1)!\,(k+1-r)!}. \tag{11}$$

Thus what has to be done is to add the two coefficients in (10) and (11) and to show that the coefficient in (9) is obtained. That is, it must be proved that

$$\frac{k!}{r!\,(k-r)!} + \frac{k!}{(r-1)!\,(k+1-r)!} = \frac{(k+1)!}{r!\,(k+1-r)!}. \tag{12}$$

The way to prove this is to change the terms on the left so that they look like the desired terms on the right. For example, we multiply top and bottom of the fractions on the left by $k+1$. This will give a $(k+1)!$ on top. There are other operations of a similar nature. The operations are shown below:

$$\frac{k!}{r!\,(k-r)!} = \frac{(k+1)!}{r!\,(k+1-r)!} \cdot \frac{k+1-r}{k+1}; \tag{13}$$

$$\frac{k!}{(r-1)!\,(k+1-r)!} = \frac{(k+1)!}{r!\,(k+1-r)!} \cdot \frac{r}{k+1}. \tag{14}$$

And now the question is: Is the sum of the two expressions in (13) and (14) equal to the expression on the right-hand side of (12)? The answer is obviously "yes." The reason for this is that

$$\frac{k+1-r}{k+1} + \frac{r}{k+1} = 1. \tag{15}$$

This finishes the proof.

It should be noted that for the coefficient (5) we can write

$$\frac{n!}{r!\,(n-r)!} = \frac{n(n-1)(n-2)\cdots(n-r+1)}{1\cdot 2\cdot 3\cdots(r-1)r}. \tag{16}$$

This is due to the fact that

$$n! = [n(n-1)\cdots(n-r+1)]\cdot(n-r)!. \tag{17}$$

This fact is useful in calculations.

Consider some simple applications of the theorem. Let us expand $(x-1)^5$. First write $(x-1)^5 = [x + (-1)]^5$ and then apply the expansion. This gives

$$(x-1)^5 = x^5 + 5x^4(-1) + \frac{5\cdot4}{1\cdot2}x^3(-1)^2 + \frac{5\cdot4\cdot3}{1\cdot2\cdot3}x^2(-1)^3$$

$$+ \frac{5\cdot4\cdot3\cdot2}{1\cdot2\cdot3\cdot4}x(-1)^4 + \frac{5\cdot4\cdot3\cdot2\cdot1}{1\cdot2\cdot3\cdot4\cdot5}(-1)^5 \tag{18}$$

$$= x^5 - 5x^4 + 10x^3 - 10x^2 + 5x - 1.$$

Suppose now we wish to obtain the expansion of $(x + 2y)^3$. Thus,

$$(x+2y)^3 = x^3 + 3x^2(2y) + \frac{3\cdot2}{1\cdot2}x(2y)^2 + \frac{3\cdot2\cdot1}{1\cdot2\cdot3}(2y)^3 \tag{19}$$

$$= x^3 + 6x^2y + 12xy^2 + 8y^3.$$

An easy consequence of the Binomial Theorem is given below.

VII–2 Corollary

For any natural number n,

$$1 + n + \frac{n(n-1)}{2} + \cdots + \frac{n!}{r!\,(n-r)!} + \cdots + \frac{n(n-1)}{2} + n + 1 = 2^n.$$

$$\tag{20}$$

PROOF: Set $x = 1$, $y = 1$ in the binomial expansion (4).

PROBLEM: Calculate $(1.02)^{17}$.

SOLUTION: Set $1.02 = 1 + x$ where $x = 0.02$ and apply the binomial expansion. If the precise answer is wanted, we have to calculate all of the 18 terms, which is quite a task. Note however, that all the terms involving high powers of 0.02 are small. For that reason the number $(1.02)^{17}$ is given rather accurately by using the first few terms of the binomial expansion. Thus we obtain,

$$(1 + 0.02)^{17} = 1 + 17 \times 0.02 + \frac{17 \times 16}{2}(0.02)^2$$

$$+ \frac{17 \times 16 \times 15}{6}(0.02)^3 + \cdots \tag{21}$$

$$= 1 + 0.34 + 0.0544 + 0.00544 + 0.0003808 + \cdots$$

$$\approx 1.400.$$

Exercises VII.2.a

1. Expand

(a) $(x + y)^8$;

(b) $(1 + x)^6$;

(c) $(2x - 3y)^5$;

(d) $\left(\dfrac{x}{y} + \dfrac{y}{x}\right)^4$;

(e) $(\tfrac{1}{3} + \tfrac{2}{3})^4$;

(f) $\left(\dfrac{x}{2} - 3y\right)^5$;

(g) $(\sqrt{x} + \sqrt{y})^4$;

(h) $\left(x - \dfrac{1}{x}\right)^6$.

2. Calculate $(1 + 1/n)^n$ for $n = 1, 2, 3, 4$.

3. Calculate the approximate value of

(a) $(0.97)^{10}$;

(b) $(103)^8$ [*Hint*: $103 = 100(1 + 0.03)$];

(c) $(51)^7$;

(d) $(\cos 0.0349)^{10}$.

4. Assuming that $p + q = 1$, write down the expansion of $(p + q)^n$ for $n = 1, 2, 3, 4$. Verify that the sum is 1 if $p = q = \tfrac{1}{2}$ and $n = 1, 2, 3$; if $p = \tfrac{1}{6}, q = \tfrac{5}{6}$, and $n = 2$.

5. Expand

(a) $(e^x - e^{-x})^4$;

(b) $(a + b + c)^3$ (substitute $d = b + c$);

(c) $(\sin t + \cos t)^5$;

(d) $(a + b + c + d)^2$.

6. (a) Prove that the signs in the expansion of $(a - b)^n$ are alternately positive and negative.

(b) Verify from the expansion that $(1 - 1)^n = 0$, in the case where n is odd. The case where n is even gives a new relation similar to that in Corollary VII–2.

Historical Note. The Binomial Theorem for integral exponents (the one proved above) is very old. The coefficients had been studied by the Italian mathematician Geronimo Cardano (1501–1576), and the French mathematician Blaise Pascal (1623–1662). The English mathematician Isaac Newton (1642–1727), extended the theorem to nonintegral exponents. Here one is interested in $(1 + x)^n$. The theorem for this case gives an infinite series.

3. THE EXPONENTIAL FUNCTION

As was seen in Chapter V, the exponential function exp satisfies the functional equation

$$\exp(u + v) = \exp(u) \cdot \exp(v). \tag{1}$$

The proof given there includes the following step requiring an induction argument, which we shall now examine: Writing the power series in the product $\exp(u) \cdot \exp(v)$ we have [see Equation (15), Chapter V, Section 4],

$$\exp(u) \cdot \exp(v) =$$

$$\left(1 + u + \frac{u^2}{2!} + \cdots + \frac{u^q}{q!} + \cdots\right)\left(1 + v + \frac{v^2}{2!} + \cdots + \frac{v^r}{r!} + \cdots\right).$$

This product is to be expanded and the resulting terms are to be arranged in an order that will now be indicated. The terms in the product in (2) are of the form $u^q v^r / q!\, r!$. Now select a fixed integer n and bring together all terms of this type such that $q + r = n$. This gives $q = n - r$ and hence the above term becomes $u^{n-r} v^r / (n - r)!\, r!$. Substituting the values $r = 0, 1, \cdots, n - 1$, n in the above and summing as is required by (2), gives

$$\frac{u^n}{n!} + \frac{u^{n-1}v}{(n - 1)!} + \cdots + \frac{u^{n-r}v^r}{(n - r)!r!} + \cdots + \frac{uv^{n-1}}{(n - 1)!} + \frac{v^n}{n!}. \qquad (3)$$

This in turn may be written in the form

$$\frac{1}{n!}\left(u^n + nu^{n-1}v + \cdots + \frac{n!}{(n - r)!r!} u^{n-r}v^r + \cdots + nuv^{n-1} + v^n\right). \qquad (4)$$

However, the quantity that is in parenthesis in (4) is precisely $(u + v)^n$ [see Equation (4) of Section 2]. This shows that by expanding, rearranging, and collecting terms, we obtain

$$\left(1 + u + \frac{u^2}{2!} + \cdots + \frac{u^q}{q!} + \cdots\right)\left(1 + v + \frac{v^2}{2!} + \cdots + \frac{v^r}{r!} + \cdots\right)$$

$$= 1 + (u + v) + \frac{(u + v)^2}{2!} + \cdots + \frac{(u + v)^n}{n!} + \cdots. \qquad (5)$$

This completes the proof of (1).

To see the above argument a little more clearly, consider the case $n = 5$. Then the powers $u^q v^r$ for which $q + r = 5$ are $u^5, u^4v, u^3v^2, u^2v^3, uv^4$, and v^5. These appear in (5) with the coefficients

$$\frac{u^5}{5!}, \quad \frac{u^4}{4!} \cdot \frac{v}{1!}, \quad \frac{u^3}{3!} \cdot \frac{v^2}{2!}, \quad \frac{u^2}{2!} \cdot \frac{v^3}{3!}, \quad \frac{u}{1!} \cdot \frac{v^4}{4!}, \quad \frac{v^5}{5!}. \qquad (6)$$

Summing these after factoring out the constant $1/5!$, we obtain

$$\frac{1}{5!}\left(u^5 + \frac{5!}{4!\,1!}u^4v + \frac{5!}{3!\,2!}u^3v^2 + \frac{5!}{2!\,3!}u^2v^3 + \frac{5!}{1!\,4!}uv^4 + v^5\right) = \frac{1}{5!}(u + v)^5. \qquad (7)$$

Of course, the whole point of the argument is to be able to recognize that the expression in (4) equals $(1/n!)(u + v)^n$. This recognition is possible by virtue of the Binomial Theorem, and the Binomial Theorem was established by an induction argument.

Exercises VII.3.a

1. Write down the first few terms of the binomial expansion of $(1 + 1/n)^n$ where n is a large natural number. Compare each of the first four terms with the corresponding terms in the expression for e given in Chapter V, Section 4, Equation (17). Calculate their differences for $n = 10$. Calculate their differences for each of the first five terms and $n = 100$. What conclusion are you thinking of reaching?

2. Let x be any positive rational number and let n be a large natural number so chosen that nx is a natural number. Then, assuming as known that $e \approx (1 + 1/n)^n$, we have $(1 + 1/n)^{nx} \approx e^x$. Write down the first few terms of the binomial expression for $(1 + 1/n)^{nx}$ and also the series expansion for e^x. Compare the first few terms.

3. In Exercise 2, write $m = nx$. This gives a new approximation for e^x in terms of powers of $(1 + x/m)$. Write down the first few terms of the binomial expansion of $(1 + x/m)^m$ and compare it with the series expansion of e^x.

Chapter VIII

TRIGONOMETRY

1. ANGLES AND TRIANGLES

Angles have been discussed earlier (see Definition VI–1). The essential features that enter into the concept of angle are these:

Consider a fixed point O and a fixed half-line or ray OP_0. A second ray OP_1 is produced by a certain amount of winding around the point O, starting in the position OP_0. The resulting figure, consisting of the two rays OP_0, OP_1 and of the amount of winding, is called an angle. The ray OP_0 is called the initial side of the angle; the ray OP_1 is called the terminal side of the angle; the point O is called the vertex of the angle. See Figure VIII.1.

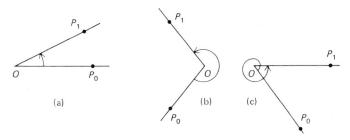

Figure VIII.1

Angles are frequently represented by lower-case letters of the Greek alphabet α, β, γ, θ, $\cdots$ (read: alpha, beta, gamma, theta, $\cdots$).

The winding can take place in two directions: clockwise (like the hands of a clock) and counterclockwise (opposite to the hands of a clock). Counterclockwise angles have a positive measure; clockwise angles have a negative measure (see the discussion in Chapter VI, Section 1).

The measure of an angle means the amount of winding which is involved in the definition of the angle. Thus we can consider angles whose measure is $30°$, -2 revolutions, 1 right angle, and $2\pi/3$ radians. If the angle α has a measure of $30°$, we say for short "α is an angle of $30°$" (or: α is a $30°$ angle) instead of saying "α is an angle whose measure is $30°$." Two angles are defined to be equal providing they have the same measure. Thus, if α and β are $30°$ angles, $\alpha = \beta$. In other words, the symbol α is used interchangeably for an angle and for its measure.

Consider a geometric configuration consisting of two rays emanating from the same point. Such a configuration is shown in Figure VIII.2(a). There are many ways to complete the configuration so that it becomes an angle. We must choose one of the two rays to be the initial ray; this automatically determines the terminal ray. There is then the question of setting down the amount of winding that carries us from the initial side to the terminal side. As we already know, there are many choices possible for this amount of winding. Two such are shown in Figure VIII.2(b) and (c).

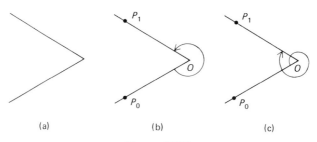

(a)   (b)   (c)

Figure VIII.2

In the configuration of Figure VIII.2(a), there is precisely one way of selecting an initial side and an amount of winding so that the measure of the angle lies between $0°$ and $180°$. This point is illustrated in Figure VIII.3. This fact is of great importance in connection with the study of triangles and polygons.

A triangle is the geometric configuration consisting of three points A, B, C lying in a plane; of the three line segments $\overline{AB}$, $\overline{BC}$, $\overline{AC}$ which they determine; and of the three angles which they determine. (The symbol $\overline{AB}$ is used interchangeably for the segment from A to B and for its length.) Notice that each point is the vertex of an angle. For example, A is the vertex of an angle whose initial and terminal sides pass through B and C. There is a unique way

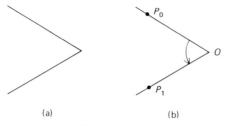

Figure VIII.3

of selecting the initial and terminal sides and of selecting the amount of winding so that each of the angles in the triangle has a measure between 0° and 180°. We shall assume that this has been done. In what follows, it will be assumed that the points *A*, *B*, *C* are not collinear (do not lie on the same line). Some triangles are shown in Figure VIII.4. In each case, curved arrows indicate the selection made of the initial side, the terminal side, and the amount of rotation. Check that each angle has a measure that is positive and less than 180°.

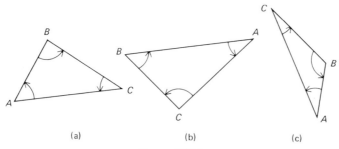

Figure VIII.4

A given triangle *ABC* has associated with it several quantities: the lengths of the three sides, $\overline{AB}$, $\overline{BC}$, $\overline{AC}$, the measures of the three angles at *A*, *B*, *C*, its area, and so on. In order to fix the triangle it is not necessary to give each of these quantities. For example, if two angles and the length of one side of a triangle are given, the triangle is completely determined. Similarly, if the lengths of the three sides are given, the triangle is completely determined. (Remember here that the sum of any two lengths exceeds the third.)

Trigonometry, in its narrow sense, is that branch of mathematics which studies the interrelations between the various quantities of a triangle. For example, any formula relating the sides and the angles is a formula of trigonometry. At least two such identities, called *laws*, will be derived later. If we are given a triangle by being told the magnitude of some of its sides and angles, to *solve* the triangle means to calculate the remaining quantities. The problem is considered completely worked out when the three sides and three angles have been calculated.

To facilitate the work, let us agree on a simple nomenclature. If the vertices of a triangle are A, B, C, then the side opposite A is called a, that opposite B is called b, and that opposite C is called c. Also the angle at A is denoted by α, that at B by β, that at C by γ. The notation is indicated in Figure VIII.5.

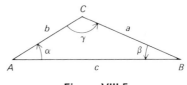

Figure VIII.5

Consider some examples.

EXAMPLE 1:   Solve the triangle ABC for which $a = 1$, $b = 1$, and $\gamma = 90°$.

SOLUTION: First, make a diagram. Then note that since $a = b$, $\alpha = \beta$. By Equation (1) below we have $\alpha = 45°$. The Pythagorean Theorem gives $c = \sqrt{2}$.

EXAMPLE 2:   Solve the triangle ABC for which $a = 2$, $c = 2$, and $\alpha = 30°$.

SOLUTION: As a first step make a reasonably careful diagram (preferably drawn free-hand). This diagram should, like all good diagrams, give constructive ideas and eliminate the possibility of making gross errors. See Figure VIII.6. It is immediately obvious that $\gamma = 30°$ since the sides a and c are equal. Furthermore, since for any triangle,

$$\alpha + \beta + \gamma = 180°, \tag{1}$$

we obtain $\beta = 180° - \alpha - \gamma = 180° - 60° = 120°$.

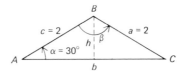

Figure VIII.6

To obtain b, draw the perpendicular h from B to the side $\overline{AC}$. This perpendicular bisects the side $\overline{AC}$ and also bisects the angle β. Simple considerations concerning relations in the well-known (30°, 60°) right triangle show that $h = 1$ and $b/2 = \sqrt{3}$. Thus $b = 2\sqrt{3}$. This completes the solution.

These two examples, along with some simple variations, provide a complete list of triangles that can be solved on the basis of a knowledge of elementary geometry alone. To proceed further, we must call upon our knowledge of the circular functions developed in Chapter VI; also, we must have access to tables of these functions. The solution of one or two exercises below will be simplified after reading the next section.

Exercises VIII.1.a

1. Make reasonably careful free-hand drawings of the triangles given below. Estimate the size of the unknown angles and sides. Make a new drawing with ruler and protractor and once more measure the unknown angles and sides.

   (a) $a = 3$, $b = 4$, $c = 5$;   (b) $\alpha = 20°$, $\beta = 30°$, $c = 2$;
   (c) $\alpha = 50°$, $b = 4$, $c = 3$;   (d) $\alpha = 30°$, $a = 1.5$, $c = 2$.

2. Solve the triangles given below.

   (a) $b = 3$, $\alpha = 120°$, $\beta = \gamma$;   (b) $c = 8$, $a = 4\sqrt{2}$, $\gamma = 90°$;
   (c) $b = 7$, $\alpha = 60°$, $\beta = 60°$;   (d) $a = 8$, $b = 4\sqrt{2}$, $\gamma = 45°$;
   (e) $c = 1$, $\alpha = 15°$, $\gamma = 90°$.

3. A square is inscribed in a circle of radius 5. Find the edge of the square. A circle is inscribed in this square and a second square is inscribed in the smaller circle. Find the area of this second square.

4. Calculate the ratio of the area of a regular hexagon to the area of the circle that circumscribes it.

5. A regular octagon is inscribed in a circle of radius 4. Find the length of the side and also the radius of the inscribed circle. Use no tables. Express the result in terms of radicals.

6. Show how to find the side of a regular pentagon inscribed in a circle of radius r without referring to the tables. (See Exercise 6 in Chapter VI, Section 6.)

2. RIGHT TRIANGLES

Let ABC be a right triangle. Suppose that the angle at C is the right angle. It is possible to pass rectangular axes, which will be called (u, v) axes, in such a way that the origin of the coordinate system is the point B, the point C lies on the positive side of the u-axis, and the point A has both coordinates positive. Figure VIII.7 indicates the coordinates of the three points A, B, C for this choice.

We now give a convention that will save a great deal of time in writing formulas and in making statements. Like all conventions, its meaning should

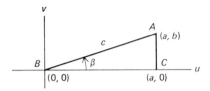

Figure VIII.7

be completely understood so that it will not lead to errors or misunderstandings. The convention will now be described.

We have seen that the circular functions are defined for real numbers and have real values. Thus the symbol cos x means the value of the cosine function for the real number x. We have seen how to associate an angle to x, namely the angle whose measure is x radians. If α is an angle *we shall now agree* to write sin α, cos α, and so on, instead of sin x, cos x, and so on, where x is the measure in radians of α. Thus throughout this chapter we shall act as if the circular functions were defined for angles. In a similar way, we shall write sin $43°$, cos $43°$ instead of sin x, cos x where x is the radian measure of the angle whose degree measure is 43. Thus, in view of this agreement, an equation such as sin $30° =$ sin $\pi/6$ is meaningful and correct. The student may wish to reread Chapter VI, Section 2 where the relations that the circular functions have to angles are discussed.

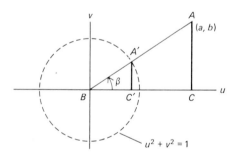

Figure VIII.8

Let β be an acute angle, that is, suppose $0 < \beta < 90°$. In Figure VIII.8 find two similar right triangles ABC and $A'BC'$ having β as an acute angle. The triangles are placed in a coordinatized plane as was shown above in Figure VIII.7. Furthermore, it is assumed $\overline{BA'} = 1$, that is, the point A' lies on the circle $u^2 + v^2 = 1$. The point A has the coordinates (a, b) since the triangle ABC has sides a, b, and c. The coordinates of A' are (u, v) where $u = $ cos β and $v = $ sin β (this is the definition of the sine and cosine). Now by similar triangles

$$\frac{\overline{A'C'}}{\overline{A'B}} = \frac{\overline{AC}}{\overline{AB}} = \frac{b}{c}. \tag{1}$$

Since $\overline{A'B} = 1$ and $\overline{A'C'} = v = \sin \beta$, this gives

$$\sin \beta = \frac{b}{c}. \qquad (2)$$

Similarly,

$$\cos \beta = \frac{a}{c}. \qquad (3)$$

These formulas give the sine and the cosine of an acute angle in a right triangle in terms of the lengths of the sides a, b, c of that triangle. Notice that the sine of the angle is the ratio of the side opposite the angle over the hypotenuse. Thus for the sine and cosine of the angle α,

$$\sin \alpha = \frac{a}{c}, \qquad \cos \alpha = \frac{b}{c}. \qquad (4)$$

Another formula of value here is

$$\tan \alpha = \frac{a}{b}. \qquad (5)$$

This is immediately derivable from (4) plus the identity $\tan \alpha = \sin \alpha / \cos \alpha$.

We remind the reader of the Pythagorean Theorem: In a right triangle ABC with right angle at C,

$$c^2 = a^2 + b^2. \qquad (6)$$

The formulas above are just what is needed to solve right triangles. This will be seen by considering the examples below.

EXAMPLE 1: Let ABC be a right triangle (as usual, the right angle is at C!) for which $\alpha = 14°$ and $c = 5$. Find a, b, and β.

SOLUTION: First of all, obviously, $\alpha + \beta = 90°$, hence $\beta = 90° - 14° = 76°$. Next, since $\sin \alpha = a/c$, this gives

$$a = c \sin \alpha = 5 \cdot \sin 14°. \qquad (7)$$

Table V shows that $\sin 14° = 0.2419$; hence, $a = 5 \cdot 0.2419 \approx 1.21$. Similarly, since $\cos \alpha = b/c$,

$$b = c \cdot \cos \alpha = 5 \cdot \cos 14° = 5 \cdot 0.9703 \approx 4.85. \qquad (8)$$

See Figure VIII.9.

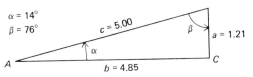

$\alpha = 14°$
$\beta = 76°$

$c = 5.00$
β
$a = 1.21$
α
A
$b = 4.85$
C

Figure VIII.9

EXAMPLE 2:   Let ABC be a right triangle for which $a = 3$ and $b = 4$. Find c, α, β.

SOLUTION: Since $c^2 = a^2 + b^2$, $c = \sqrt{9 + 16} = \sqrt{25} = 5$. Next, note that since $\sin \alpha = a/c$, this gives $\sin \alpha = 3/5 = 0.6000$. Looking up Table V gives $\alpha \approx 36° \ 50'$ (we have not used interpolation). Thus $\beta = 90° - \alpha \approx 53° \ 10'$. See Figure VIII.10.

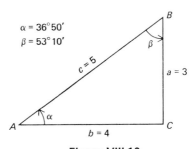

$\alpha = 36°50'$
$\beta = 53°10'$
$c = 5$
$a = 3$
$b = 4$
A C B
β α

Figure VIII.10

It will be noticed that the tables list angles in degrees and minutes, the smallest step being 10 minutes. We recall that there are 60 minutes to every degree. Thus $12° \ 15'$ can be expressed decimally (if one so wishes) as $12.25°$. We repeat here also that we are not using interpolation. The reason is that we are not interested at this point in securing highly accurate solutions. The emphasis is on understanding the methods used in solving triangles. It is good advice to spend a minimum of time carrying out the operations of multiplication and division.

We define the terms *angle of elevation* and *angle of depression* of an object. If a man is standing on a plain and sees a mountain on the horizon, the angle of elevation of the mountain top is the angle between a horizontal ray and a ray from the observer to the mountain top. See Figure VIII.11. Similarly, the angle of depression from the mountain top to the observer is the angle between a horizontal ray through the mountaintop and a ray to the object observed.

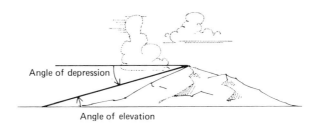

Angle of depression

Angle of elevation

Figure VIII.11

EXAMPLE 3:   At noon on March 21, a tourist in Paris measures the length of the shadow cast by the 300-meter Eiffel Tower and finds it to be 345 meters long. He claims that with a set of trigonometric tables, he can find the latitude of Paris. Show that he is correct and find the latitude.

SOLUTION: Let us find the angle of elevation α of the tower at the tip of the shadow. See Figure VIII.12. Clearly

$$\cot \alpha = \frac{345}{300} = 1.15.$$

The tables give $\alpha = 41°$.

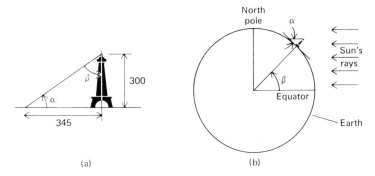

(a)   (b)

Figure VIII.12

On the twenty-first of March at noon, the sun is vertically overhead at the equator (latitude 0°) and is exactly on the horizon at the North Pole (latitude 90°). It is quite clear from the diagram that the desired latitude β is such that $\alpha + \beta = 90°$. Thus $\beta = 49°$.

The following example shows how to use logarithms and interpolations in the computations. It need not be read unless desired.

EXAMPLE 4:   Given the right triangle ABC with $\alpha = 22° \ 42'$ and $b = 47.65$, solve for c.

SOLUTION: Note that $\beta = 90° - 22° \ 42' = 67° \ 18'$. Next, since $\sin \beta = b/c$, we have $c = b/\sin \beta$. Thus [Chapter V, Section 6, Equation (7)]

$$\log_{10} c = \log_{10} b - \log_{10} \sin \beta.$$

First carry out the interpolation for $\log_{10} b$. (See Table IV.)

$$10 \begin{cases} 5 \begin{cases} \log_{10} 47.60 = 1.6776 \\ \log_{10} 47.65 = 1.6781 \end{cases} 5 \\ \log_{10} 47.70 = 1.6785 \end{cases} 9. \tag{9}$$

Next the computation of $\log_{10} \sin \beta$ gives (see Table VI),

$$10 \left\{ 8 \begin{cases} \log_{10} \sin 67° \ 10' = 0.9646 - 1 \\ \log_{10} \sin 67° \ 18' = 0.9650 - 1 \\ \log_{10} \sin 67° \ 20' = 0.9651 - 1 \end{cases} 4 \right\} 5. \tag{10}$$

Thus, we obtain

$$\begin{aligned} \log_{10} c &= \log_{10} 47.65 - \log_{10} \sin 67° \ 18' \\ &= 1.6781 - (0.9650 - 1) \\ &= 2.6781 - 0.9650 = 1.7131. \end{aligned} \tag{11}$$

The calculation of the interpolation required to find c can be carried out mentally. This gives $c = 51.65$. See Figure VIII.13.

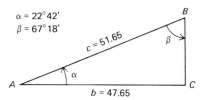

$\alpha = 22° 42'$
$\beta = 67° 18'$
$c = 51.65$
$b = 47.65$

Figure VIII.13

Exercises VIII.2.a

1. Find the unknown sides and angles of the right triangle ABC (right angle at C). Use no interpolation and no logarithms.

   (a) $a = 5, b = 12$;   (b) $\alpha = 40°, c = 100$;
   (c) $\alpha = 15°, a = 10$;   (d) $a = 15, c = 25$;
   (e) $c = 20, \beta = 35°$;   (f) $b = 50, \beta = 62°$;
   (g) $c = 10, \beta = 10°$;   (h) $b = 40, \beta = 50°$;
   (i) $a = 10, b = 17$.

2. Using logarithms and interpolation find

   (a) α and β given that $a = 31.62, c = 47.13$;
   (b) α and β given that $b = 17, c = 53$;
   (c) β and c given that $\alpha = 37° \ 42', b = 7642$;
   (d) α and β given that $a = 34.2, b = 16.1$;
   (e) β and a given that $\alpha = 68° \ 15', c = 0.1642$;
   (f) a and b given that $c = 127.31, \alpha = 17° \ 35'$.

3. A navigator on a ship measures from a height of 80 feet above water level the angle of depression of the horizon. Assuming that the radius of the earth is 4000 miles, can you calculate the answer he should get?

4. At the beginning of a trip to the moon, some astronauts measure the angle subtended by the sphere of the earth and find it to be 2° 20′. Find the distance from the earth to the spaceship at the instant the angle is measured (the radius of the earth is 4000 miles).

5. A man wishes to buy a piece of land in the form of a right triangle. The deed for the land gives the following dimensions: $\alpha = 60° 24′$, $\beta = 29° 36′$, $a = 294.1$, $b = 161.4$, $c = 326.7$. Is the deed correct? Assuming only one figure in error, which figure is it?

6. A regular nonagon (regular polygon with 9 sides) is inscribed in a circle of radius r. Find the length of the side.

7. Find the perimeter of a regular polygon of 360 sides which is inscribed in a circle of radius 1. What approximate value does this give for π? Is a four-place table of sines good enough for this problem?

3. LAWS OF SINES AND COSINES

There are several identities relating the sides a, b, c and the angles α, β, γ of an arbitrary triangle ABC. These identities are called *laws*. We shall derive two such laws in this section: the law of sines and the law of cosines. In turn, with the help of these laws it is possible to handle any triangle solution problem. The laws are very easy to obtain. The case of the sine law will be considered first.

We know that the sum of the three angles of a triangle is 180°. Thus,

$$\alpha + \beta + \gamma = 180°. \tag{1}$$

If one of the angles, say α, is obtuse (that is, $\alpha > 90°$), then the other two are acute ($\beta < 90°$, $\gamma < 90°$). In the proofs below, two diagrams are generally needed, one for a triangle with an obtuse angle and one for a triangle that has only acute angles. See Figure VIII.14. As is the case in all proofs in which several diagrams are possible, the steps in the proof apply simultaneously to all diagrams.

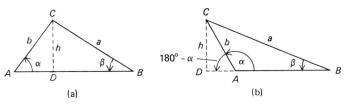

Figure VIII.14

Let ABC be any triangle. From the point C drop a perpendicular $\overline{CD}$ to the side opposite C. Let its length be h. This gives two right triangles ACD and BCD. We remind ourselves that for the angle α,

$$\sin \alpha = \sin(180° - \alpha), \qquad \cos \alpha = -\cos(180° - \alpha). \qquad (2)$$

(This can easily be seen from the identities of Chapter VI, Section 2. The identities there are written in radians: $\sin(\pi + x) = -\sin x$ and $\sin(-x) = -\sin x$. These give $\sin(\pi - x) = \sin[\pi + (-x)] = -\sin(-x) = \sin x$. (The case of the cosine is similar.)

Now, $\sin \beta = h/a$ and $\sin \alpha = h/b$. This gives

$$\frac{\sin \alpha}{\sin \beta} = \frac{h/b}{h/a} = \frac{a}{b}. \qquad (3)$$

This can be written in the form

$$\frac{\sin \alpha}{a} = \frac{\sin \beta}{b}. \qquad (4)$$

If a perpendicular is dropped from A to the side $\overline{BC}$, an equation similar to (4) is obtained, namely,

$$\frac{\sin \beta}{b} = \frac{\sin \gamma}{c}. \qquad (5)$$

This is the law of sines.

VIII–1 Law of Sines

In any triangle ABC, the sides a, b, c and the angles opposite them α, β, γ satisfy the identities

$$\frac{\sin \alpha}{a} = \frac{\sin \beta}{b} = \frac{\sin \gamma}{c}. \qquad (6)$$

Let us now derive the law of cosines. Except for lettering, we repeat Figure VIII.14, adding to it a set of coordinate axes, as shown in Figure VIII.15. The coordinates of B and C are also shown. To find the coordinates of B in Figure VIII.15(b) we use (2). The coordinates of C are obviously

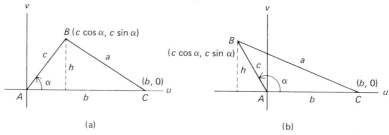

(a)   (b)

Figure VIII.15

$(b, 0)$. Those of B are $(c \cos \alpha, c \sin \alpha)$; this is easy to check. Then apply the distance formula to find the length of the segment $\overline{BC}$. This gives

$$a = \sqrt{(c \cos \alpha - b)^2 + (c \sin \alpha - 0)^2}. \tag{7}$$

Squaring and using the fact that $\sin^2 \alpha + \cos^2 \alpha = 1$, we obtain

$$\begin{aligned} a^2 &= c^2 \cos^2 \alpha - 2bc \cos \alpha + b^2 + c^2 \sin^2 \alpha \\ &= b^2 + c^2 - 2bc \cos \alpha. \end{aligned} \tag{8}$$

This is the law of cosines in one of its forms. We obtain the general formulation by appropriately permuting the letters.

VIII-2 Law of Cosines

In any triangle ABC, the sides a, b, c and the angles opposite them α, β, γ satisfy the identities

$$\begin{aligned} a^2 &= b^2 + c^2 - 2bc \cos \alpha; \\ b^2 &= a^2 + c^2 - 2ac \cos \beta; \\ c^2 &= a^2 + b^2 - 2ab \cos \gamma. \end{aligned} \tag{9}$$

Note that the law of sines contains formula (4) of Section 2 on right triangles. For if $\gamma = 90°$, $\sin \gamma = 1$ and the formula $\sin \alpha / a = \sin \gamma / c$ gives $\sin \alpha = a/c$.

Note also that the law of cosines contains the Pythagorean Theorem as a special case. For if $\gamma = 90°$, $\cos \gamma = 0$ and $c^2 = a^2 + b^2 - 2ab \cos \gamma = a^2 + b^2 - 2ab \cdot 0$; that is, $c^2 = a^2 + b^2$.

With the help of these two laws, any given triangle can be solved. We list below the given quantities in the various types of situations. The problem in each case is to find the remaining parts.

1. Given two angles and one side.
2. Given three sides.
3. Given two sides and one angle:
    (i) the angle lies between the two sides;
    (ii) the angle does not lie between the two sides.

The strategy for each of these cases will now be given. To indicate the difference between a given quantity and an unknown quantity, we shall circle the unknown. Thus $\textcircled{\alpha}$ stands for the unknown angle at A. As soon as it becomes known, we remove the circle.

PROBLEM 1: Given α, β, and c, find $\textcircled{\gamma}$, $\textcircled{a}$, and $\textcircled{b}$. First $\textcircled{\gamma} = 180° - \alpha - \beta$. Next find $\textcircled{a}$ and $\textcircled{b}$ from the sine law. The results are

$$\textcircled{a} = \frac{c \sin \alpha}{\sin \gamma}; \qquad \textcircled{b} = \frac{c \sin \beta}{\sin \gamma}.$$

PROBLEM 2: Given a, b, c, find $\textcircled{\alpha}$, $\textcircled{\beta}$, $\textcircled{\gamma}$. We apply the cosine law three times. This gives

$$\cos \textcircled{\alpha} = \frac{b^2 + c^2 - a^2}{2bc} \; ; \qquad \cos \textcircled{\beta} = \frac{c^2 + a^2 - b^2}{2ac} \; ;$$

$$\cos \textcircled{\gamma} = \frac{a^2 + b^2 - c^2}{2ab} \; .$$

From the tables we then find $\textcircled{\alpha}$, $\textcircled{\beta}$, $\textcircled{\gamma}$. If we wish, we may, after solving for $\textcircled{\alpha}$, use the sine law to find $\textcircled{\beta}$ and $\textcircled{\gamma}$. Thus,

$$\sin \textcircled{\beta} = \frac{b \sin \alpha}{a} \; ; \qquad \sin \textcircled{\gamma} = \frac{c \sin \alpha}{a} \; .$$

This leads to the values of $\textcircled{\beta}$ and $\textcircled{\gamma}$.

PROBLEM 3: (i) Given α, b, c, find $\textcircled{\beta}$, $\textcircled{\gamma}$, and $\textcircled{a}$. Apply the cosine law:

$$\textcircled{a}^2 = b^2 + c^2 - 2bc \cos \alpha.$$

Next the sine law yields

$$\sin \textcircled{\beta} = \frac{b \sin \alpha}{a} \; ; \qquad \sin \textcircled{\gamma} = \frac{c \sin \alpha}{a} \; .$$

Once more we find $\textcircled{\beta}$ and $\textcircled{\gamma}$.

PROBLEM 3: (ii) Given a, b, α, find $\textcircled{c}$, $\textcircled{\beta}$, $\textcircled{\gamma}$. The sine law gives

$$\sin \textcircled{\beta} = \frac{b \sin \alpha}{a} \; .$$

The table gives a value of $\textcircled{\beta}$. However $180° - \beta$ is also a solution by (2). Thus there may be two solutions to the problem. See below for a numerical example. Starting with β we quickly find $\textcircled{\gamma} = 180° - \alpha - \beta$. Finally $\textcircled{c}$ is obtained by the sine law. The case $180° - \beta$ proceeds similarly.

It may be asked in Problem 3(i) which value of $\textcircled{\beta}$ and $\textcircled{\gamma}$ is to be chosen after calculating $\sin \textcircled{\beta}$ and $\sin \textcircled{\gamma}$. A well-made diagram will help in making this decision. The puzzle can also be reasoned out without appealing to a diagram.

A few examples are given below to illustrate these methods. Note that the sine law involves multiplication and division; the cosine law involves these and addition also. If the data of the problem are given with high accuracy this will cause the computations to be very laborious. In case this arises, there are three possible procedures: To put the data into a computer; to develop further formulas that are a bit better to work with; to drop the undertaking with regret. Each of these methods has much to be said for it. We shall adopt the last.

EXAMPLE 1:   In a triangle ABC, $\alpha = 50°$, $\beta = 60°$, and $a = 10$. Find γ, b, and c.

SOLUTION: Obviously $\gamma = 180° - 50° - 60° = 70°$. Next, the sine law gives $b = a(\sin \beta/\sin \alpha) = 10(0.866/0.766) = 11.3$. The sine law gives also $c = a(\sin \gamma/\sin \alpha) = 10(0.940/0.766) = 12.3$.

EXAMPLE 2:   The sides of a triangle are $a = 4$, $b = 5$, $c = 6$. Find α, β, γ.

SOLUTION: By the cosine law, $a^2 = b^2 + c^2 - 2bc \cos \alpha$. Hence

$$16 = 25 + 36 - 60 \cos \alpha.$$

Hence, $60 \cos \alpha = 45$ and $\cos \alpha = 45/60 = 3/4 = 0.750$.   This   gives $\alpha = 41° 25'$.

Using the cosine law twice, once for β and once for γ, we obtain $\cos \beta = 27/48 = 9/16 = 0.5625$ and $\beta = 55° 46'$; and $\cos \gamma = 5/40 = 0.125$ and $\gamma = 82° 49'$. As a check, we add α, β, and γ, obtaining $180° 0'$. This shows that our calculations are reasonably accurate.

EXAMPLE 3:   (i) Of the triangle ABC it is known that $\alpha = 35°$, $b = 11$, $c = 10$. What are a, β, γ?

SOLUTION: First the cosine law gives $a^2 = b^2 + c^2 - 2bc \cos \alpha = 121 + 100 - 220 \times 0.819 = 221 - 180.2 = 40.8$. Hence $a = 6.4$. Next we obtain β and γ from the sine laws:

$$\sin \beta = \frac{b \sin \alpha}{a}$$

and

$$\sin \gamma = \frac{c \sin \alpha}{a}.$$

We shall not carry out the calculations here.

EXAMPLE 3:   (ii) Of the triangle ABC, it is known that $\alpha = 60°$, $a = 18$, and $b = 20$. What are the remaining parts?

SOLUTION: A diagram is instructive. (See Figure VIII.16.) It reveals immediately that there are two triangles satisfying the given conditions. The perpendicular CD of length $10\sqrt{3} = 17.3$ has also been indicated. Note that the sine law immediately gives the value of $\sin \beta$. However, a given value of the sine determines two angles, not one; their sum is $180°$.

Now, from the sine law, $\sin \beta = (b/a) \sin \alpha$ or $\sin \beta = (20/18) \times 0.866 = 0.962$. Table V gives $\beta = 74° 10'$. Another solution is $\beta' = 180° - 74° 10' = 105° 50'$. These two angles are indicated in Figure VIII.16. The values for γ and γ' are $\gamma = 45° 50'$ and $\gamma' = 14° 10'$. To find c it suffices to apply the sine law $c = a(\sin \gamma/\sin \alpha)$. Similarly for c'.

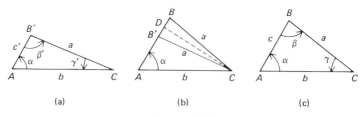

Figure VIII.16

Exercises VIII.3.a

1. In the triangle ABC with the given data solve for the missing parts.

(a) $a = 7, b = 5, c = 6$;
(b) $a = 10, \alpha = 20°, \beta = 60°$;
(c) $b = 10, c = 5, \alpha = 45°$;
(d) $a = 16, b = 30, c = 34$;
(e) $a = 30, b = 20, \alpha = 60°$;
(f) $a = 12, b = 20, \alpha = 30°$;
(g) $a = 17, b = 12, c = 21$;
(h) $a = 25, b = 40, \beta = 30°$;
(i) $a = 10, b = 12, \gamma = 45°$;
(j) $b = 18, c = 20, \beta = 48°$;
(k) $b = 9, c = 12, \beta = 80°$.

2. Two points A and B which lie at the same elevation on opposite sides of a steep mountain are to be connected by a tunnel. The mountain top C is on a vertical plane through AB. The angle of elevation of C from A is $22°$; from B it is $29°$. Given that AC has been determined to be 3.4 miles, find the length of the tunnel.

3. In trying to measure the distance of a star to the earth one may think of the following scheme. Let A and B be points on the earth's orbit about the sun which are 6 months apart, hence, $\overline{AB} = 180$ million miles. Let C denote the star. In principle, to obtain the distance of the star it is sufficient to measure the angles α and β very accurately, then use the fact that $\gamma = 180° - \alpha - \beta$ and the sine law. Assume that measurements give $\gamma = 1$ second $(=\frac{1}{60}$ minute$)$ and $\alpha = 85°$. Find the distance to the star. Use the fact that if x is small, $\sin x \approx x$. Thus the value of $\sin \gamma$ is equal to the radian measure of γ. Use the scientific notation in writing all numbers.

Given that light travels 186,000 miles per second find out whether it takes light from the star more or less than 1 year to reach us.

4. Three circles of radii 4, 5, and 6 respectively are externally tangent. Find the angles of the triangle which is formed by joining the three centers.

5. Solve the following triangles (use logarithms if this shortens the work).

(a) $a = 53.1$, $\alpha = 49° \, 15'$, $\beta = 31° \, 9'$;
(b) $a = 13.42$, $b = 22.45$, $\gamma = 61° \, 22'$;
(c) $a = 32.31$, $b = 24.62$, $c = 41.28$;
(d) $b = 213.1$, $c = 332.4$, $\gamma = 63° \, 19'$;
(e) $b = 0.325$, $c = 0.401$, $\beta = 29° \, 10'$.

6. Lavinia is told to construct a triangle ABC which has the property that $\alpha = 2\beta$ and $a = 2b$. She puzzles over the problem and reports that there is no such triangle. Is she correct? Prove your answer.

Chapter IX

POLYNOMIALS AND APPROXIMATION THEORY

1. APPROXIMATION BY POLYNOMIALS

Most of mathematics and all of applied mathematics is saturated with the notion of approximation. This fact is frequently not stressed and sometimes it is hardly even mentioned. However, it should be kept in mind as a directing force. It is always there and we should be ready to invoke it at any point. The manner in which one becomes involved in approximation is the following. We are interested in a certain problem either scientific or mathematical. The problem is given a mathematical form which calls for a solution. To carry out the solution is either impossible in the present state of knowledge, or it is impractical, or it calls for an expenditure of time and energy far beyond the value of an answer to the original problem. In some cases several of these evaluations are valid simultaneously. What is done at that stage? One approximates!

Let us give some examples that have a certain history. The Newtonian laws of motion and of gravitational attraction show how the sun and planets should move relative to one another. If it is assumed that there are only two bodies, the sun and one planet (approximation number one), it is easy to prove that the motion of the planet is elliptic about the sun. But if instead of considering just two bodies, we wish to consider three or four simultaneously, the sun, the earth, the moon, and Jupiter, then the mathematical solution is not at hand and various approximations must be introduced.

Another example will show why the solution to a problem, even if at hand, cannot be obtained for practical reasons. Everyone is interested in the weather, everyone talks about it, and the mathematicians do something about it. Conceptually, it is possible to write down differential equations whose solution will give the weather accurately for tomorrow and also the next day. However, obtaining the solution of these differential equations might take as much as several months. For obvious reasons, weather is not predicted by this method. We pay the price in accuracy but at least we get a forecast in time to use it in our decision processes.

An example of approximation in pure mathematics occurred in Chapter VII in the discussion of the Binomial Theorem. At the end of Section 2, we calculated $(1.02)^{17}$. The correct answer is given by expanding $(1 + 0.02)^{17}$ by the binomial formula and adding up the 18 terms so obtained. However, it was decided to settle for less than complete accuracy (in fact, a completely accurate answer would have been embarrassing). Thus it was decided to consider only the first few terms of the binomial expansion. This gave $(1.02)^{17} \approx 1.400$. Note that in order to indicate that this was an approximation, we wrote "$\approx$" instead of "$=$." We shall go back to examples much more general than this in the present section.

In Chapter III, Section 1, we discussed a most important type of approximation. It was entitled: The behavior of polynomials at infinity. It results from that discussion that a polynomial

$$f(x) = a_n x^n + a_{n-1} x^{n-1} + \cdots + a_0, \qquad a_n \neq 0$$

behaves very much like the polynomial

$$g(x) = a_n x^n$$

for large values of x. This is seen by the device of factoring out the term $a_n x^n$ from the expression for $f(x)$, giving

$$f(x) = a_n x^n \left(1 + \frac{a_{n-1}}{a_n x} + \cdots + \frac{a_0}{a_n x^n} \right),$$

and then noting that when $|x|$ is large, the second, third, $\cdots$ terms in the parenthesis above are small. Thus the parenthesis in the expression for $f(x)$ is *approximately* equal to 1 when x is large and therefore the polynomial f is *approximately* equal to the polynomial g.

In the present chapter, we shall be interested in approximations to f, not for large values of x, but for *small* values of x (close to 0).

Here are a few more examples of approximations which are familiar: Writing $\sqrt{2} = 0.1414$, $\pi = 3.1416$, $e = 2.71828$—all these are approximations. If higher accuracy is desired, it can be obtained, but at a price. The above are examples of approximations to numbers. At this stage, we are also aware of approximation of one curve by another curve. For example, we are ready to *approximate* to a circle by a regular inscribed polygon of 16 sides, or of 256 sides. Incidentally, a sophisticated approximator is ready to approximate to a circle by a regular inscribed polygon of 3 sides or 4 sides! In fact, a good approximator is one who (among other things) is ready to go out of his way to make bad approximations—to find out how bad they are.

All this points to the fact that all of us have had a fair amount of experience in approximation theory. However, except for his brief experience in Chapter III, and a passing exercise or two, this book has provided no experience in approximating one function by another function. This will be the type of approximation considered in this chapter. Thus the problem of approximation of functions is the following: Given a function f, approximate to f by a function g of a simpler type. Of course, everything depends on what one is looking for in a function. It is one thing to be interested in the function e^x. It is something quite different to be interested in the function e^x for small values of x. As an example along these lines, let us refer to Exercise 3 in VI.2.b. The purpose of the exercise is to show that for small values of x, $\sin x \approx x$. As the tables show, the approximation is phenomenally good for such values. However, it is no good at all for $x = \pi$, and it is hopeless for $x = 100$, or 10^{10}.

As was just said, in approximation theory for functions, we consider a function f which is complicated and wish to approximate to it by a function g which is simpler. We start out with the agreement that the simple functions are the polynomials. Thus, we are discussing *polynomial* approximation. Having made this decision, a whole new dimension (so to speak) is open to us. Polynomials have degrees: $n = 0, 1, 2, \cdots$, and hence, we can approximate by polynomials of degree 0, of degree 1, of degree 2, $\cdots$. Thus, for each degree there is an approximation problem. For example, given the degree 2 and the function exp, we can ask:

Which polynomial $g(x)$ of degree 2 or less best approximates $\exp(x)$ for small values of x?

The problem is precise and the solution is not easy. [It is $g(x) = 1 + x + x^2/2$.] The answer requires for its elaboration substantial knowledge of calculus. Similarly, the question:

Which polynomial $g(x)$ of degree 1 or less approximates most closely the function $\sin x$ for small values of x? The answer here is $g(x) = x$. Calculus books usually have quasiproofs of this fact; however, these proofs appeal more to the eye than to the mind. The real proof calls for high altitude performance.

In this chapter, we shall be concerned with the approximation of polynomials by polynomials. Thus the questions asked will be:

Given a polynomial $f(x)$, find the polynomials $g(x)$ of degree at most 0, at most 1, at most 2, $\cdots$ which approximate most closely to $f(x)$. Each of these questions will be answered completely.

Let us start with a numerical example. Given

$$f(x) = 1 + 2x + x^2, \tag{1}$$

find that polynomial $g(x)$ of degree 0 which most closely approximates to $f(x)$ for small values of x. The polynomial $g(x)$ of degree 0 is, of course, a constant: $g(x) = b$. We indicate in Figure IX.1 the graph of f and also the graph of g for various values of b.

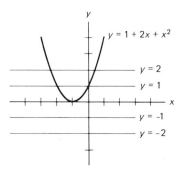

Figure IX.1

Clearly, for small x, the answer is $b = 1$. That is, the best approximation g is given by $g(x) = 1$. Now, how do we obtain this answer? The first step is to notice that if g is very close to f, then $f - g$ is very close to 0. We obtain

$$f(x) - g(x) = 1 + 2x + x^2 - b = (1 - b) + 2x + x^2. \tag{2}$$

If x is close to 0 (that is, if $|x|$ is small), then $2x + x^2$ is small also. In fact $2x + x^2 = x(2 + x)$. Thus, if x is small, $2 + x$ is close to 2, and x multiplied by $2 + x$ is close to $2x$, which is small. Thus for small x, $f(x) - g(x) \approx 1 - b$. If this is to be made small there is one and only one choice for b, namely, $b = 1$.

The above discussion about making something small can all be concretized. Suppose someone challenges us to make $2x + x^2$ less than $1/1000$ by making x sufficiently small. Very well. First choose $|x| < 1$; hence $|2 + x| < 3$. Then $|2x + x^2| = |x(2 + x)| = |x||2 + x|$ and all that is required is to make $|x| < 1/10,000$. The reader will notice the very close resemblance between this kind of argument and that which is found in Chapter III, Section 1.

Let us go on with this same function f given in (1) and let us find that polynomial h of degree at most 1 which most closely approximates to f for small values of x.

The polynomial h of degree at most 1 will be written in the form $h(x) = b + mx$. Thus the problem is to find the values b and m such that

$$\begin{aligned} f(x) - h(x) &= (1 + 2x + x^2) - (b + mx) \\ &= (1 - b) + (2 - m)x + x^2 \end{aligned} \tag{3}$$

is small when $|x|$ is small. Now, if x is small, then no matter what value m has, $(2 - m)x + x^2 = x[(2 - m) + x]$ is small. Thus for x small, $f(x) - h(x) \approx 1 - b$. If the approximation is to be good, we must have $b = 1$.

So far, so good. Now to find m.

Write (because $b = 1$)

$$f(x) - h(x) = (2 - m)x + x^2$$
$$= x[(2 - m) + x].$$ **(4)**

It is required to make this quantity small. In a certain sense, any value of m leaves the quantity small if x is small. This is true because in multiplication "a small quantity times a moderate quantity gives a small quantity." However, there is one value of m which makes $x[(2 - m) + x]$ not merely small, but small compared to x. In other words, it makes it *very* small. (For example, if x is small, $2x^2$ is small. But $2x^2$ is small even by using x as a standard because $2x^2/x = 2x$ which is again small. Our mathematical ancestors would have called $2x^2$ an infinitesimal of higher order as compared to the infinitesimal x.) That value of m which makes $x[(2 - m) + x]$ very small is $m = 2$. This gives the answer to the approximation problem:

$$h(x) = 1 + 2x.$$ **(4)**

In Figure IX.2, the geometrical meaning of the choice is made clear. All lines $y = 1 + mx$ pass through the point $(0, 1)$ on the graph of the parabola $y = 1 + 2x + x^2$. Of these lines, there is one which best approximates to the parabola. It is the one for which $m = 2$. In geometrical language, this would be stated by saying that $y = 1 + 2x$ is the tangent line to the curve $y = 1 + 2x + x^2$ at the point $(0, 1)$.

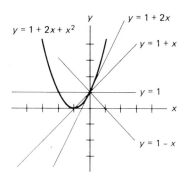

Figure IX.2

It seems from this example that the problem of finding the function $h(x) = b + mx$ which best approximates $f(x) = 1 + 2x + x^2$ for small x has as its solution the function whose graph is the tangent line to the graph of $f(x)$ at the point $(0, 1)$. Let us state that this is the case.

At this point we change the notation slightly. Let g_0, g_1, g_2, g_3, and so on, be the polynomials of degrees at most 0, 1, 2, 3, and so on, which most closely approximate to the polynomial f given above. Then we have

$$g_0(x) = 1;$$
$$g_1(x) = 1 + 2x.$$ **(5)**

Note that the answer consists of the beginning of the expression for f. This will be the case for all functions f and for g_2, g_3, g_4, and so on. This will be proved.

Consider now the general case. Let

$$f(x) = a_0 + a_1 x + \cdots + a_m x^m \tag{6}$$

be a polynomial. Let us find the polynomials $g_0, g_1, g_2, \cdots$ of degrees at most 0, 1, 2, $\cdots$ which approximate most closely to f for small values of x. It will be shown that

$$\begin{aligned} g_0(x) &= a_0; \\ g_1(x) &= a_0 + a_1 x; \\ g_2(x) &= a_0 + a_1 x + a_2 x^2; \\ &\cdots \end{aligned} \tag{7}$$

The proof will be given for g_2. Suppose that the answer is

$$g_2(x) = b_0 + b_1 x + b_2 x^2. \tag{8}$$

Then, since g_2 approximates most closely to f for $|x|$ small, we see that $f - g_2$ is closest to 0 for $|x|$ small. Now

$$f(x) - g_2(x) = (a_0 - b_0) + (a_1 - b_1)x + (a_2 - b_2)x^2 + a_3 x^3 + \cdots + a_m x^m. \tag{9}$$

This can be written

$$f(x) - g(x) = a_0 - b_0 + x[(a_1 - b_1) + (a_2 - b_2)x + a_3 x^2 + \cdots + a_m x^{m-1}]. \tag{10}$$

When $|x|$ is small, the quantity in brackets is close to $|a_1 - b_1|$ in value. Thus for small $|x|$, $f(x) - g(x) \approx (a_0 - b_0) + x(a_1 - b_1)$. If $f(x) - g(x)$ is to be small, it is clear that $a_0 - b_0 = 0$. This gives the value of b_0: $b_0 = a_0$.

We move forward and find the value of b_1. We have

$$\begin{aligned} \frac{f(x) - g(x)}{x} &= (a_1 - b_1) + (a_2 - b_2)x + a_3 x^2 + \cdots + a_m x^{m-1} \\ &= (a_1 - b_1) + x[(a_2 - b_2) + a_3 x + \cdots + a_m x^{m-2}]. \end{aligned} \tag{11}$$

We repeat the argument given above for (10) and see quickly that the way to make $[f(x) - g(x)]/x$ small [and hence $f(x) - g(x)$ "doubly" small] is to set $a_1 - b_1 = 0$. Hence $b_1 = a_1$.

The solution for b_2 is $b_2 = a_2$ and it is found by writing down the expression for $[f(x) - g(x)]/x^2$ making use of the fact that $a_0 = b_0$ and $a_1 = b_1$. This concludes our proof.

The answers to the approximation problem are simple. Given a polynomial f in (6), if we wish to approximate to f for small values of $|x|$ by polynomials of various degrees, we merely write down the first few terms (the beginning terms). For high-order approximation, we write down more terms (and obtain a more complicated polynomial). For approximation that is less demanding, we write down fewer terms. A commonly used decision is to write down two terms: $g_1(x) = a_0 + a_1 x$. This gives a first degree polynomial whose graph is the tangent line. Remember that the approximation is good only if $|x|$ is small. It is called an approximation *near* $x = 0$, also *at* $x = 0$. In the next section we shall learn how to get approximations near $x = c$ where c is any constant. Thus this section and the next give a complete theory of polynomial approximation of this type.

EXAMPLE 1:   Find the equation of the tangent line to the graph of $y = -3x + 2x^2 + x^5$ at the point for which $x = 0$.

SOLUTION: Applying directly the results obtained before gives $y = -3x$ as the equation of the tangent line.

EXAMPLE 2:   Find the polynomial of the first degree which approximates most closely to the polynomial given by $f(x) = (2 + 3x)^3$ at $x = 0$.

SOLUTION: First of all $(2 + 3x)^3 = 8 + 36x + 54x^2 + 27x^3$. Applying the previous results yields: The polynomial g of degree 1 which approximates most closely to f for $x = 0$ is given by $g(x) = 8 + 36x$.

EXAMPLE 3:   Find for the function f given by

$$f(x) = 1 + 2x + 3x^2 + 4x^3 \tag{12}$$

the polynomials of degree 0, 1, 2 which approximate most closely to f near $x = 0$. Graph the results.

SOLUTION: The answers are

$$\begin{aligned} g_0(x) &= 1; \\ g_1(x) &= 1 + 2x; \\ g_2(x) &= 1 + 2x + 3x^2. \end{aligned} \tag{13}$$

Note that g_3, g_4, g_5, and so on, are all equal to f. The approximation in the case of $g_3, g_4, g_5, \cdots$ is perfect for *all* x.

The graphs appear in Figure IX.3.

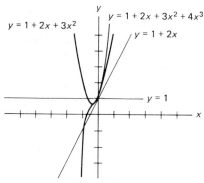

Figure IX.3

We return to the problem of making one quantity small by making another one small. In order to understand this better we consider a specific problem.

PROBLEM: If $h(u) = 2u - u^2 + 7u^3$, find a number k such that if $|u| \leq k$, $|h(u)| \leq 1/100$.

SOLUTION: The first decision is that $k < 1$. Thus $|u| \leq k$, gives $|u|^2 \leq k^2 < k$, $|u|^3 \leq k^3 < k$, and so on. Now by the often used triangle inequality and its extensions (Chapter I),

$$|h(u)| = |2u - u^2 + 7u^3| \leq |2u| + |u^2| + |7u^3|$$
$$= 2|u| + |u|^2 + 7|u|^3. \tag{14}$$

If $|u| \leq k$ and $k < 1$, then

$$|h(u)| < 2k + k + 7k = 10k. \tag{15}$$

If we now set $k = \frac{1}{1000}$, we obtain $|h(u)| \leq 10 \cdot \frac{1}{1000} = \frac{1}{100}$. This solves the problem.

The reader may be interested in knowing the answer to certain approximation problems not treated here. For instance, what are approximating polynomials to exp? The answer is easy to give: They are the beginning of the infinite series given in Chapter V, Section 4, Equation (8). The proof of this fact is within our reach; certainly a correct sketch of a proof could be given at this point. What about approximating polynomials to sin and cos? Here we can give a few answers but no proofs. It has been stated that for small $|x|$, $\sin x \approx x$. This gives a first degree approximation. A second degree approximation to cos is $\cos x \approx 1 - x^2/2$. Notice that if we set $x = \pi/3$ in this last equation, we obtain $\cos \pi/3 \approx 1 - \frac{1}{2}(\pi^2/9)$ or $\cos \pi/3 \approx 1 - 0.555 = 0.444$. Not bad! The correct answer is $\cos \pi/3 = \frac{1}{2} = 0.500$. Of course, $\pi/3$ is not exactly a small number. For $x = \frac{1}{10}$, the approximation gives $\cos \frac{1}{10} \approx 1 - \frac{1}{2} \frac{1}{100} = 1 - 0.005 = 0.9950$. The tables give (with interpolation) $\cos \frac{1}{10} = 0.9950$. In other words, the cosine approximation seems to give accuracy to four figures for angles between 0 and $\frac{1}{10}$—hence between $0°$ and $5°$. It is clear that these approximations are powerful.

Exercises IX.1.a

1. Find the polynomials of degree at most 0, 1, 2 which approximate most closely at $x = 0$ to the function $f(x)$ given below.

   (a) $f(x) = 3 - 6x + x^2$;
   (b) $f(x) = 1 + 3x + 6x^2 + 9x^3$;
   (c) $f(x) = 2 + x^2$;
   (d) $f(x) = (x + 1)^2(x - 1)$;

(e) $f(x) = 1 + 3(x + 1) - 2(x + 1)^2 + (x + 1)^3$;
(f) $f(x) = 8 - x^3$;
(g) $f(x) = 2$;
(h) $f(x) = (1 + x)^3$;
(i) $f(x) = 7x + x^2 - 4x^4$.

2. In Problem 1, compute the value of $f(x)$ and that of its approximating polynomials of degrees 0, 1, 2, for

$$x = 0; \qquad x = \frac{1}{2}; \qquad x = -\frac{1}{2}; \qquad x = \frac{1}{10}; \qquad x = 1.$$

The answers indicate the values of x for which the approximation is good.

3. By taking 1, 2, 3, 4 terms in the appropriate binomial expansion, obtain approximations to

(a) $(1 + 0.02)^{10}$; (b) $(0.97)^{13}$;
(c) $(0.101)^5$; (d) $(\frac{5}{4})^8$.

4. Assuming that the formulas $\exp x \approx 1 + x + x^2/2$, $\sin x \approx x - x^3/6$, $\cos x \approx 1 - x^2/2$, $\tan x \approx x + x^3/3$ are valid, compute the following (compare with answers given in the tables).

(a) $\exp 1$; (b) $\exp(\frac{1}{2})$;
(c) $\exp(-0.1)$; (d) $\sin(0.1)$;
(e) $\sin(3\frac{3}{4}°)$; (f) $\cos(0.3)$;
(g) $\tan(0.1)$; (h) $\cos(1°)$;
(i) $\tan(7\frac{1}{2}°)$.

5. Given the polynomial f below, find a number k such that if $|x| \le k$, then $|f(x)| \le 10$; $1/10$; $1/10^6$.

(a) $f(x) = 2x$;
(b) $f(x) = x^2$;
(c) $f(x) = x + x^2$;
(d) $f(x) = x + 2x^2 + 16x^3$;
(e) $f(x) = x + x^2 + x^3 + \cdots + x^{10}$;
(f) $f(x) = x$;
(g) $f(x) = x^n$, $n \ge 1$;
(h) $f(x) = ax^2$, $a > 0$.

2. EXPANSIONS ABOUT A POINT

The material of the preceding section gives us a considerable amount of insight on the behavior of a polynomial function near $x = 0$ but gives us none about its behavior near other values of x, say $x = 2$. In this section we shall show how to transform an expression for f given in powers of x,

$$f(x) = a_0 + a_1x + \cdots + a_nx^n,$$

into another expression given in powers of $x - 2$ (say),

$$f(x) = b_0 + b_1(x - 2) + \cdots + b_n(x - 2)^n.$$

It will be seen that there is a unique selection of the coefficients $b_0, \cdots, b_n$ which renders this possible.

Consider a special case. Suppose we have

$$f(x) = 2x^2 - 11x + 15. \tag{1}$$

Write

$$f(x) = b_0 + b_1(x - 2) + b_2(x - 2)^2. \tag{2}$$

Expanding this, we find that

$$f(x) = b_0 + b_1x - 2b_1 + b_2x^2 - 4b_2x + 4b_2. \tag{3}$$

Collecting terms of like powers of x, this gives

$$f(x) = (b_0 - 2b_1 + 4b_2) + (b_1 - 4b_2)x + b_2x^2. \tag{4}$$

Equating coefficients between the two expressions (1) and (4) for f yields

$$\begin{aligned} b_2 &= 2; \\ b_1 - 4b_2 &= -11; \\ b_0 - 2b_1 + 4b_2 &= 15. \end{aligned} \tag{5}$$

This system of equations for b_2, b_1, b_0 is obviously solvable uniquely. The solution is

$$b_2 = 2, \qquad b_1 = -3, \qquad b_0 = 1; \tag{6}$$

and the expression for f in powers of $x - 2$ is

$$f(x) = 1 - 3(x - 2) + 2(x - 2)^2. \tag{7}$$

We say that the above is the *expansion of f in powers of x* $-$ 2; we also call it the *expansion of f around x* $= 2$. Finally it is also called *the Taylor expansion of f* around $x = 2$.

It is clear that the method illustrated above is valid for any polynomial f. We shall not attempt to write down general formulas for the coefficients of f in the expansion around $x = c$. These formulas are well known in the calculus.

We note that this section and the preceding one put us in a position to approximate to f, by polynomials of arbitrary degree for values of x close to any point $x = c$. The argument is the same as before except that now, if x is close to c, then $x - c$ is small and so are $(x - c)^2$, $(x - c)^3$, and so on.

Thus for the function given in (1), the approximating polynomials of degree 0, 1, 2 for x near 2 can be read off from (7). They are

$$
\begin{aligned}
g_0(x) &= 1, \\
g_1(x) &= 1 - 3(x - 2), \\
g_2(x) &= 1 - 3(x - 2) + 2(x - 2)^2.
\end{aligned}
\tag{8}
$$

The graph of the function g_1 is the tangent line to the graph of f at the point $(2, f(2))$. Note that the best approximant of degree 2 is the function itself.

We mention very briefly the fact that with the methods of the calculus we can obtain polynomial approximations of the type discussed in this section for all the classical functions: exp, ln, sin, cos, tan, and so on. For example, an interesting formula is: $\ln x \approx (x - 1) - (x - 1)^2/2$. If, in this formula, we set $x = \frac{3}{2}$, we obtain $\ln \frac{3}{2} \approx \frac{1}{2} - \frac{1}{8} = \frac{3}{8} = 0.3750$. The tables give $\ln \frac{3}{2} = 0.4055$. On the other hand, $\ln \frac{5}{4} \approx \frac{1}{4} - \frac{1}{32} = 0.2188$; the tables give $\ln 1.25 = 0.2231$ which is a little better.

Exercises IX.2.a

1. Find the polynomials of degrees at most 0, 1, 2 approximating most closely at the indicated point to

(a) $f(x) = 1 + 3x + x^2$, $\qquad c = 1$;
(b) $f(x) = 2 - 3x^2 + x^3$, $\qquad c = 2$;
(c) $f(x) = 2 - x + 2x^2$, $\qquad c = -1$;
(d) $f(x) = 3 + 2x - x^4$, $\qquad c = 0$;
(e) $f(x) = (2 - x)^3$, $\qquad c = 1$;
(f) $f(x) = (x - 3)^5 + 1$, $\qquad c = 3$;
(g) $f(x) = 2 + x^2$, $\qquad c = -1$;
(h) $f(x) = (x + 1)^2(x - 1)$, $\qquad c = -1$;
(i) $f(x) = 2 + x^2$, $\qquad c = 1$;
(j) $f(x) = -3$, $\qquad c = 2$;
(k) $f(x) = 1 + x + x^2 + x^3$, $\qquad c = -1$.

2. Find the Taylor expansion around the indicated point for the functions

(a) $f(x) = 2 - x + x^2$, $\qquad c = 2$;
(b) $f(x) = 3 + 4x$, $\qquad c = -4$;
(c) $f(x) = 5$, $\qquad c = 3$;
(d) $f(x) = (1 - x)^3$, $\qquad c = -1$;
(e) $f(x) = (x + 1)(x - 2)^2$, $\qquad c = 2$;
(f) $f(x) = x^4 - 2x^2 + 2$, $\qquad c = 0$;
(g) $f(x) = 2x^2 + 3x - 4$, $\qquad c = 1$;
(h) $f(x) = 2x^2 + 3x - 4$, $\qquad c = -1$.

3. Given $f(x) = 2 - 3x + x^2$, find the expansion of f around the point $x = c$. Obtain by substituting the value $c = \frac{3}{2}$ the approximating polynomials to f of degrees at most 0, 1, 2 at the indicated point.

4. Given $f(x) = 2x - 3x^2 + x^3$, find the expansion for f about the point $x = c$. For what values of c is the tangent line to the graph parallel to the x-axis?

5. Using the approximation formulas $\ln x \approx (x - 1) - (x - 1)^2/2$ and $\ln x \approx (x - 1) - (x - 1)^2/2 + (x - 1)^3/3$, calculate the following numbers. Compare the results with those given in the tables.

(a) $\ln \frac{3}{2}$;   (b) $\ln \frac{5}{4}$;

(c) $\ln \frac{1}{2}$;   (d) $\ln \frac{3}{4}$;

(e) $\ln \frac{4}{3}$.

Historical Note. The Taylor series expresses a function in terms of powers of $(x - c)$ and gives formulas for the coefficients. Its name comes from Brook Taylor (1685–1731), an English mathematician, who wrote on the series in 1715. The special case $c = 0$ was named after Colin Maclaurin (1698–1746), a Scottish mathematician, although his work comes 27 years after Taylor in 1742! To make matters even more topsy-turvy, Taylor had been anticipated by James Gregory (1638–1675), a Scottish predecessor of the great Isaac Newton (1642–1727). Gregory discovered the Taylor series 40 years before Taylor. Even this is not the end of the historical tangle, since elements in the series formula can be found in India a hundred years earlier.

3. GRAPHS OF POLYNOMIAL FUNCTIONS

In this section, we shall consider the problem of graphing an arbitrary polynomial function. In Chapter II the graphs of polynomials of degrees 0, 1, and 2 were completely discussed. Thus, it will be assumed here that the degree of the given function is at least 3. It is to be expected that as the degree increases, the graph becomes more complicated. This indeed happens. This phenomenon can be looked at from another point of view. A polynomial f of degree 0 is determined if one coefficient a_0 is given [since $f(x) = a_0$]. A polynomial f of degree 1 is determined if two coefficients a_0 and a_1 are given [since $f(x) = a_0 + a_1x$]. And in general, for a polynomial f of degree n, $n + 1$ coefficients have to be given: $a_0, a_1, \cdots, a_n$ [since $f(x) = a_0 + a_1x + \cdots + a_nx^n$]. Thus, as the degree increases, the freedom of choice increases, and this will increase the degree of complexity very substantially.

We have at our disposal a few concepts that may simplify our graphing problem. There is the question of possible symmetry about the y-axis or about some line parallel to it.

We may receive help from the concept of maximum or minimum (it has been seen how these concepts played a role in graphing second degree polynomial functions).

Let us first examine the question of symmetry about the y-axis. If f has a graph that is symmetric about the y-axis, then $f(-x) = f(x)$; that is, f is an even function. Suppose f is given by

$$f(x) = a_0 + a_1 x + a_2 x^2 + \cdots + a_n x^n. \tag{1}$$

Then

$$f(-x) = a_0 + a_1(-x) + a_2(-x)^2 + \cdots + a_n(-x)^n$$
$$= a_0 - a_1 x + a_2 x^2 - \cdots + (-1)^n a_n x^n.$$

Thus if $f(x) = f(-x)$, then $f(x) - f(-x) = 0$; hence,

$$0 = 2a_1 x + 2a_3 x^3 + \cdots. \tag{2}$$

Thus (by the Unique Representation Theorem III–5), $a_1 = 0, a_3 = 0, a_5 = 0$, and so on. In other words, if f is even, all odd coefficients are zero. The converse is left as an easy exercise. That is, if the odd coefficients in f are zero, then $f(x) = f(-x)$. (See Exercise 4.) Thus the graph of f is symmetric about the y-axis if and only if all the odd coefficients are zero.

Similarly, it can be shown that if a polynomial function f is an odd function, then all the even coefficients are 0. Thus $a_0 = 0, a_2 = 0, a_4 = 0$, and so on (see Exercise 5).

Consider now the question of asymptotes. We shall see immediately that the graph of a polynomial of degree greater than 0 has no horizontal asymptotes. This is so because as $|x|$ becomes large $f(x)$ does not approach a constant value, a fact that follows immediately from Theorem III–2. It was proved there that for any polynomial f of degree greater than 0, $|f(x)|$ becomes arbitrarily large when $|x|$ becomes large. There are no vertical asymptotes either. This follows from the fact that in any interval $-a \le x \le a$, the set of values $f(x)$ is bounded. That is, there exists a number b such that $-b \le f(x) \le b$. [To convince ourselves of this fact, it should be tried out on some special case. Suppose f is given by $f(x) = 2x - x^3$ and $a = 10$. Then since $|x| \le 10$ we have $|f(x)| = |2x - x^3| \le 2|x| + |x|^3 \le 20 + 1000 = 1020$.]

We say f has a *maximum* at some value $x = h$ providing that $f(h) \ge f(x)$ when $|x - h|$ is small. More precisely, we speak of a *local maximum*. There is a similar definition for a minimum. Clearly, the tangent to the graph of f at $x = h$ must be parallel to the x-axis when f has a maximum or a minimum at h. This is clear from Figure IX.4 and follows rigorously from our discussion of approximation. The meaning of this is the following: If

$$f(x) = b_0 + b_1(x - h) + b_2(x - h)^2 + \cdots \tag{3}$$

is the expansion of f around the point $x = h$ at which f has a maximum or a minimum, then we must have $b_1 = 0$. This is so because the linear function

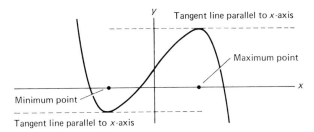

Figure IX.4

whose graph is the tangent line at $x = h$ is given by

$$g_1(x) = b_0 + b_1(x - h), \tag{4}$$

and its graph is parallel to the x-axis only if $b_1 = 0$.

Note that the tangent line may be parallel to the x-axis without yielding a local maximum or minimum. This is evident for the function f given by $f(x) = 1 + x^3$ at the point $h = 0$. See Figure IX.5. Points h at which the tangent is parallel to the x-axis are called *critical points* of f.

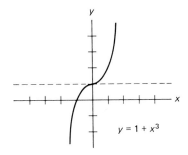

Figure IX.5

Consider now two examples that will illustrate some of these ideas. Let us find the graph of the cubic f defined by

$$f(x) = 2x^3 + 3x^2 - 1. \tag{5}$$

We first look about to find any obvious zeros. In this case $x = -1$ is such a zero. By Theorem III–11, $x + 1$ is a factor of $f(x)$: $f(x) = (x + 1)$ $(2x^2 + x - 1)$. And since $2x^2 + x - 1 = (x + 1)(2x - 1)$, we have

$$f(x) = (x + 1)^2(2x - 1).$$

The double zero at $x = -1$ should be a signal to follow up. Let us now look for maxima and minima. The method for so doing is to write the cubic in powers of $x - h$ without specifying h and then determining what values of

h will make the coefficient of $(x - h)$ equal to 0. We write, in accordance with the method given before (see Section 2),

$$\begin{aligned} f(x) &= b_3(x - h)^3 + b_2(x - h)^2 + b_1(x - h) + b_0 \\ &= b_3 x^3 + (b_2 - 3b_3 h)x^2 + (b_1 - 2b_2 h + 3b_3 h^2)x \\ &\quad + (b_0 - b_1 h + b_2 h^2 - b_3 h^3). \end{aligned} \tag{6}$$

This gives

$$\begin{aligned} b_3 &= 2, \\ b_2 - 3b_3 h &= 3, \\ b_1 - 2b_2 h + 3b_3 h^2 &= 0, \end{aligned} \tag{7}$$

and another equation that will not be needed. Thus

$$b_3 = 2, \qquad b_2 = 3 + 6h, \qquad b_1 = 2(3 + 6h)h - 6h^2 = 6h + 6h^2.$$

Now, for a maximum or minimum, $b_1 = 0$, that is, $6h + 6h^2 = 0$. This gives $h = 0$ and $h = -1$. Thus the tangent line to the graph is parallel to the x-axis at the points $(0, -1)$ and $(-1, 0)$.

Now find a few points on the graph. These include the points of special interest above. The graph is shown in Figure IX.6.

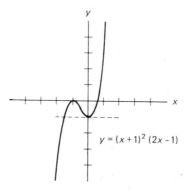

$$y = (x + 1)^2 (2x - 1)$$

Figure IX.6

It is worth noting that we had a reasonable amount of information about the curve even before finding the maximum and minimum points. We shall make further remarks about this situation later. The next example involves some harder computations.

Consider the quartic f defined by

$$f(x) = (x^2 - 4)(x - 1)^2 = x^4 - 2x^3 - 3x^2 + 8x - 4. \tag{8}$$

The zeros of f are 2, 1, 1, and -2. We find as before the development of f in powers of $x - h$ where h will be determined later. Thus we write

$$f(x) = (x - h)^4 + b_3(x - h)^3 + b_2(x - h)^2 + b_1(x - h) + b_0. \tag{9}$$

By expanding this expression and equating the coefficients to those given in (8), we find

$$b_3 - 4h = -2,$$
$$b_2 - 3b_3h + 6h^2 = -3,$$
$$b_1 - 2b_2h + 3b_3h^2 - 4h^3 = 8.$$

This gives first of all

$$b_3 = 4h - 2.$$

Solve for b_2 above and substitute this value for b_3. This gives

$$b_2 = 6h^2 - 6h - 3.$$

Finally, we solve for b_1 and substitute the values of b_3 and b_2 just found. This gives

$$b_1 = 4h^3 - 6h^2 - 6h + 8. \tag{10}$$

(The steps in the calculation are left to the reader.) The critical points (including local maxima and minima) are those for which $b_1 = 0$. Thus we must solve the cubic in h given by $b_1 = 0$.

Now, a little experience shows that because f has a double zero at $x = 1$, it has a critical point at $x = 1$. In fact, it is seen immediately that $h = 1$ makes $b_1 = 0$. Thus $(h - 1)$ is a factor of b_1. One finds by division that

$$b_1 = 2(h - 1)(2h^2 - h - 4). \tag{11}$$

The zeros of the quadratic term are $\frac{1}{4}(1 \pm \sqrt{33}) \approx 1.7, -1.2$. We now calculate roughly a few points on the graph and sketch it as shown in Figure IX.7.

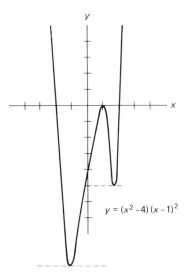

$$y = (x^2 - 4)(x - 1)^2$$

Figure IX.7

Some remarks are in order. Most evident is the fact that problems of this nature require time and patience. These problems have shown how complicated a cubic and a quartic can be and it may well be imagined that sextics will really be trying. There is not much that one can do about this. Another remark concerns the formula for b_1. At our stage, it requires a fair amount of work to obtain this. In the differential calculus a method is devised for obtaining b_1 without expenditure of energy. It is interesting to know that without the elaborate techniques of the calculus, we are in a position to compute maxima and minima for polynomials.

The reader will have noticed that in order to find the critical points of a cubic, a quadratic must be solved (in our first example, this was the quadratic $6h + h^2 = 0$). In order to find the critical points of a quartic, a cubic must be solved (in our second example, this was the cubic $4h^3 - 6h^2 - 6h + 8 = 0$). This process goes on. In order to find the critical points of a polynomial of degree n, it is necessary to find the zeros of a polynomial of degree $n - 1$. There is no getting around this. No magic will come to the rescue. One either meets the situation head on or surrenders gracefully.

Exercises IX.3.a

1. Find the graph of the function f given below.

(a) $f(x) = x^3 + 1$;
(b) $f(x) = (x - 1)^3$;
(c) $f(x) = x(x^2 - 1)$;
(d) $f(x) = x^3 + x^2 - 2x$;
(e) $f(x) = -x^3 + x^2 - x + 1$;
(f) $f(x) = x^3 - 3x - 1$.

2. Find the graph of the function f given below.

(a) $f(x) = (x^2 - 1)(x^2 - 4)$;
(b) $f(x) = (x^2 + 1)^2$;
(c) $f(x) = x^2(x^2 - 1)$;
(d) $f(x) = x^2(x^2 - 1) - 1$;
(e) $f(x) = x^4 - 2x^3 - 5x^2 + 6x$;
(f) $f(x) = x^4 - x^3 + x^2 - x$.

3. Find the graph of the function f given below.

(a) $f(x) = x^6 - 1$;
(b) $f(x) = (x - 1)^5 + 11$;
(c) $f(x) = x^{10}$.

4. Let $f(x) = a_0 + a_1x + a_2x^2 + \cdots + a_nx^n$. Suppose that $a_1 = 0, a_3 = 0, a_5 = 0$, and so on. Show that $f(x) = f(-x)$.

5. Show that if $f(-x) = -f(x)$, then $a_0 = 0, a_2 = 0, a_4 = 0$, and so on. Show the converse. [Use Equation (1) and the equation for $f(-x)$ and apply the definition of an odd function.]

6. An alternative method that may be used for finding expansions around $x - h$ will be illustrated. Given $f(x) = x^3$, write $x = (x - h) + h$ and expand. This gives

$$f(x) = x^3 = [(x - h) + h]^3$$
$$= (x - h)^3 + 3h(x - h)^2 + 3h^2(x - h) + h^3.$$

Use this method to obtain the expansions given in the text for the functions below.

(a) $f(x) = 2x^3 + 3x^2 - 1$;
(b) $f(x) = x^4 - 2x^3 - 3x^2 + 8x - 4$.

4. ABSTRACT POWER SERIES

Our description of polynomials started off as follows: (1) polynomials are first of all functions; (2) next they are functions of a certain type, namely, a sum of powers with constant coefficients. The fact that they are functions bound us by a whole collection of definitions concerning functions: we knew in advance when two polynomials are equal, we knew how to add and multiply polynomials. It was only later that we discovered (by means of a proof) that two polynomials are equal only if their coefficients are respectively equal; and also that the addition and multiplication of polynomials can be described completely by saying what happens to their coefficients. This led us to state that polynomials seemed to lead a life of their own apart from being functions. That is, much of the theory of polynomials can be developed by replacing the function f for which $f(x) = a_0 + a_1 x + \cdots + a_n x^n$ by an ordered n-tuple $(a_0, a_1, \cdots, a_n)$.

We shall carry out this development in the present section, but we shall carry it out on a new type of object. These objects are called *abstract power series*. There is no need to worry too much about the name. We specify that we shall *not* introduce power series. As for the adjective "abstract" it is customary to use it to describe something seemingly mysterious and not completely run-of-the-mill, and according to this criterion, it is used appropriately here. The mystery won't last very long.

In the definition of real functions, given in Chapter II, we considered the set of real numbers $\mathbf{R}$ and a rule or formula f which assigned to each number x in $\mathbf{R}$ a real number $f(x)$. We wrote $f: \mathbf{R} \to \mathbf{R}$. Now, there is no reason for restricting ourselves to the real numbers. We may substitute an arbitrary set for the $\mathbf{R}$ on the left, or for that on the right, or for both. For our purposes, consider a function a defined on the natural numbers $\mathbf{N} = \{0, 1, 2, \cdots\}$ and having values in $\mathbf{R}$:

$$a: \mathbf{N} \to \mathbf{R}. \tag{1}$$

(Remember that 0 is an element of $\mathbf{N}$). If n is a natural number, then the value of the function a on the number n is usually denoted by a_n instead of $a(n)$.

Thus the function a is known if we know the real number a_n for each n. The values a_n are frequently written out in a row, as follows:

$$(a_0, a_1, a_2, \cdots); \tag{2}$$

or also

$$(a_0, a_1, a_2, \cdots, a_n, \cdots). \tag{3}$$

For example, one might have

$$(0, 1, 4, 9, \cdots, n^2, \cdots);$$

here $a_n = n^2$. Or again one might have

$$(0, 1, 2, 3, \cdots);$$

presumably, here $a_n = n$.

Functions from the natural numbers to the real numbers are also called sequences. Note that if f is a polynomial of degree m, and its coefficients are $b_0, b_1, \cdots, b_m$ then we may make a sequence out of these coefficients by filling in the remaining places with zeros. We then obtain the sequence

$$(b_0, b_1, \cdots, b_m, 0, 0, 0, \cdots). \tag{4}$$

Thus the polynomials correspond precisely to the sequences all of whose terms are 0 from some point on.

Since sequences are functions defined on $\mathbf{N}$ and with real values, they are to be added and multiplied in the usual way as functions. Thus if we have two sequences

$$a: \mathbf{N} \to \mathbf{R} \qquad \text{and} \qquad b: \mathbf{N} \to \mathbf{R},$$

then $a + b$ is the sequence whose value at the number n is $a_n + b_n$. In other words,

$$(a + b)_n = a_n + b_n. \tag{5}$$

Similarly, $a \cdot b$ is that sequence whose value at the integer n is $a_n \cdot b_n$. In other words,

$$(a \cdot b)_n = a_n \cdot b_n. \tag{6}$$

[All we have done here is to write in the new notation what we wrote previously as $(f + g)(x) = f(x) + g(x)$ and $(f \cdot g)(x) = f(x) \cdot g(x)$.]

We may therefore write

$$(a_0, a_1, a_2, \cdots) + (b_0, b_1, b_2, \cdots) = (a_0 + b_0, a_1 + b_1, a_2 + b_2 \cdots), \tag{7}$$

and

$$(a_0, a_1, a_2, \cdots) \cdot (b_0, b_1, b_2, \cdots) = (a_0 b_0, a_1 b_1, a_2 b_2, \cdots). \tag{8}$$

Thus the sequences, as functions, form a ring: the sum of sequences is a sequence, the product of sequences is a sequence, and these operations are commutative, associative, and distributive. (The proof is straightforward. It is based on the definition of equality of functions and properties of $\mathbf{R}$.)

We shall not be interested in this ring. We shall be interested in another ring in which the objects are the same as above—that is, sequences— in which addition is the same as above, but multiplication is different.

The multiplication we propose to introduce is suggested by the formulas concerning polynomial coefficients [Chapter III, Section 2, Equation (9)]. It was seen there that if we have two polynomials whose coefficients are

$$(a_0, a_1, \cdots, a_m) \qquad \text{and} \qquad (b_0, b_1, \cdots, b_n),$$

then their product has coefficients

$$(a_0 b_0, a_0 b_1 + a_1 b_0, a_0 b_2 + a_1 b_1 + a_2 b_0, \cdots, a_m b_n). \tag{9}$$

Notice that this type of multiplication can be carried out on arbitrary sequences. We shall call this multiplication *convolution* and when using this type of multiplication we shall refer to sequences as *abstract power series*. Let us state:

IX–1 Definition

Let $(a_0, a_1, a_2, \cdots)$ and $(b_0, b_1, b_2, \cdots)$ be two abstract power series. By the product of these two is meant the abstract power series $(c_0, c_1, c_2, \cdots)$ whose coefficients are given by the equations

$$\begin{aligned}
c_0 &= a_0 b_0, \\
c_1 &= a_0 b_1 + a_1 b_0, \\
c_2 &= a_0 b_2 + a_1 b_1 + a_2 b_0,
\end{aligned} \tag{10}$$

and so on.

The product is written $a * b$.

Several things are to be noted about the set of abstract power series (called a.p.s. for short). First, two a.p.s. are equal if and only if their respective coefficients are equal. Next, addition is to be carried out as indicated in (7). Next, multiplication is commutative (this is easy to check, see Exercise 3). It is also associative (this requires a little patience and some pencil and paper: Exercise 8). Finally multiplication is distributive with respect to addition (Exercise 9). What is being said here is that if a, b, c are three a.p.s., then

$$\begin{array}{ll}
a * b = b * a & \text{(commutativity)}; \\
(a * b) * c = a * (b * c) & \text{(associativity)}; \\
a * (b + c) = a * b + a * c & \text{(distributivity)}.
\end{array} \tag{11}$$

Let us continue with our observations. Note that all polynomials are represented among our a.p.s. In fact, an a.p.s. is a polynomial if (and only if) the a.p.s. is terminating; that is, consists only of zeros from some point on. More important is that polynomial multiplication and a.p.s. multiplication are identical; our definition of convolution was so phrased as to bring this about. Hence the system of all a.p.s. contains the system of polynomials. It is an extension of the system of polynomials. It is precisely for this reason that it is proper to study them briefly in this chapter which is dedicated to poly-nomials.

Two a.p.s. have special properties; they are

$$(0, 0, 0, \cdots) \quad \text{and} \quad (1, 0, 0, \cdots). \tag{12}$$

For any a.p.s. $(a_0, a_1, a_2, \cdots)$,

$$(a_0, a_1, a_2, \cdots) + (0, 0, 0, \cdots) = (a_0, a_1, a_2, \cdots),$$
$$(a_0, a_1, a_2, \cdots) * (1, 0, 0, \cdots) = (a_0, a_1, a_2, \cdots). \tag{13}$$

The last equation should be checked (Exercise 4). These special a.p.s. play the role of "zero" and "one."

So far, the theory of a.p.s. has been very much like that of polynomials. But from this point on the development is quite different. For polynomials there is a remainder theorem. This does not exist for a.p.s. The reason is simple. A polynomial had a degree and a leading coefficient. Thus if we want to divide, we start out "at the top," that is, with the term of highest degree. An a.p.s. has no degree and no term at the top. What one does is to divide by starting at the bottom. It will be shown at the end of this section that an a.p.s. $(a_0, a_1, a_2 \cdots)$ is exactly divisible by an a.p.s. $(b_0, b_1, b_2, \cdots)$ if $b_0 \neq 0$. Thus we see that a factorization theory such as we had for polynomials falls by the wayside for a.p.s. We do not speak of zeros of an a.p.s.; indeed, an a.p.s. is not a function defined over $\mathbf{R}$ in the sense that polynomials were defined over $\mathbf{R}$. Thus there is no fundamental theorem nor graph to worry about.

This is not to say that at some future moment, life as functions over $\mathbf{R}$ will not be given to some of these a.p.s. The expectation of this future life as a function is in fact one of the excellent reasons for studying them now.

Let us consider an example. Start with the easily established fact that

$$(1, -1, 0, 0, \cdots) * (1, 1, 1, 1, \cdots) = (1, 0, 0, 0, \cdots).$$

Now it has been said that the a.p.s. $(1, 0, 0, \cdots)$ represents "one" and we shall write it as 1. Also, the a.p.s. $(1, -1, 0, \cdots)$ represents the polynomial $1 - x$. Thus the above equation states, after division, that

$$\frac{1}{1 - x} = (1, 1, 1, \cdots). \tag{14}$$

All this becomes a little more meaningful if we remember the result of the study of geometric series which states that if $|x| < 1$, then

$$\frac{1}{1 - x} = 1 + x + x^2 + x^3 + \cdots. \tag{15}$$

If the expression $1 + x + x^2 + \cdots$ is to receive an interpretation as an a.p.s. it would be by $(1, 1, 1, \cdots)$. This means that not only polynomial functions have representations as a.p.s. but certain other functions as well; for example, the rational function given by $f(x) = 1/(1 - x)$. It is proved in the calculus that all functions that are "smooth" at $x = 0$ have representations as a.p.s. In fact, one of the aims of the calculus is to show that for these functions the adjective "abstract" may be dropped and one speaks for short of power series.

We recall another example, one of the most striking in all of analysis discussed at length in Chapter V and also in Chapter VII.

Let s and t be arbitrary fixed real numbers. Consider the a.p.s.

$$\left(1, s, \frac{s^2}{2!}, \frac{s^3}{3!}, \frac{s^4}{4!}, \cdots\right),$$

and

$$\left(1, t, \frac{t^2}{2!}, \frac{t^3}{3!}, \frac{t^4}{4!}, \cdots\right).$$

(16)

Let us find their convolution product. Letting the product be represented by $(a_0, a_1, a_2, \cdots)$, we obtain

$$a_0 = 1,$$
$$a_1 = s + t,$$

$$a_2 = \frac{s^2}{2!} + st + \frac{t^2}{3!},$$

(17)

$$a_3 = \frac{s^3}{3!} + \frac{s^2 t}{2!} + \frac{st^2}{2!} + \frac{t^3}{3!},$$

and so on. Since

$$\frac{s^2}{2!} + st + \frac{t^2}{2!} = \frac{(s+t)^2}{2!} \quad \text{and} \quad \frac{s^3}{3!} + \frac{s^2 t}{2!} + \frac{st^2}{2!} + \frac{t^3}{3!} = \frac{(s+t)^3}{3!},$$

(18)

we surmise that, in general, we have

$$a_n = \frac{(s+t)^n}{n!}.$$

(19)

This surmise is correct. It was established by mathematical induction in Chapter VII. We restate our result in the form

$$\left(1, s, \frac{s^2}{2!}, \cdots\right) * \left(1, t, \frac{t^2}{2!}, \cdots\right) = \left(1, s + t, \frac{(s+t)^2}{2!}, \cdots\right).$$

(20)

This formula is the formulation in a.p.s. terms of the functional equation for exp.

We return briefly to the problem of dividing one a.p.s. by another. Let us look into this problem by trying an example. Divide

$$(1, 4, 13, 40, \cdots) \quad \text{by} \quad (1, 3, 9, 27, \cdots).$$

(21)

Let the result of the division be $(a_0, a_1, a_2, \cdots)$. Thus,

$$(a_0, a_1, a_2, a_3, \ldots) * (1, 3, 9, 27, \cdots) = (1, 4, 13, 40, \cdots). \tag{22}$$

Multiplying the two a.p.s. on the left in (22) gives

$$(a_0, \ a_1 + 3a_0, \ a_2 + 3a_1 + 9a_0, \ a_3 + 3a_2 + 9a_1 + 27a_0, \ \cdots). \tag{23}$$

Equating the coefficients so obtained to those on the right side of (22), a system of equations is obtained of which the first 4 are:

$$\begin{aligned}
a_0 &= 1, \\
a_1 + 3a_0 &= 4, \\
a_2 + 3a_1 + 9a_0 &= 13, \\
a_3 + 3a_2 + 9a_1 + 27a_0 &= 40.
\end{aligned} \tag{24}$$

These equations happen to be easy to solve. The solution is $a_0 = 1$, $a_1 = 1, a_2 = 1, a_3 = 1, \cdots$.

We shall not write down the solution of the division problem in general. The only thing to note is that if an a.p.s. is divided by $(b_0, b_1, \cdots)$ it is always possible to solve the equations of the type (24) providing that $b_0 \neq 0$.

It has been underlined most strongly that functions and abstract power series are closely related. This is true of all polynomial functions. It is true of exp. What about sin and cos? Here again, there are abstract power series that are the skeletons of sin and cos. These skeletons are only visible through the x-ray eyes of advanced analysis. We write them down, calling them $s(x)$ and $c(x)$, respectively.

$$s(x) = \left(0, x, 0, -\frac{x^3}{3!}, 0, \frac{x^5}{5!}, 0, \cdots \right);$$

$$c(x) = \left(1, 0, -\frac{x^2}{2!}, 0, \frac{x^4}{4!}, 0, \cdots \right). \tag{25}$$

It can then be shown (using mathematical induction to nail down the proof thoroughly) that

$$s(x) * s(x) + c(x) * c(x) = (1, 0, 0, \cdots). \tag{26}$$

This is, in disguise, our old friend $\sin^2 x + \cos^2 x = 1$.

It is also possible to show that

$$\begin{aligned}
s(x + y) &= s(x) * c(y) + c(x) * s(y), \\
c(x + y) &= c(x) * c(y) - s(x) * s(y).
\end{aligned} \tag{27}$$

These correspond to the functional equations for sin and cos. [For example, $\sin(x + y) = \sin x \cos y + \cos x \sin y$.] The proof of Equations (26) and (27) is left to the exercises.

Exercises IX.4.a

1. Prove that $(1, 1, 1, \cdots) * (1, 1, 1, \cdots) = (1, 2, 3, \cdots)$.

2. Obtain the value of $(1, 1, 1, \cdots) * (1, 2, 3, \cdots)$.

3. Prove that the multiplication of a.p.s. is commutative; that is,

$$(a_0, a_1, a_2, \cdots) * (b_0, b_1, b_2, \cdots) = (b_0, b_1, b_2, \cdots) * (a_0, a_1, a_2, \cdots).$$

4. Prove that $(a_0, a_1, a_2, \cdots) * (1, 0, 0, \cdots) = (a_0, a_1, a_2, \cdots)$.

5. Show that

$$(a_0, a_1, a_2, \cdots) * (0, 1, 0, 0, \cdots) = (0, a_0, a_1, a_2, \cdots).$$

6. For any natural number n let A_n represent $(a_0, a_1, \cdots)$ where $a_i = 0$ if $i \neq n$, $a_i = 1$ if $i = n$. Show that $A_n * A_m = A_{n+m}$.

7. Show that

$$\left(1, 1, \frac{1}{2!}, \frac{1}{3!}, \cdots\right) * \left(1, -1, \frac{1}{2!}, -\frac{1}{3!}, \cdots\right) = (1, 0, 0, \cdots).$$

8. Show that multiplication of a.p.s. is associative. [Carry out the operations indicated in the two sides of (11) and compare the results.]

9. Show that multiplication of a.p.s. is distributive with respect to addition [see (11)].

10. Establish Equation (26).

11. Establish Equations (27).

Table I

Powers and Roots of Integers n ($n = 1$ through 100)

n	n^2	$\sqrt{n}$	n^3	$\sqrt[3]{n}$	n	n^2	$\sqrt{n}$	n^3	$\sqrt[3]{n}$
1	1	1.000	1	1.000	51	2,601	7.141	132,651	3.708
2	4	1.414	8	1.260	52	2,704	7.211	140,608	3.732
3	9	1.732	27	1.442	53	2,809	7.280	148,877	3.756
4	16	2.000	64	1.587	54	2,916	7.348	157,464	3.780
5	25	2.236	125	1.710	55	3,025	7.416	166,375	3.803
6	36	2.449	216	1.817	56	3,136	7.483	175,616	3.826
7	49	2.646	343	1.913	57	3,249	7.550	185,193	3.848
8	64	2.828	512	2.000	58	3,364	7.616	195,112	3.871
9	81	3.000	729	2.080	59	3,481	7.681	205,379	3.893
10	100	3.162	1,000	2.154	60	3,600	7.746	216,000	3.915
11	121	3.317	1,331	2.224	61	3,721	7.810	226,981	3.936
12	144	3.464	1,728	2.289	62	3,844	7.874	238,328	3.958
13	169	3.606	2,197	2.351	63	3,969	7.937	250,047	3.979
14	196	3.742	2,744	2.410	64	4,096	8.000	262,144	4.000
15	225	3.873	3,375	2.466	65	4,225	8.062	274,625	4.021
16	256	4.000	4,096	2.520	66	4,356	8.124	287,496	4.041
17	289	4.123	4,913	2.571	67	4,489	8.185	300,763	4.062
18	324	4.243	5,832	2.621	68	4,624	8.246	314,432	4.082
19	361	4.359	6,859	2.668	69	4,761	8.307	328,509	4.102
20	400	4.472	8,000	2.714	70	4,900	8.367	343,000	4.121
21	441	4.583	9,261	2.759	71	5,041	8.426	357,911	4.141
22	484	4.690	10,648	2.802	72	5,184	8.485	373,248	4.160
23	529	4.796	12,167	2.844	73	5,329	8.544	389,017	4.179
24	576	4.899	13,824	2.884	74	5,476	8.602	405,224	4.198
25	625	5.000	15,625	2.924	75	5,625	8.660	421,875	4.217
26	676	5.099	17,576	2.962	76	5,776	8.718	438,976	4.236
27	729	5.196	19,683	3.000	77	5,929	8.775	456,533	4.254
28	784	5.291	21,952	3.037	78	6,084	8.832	474,552	4.273
29	841	5.385	24,389	3.072	79	6,241	8.888	493,039	4.291
30	900	5.477	27,000	3.107	80	6,400	8.944	512,000	4.309
31	961	5.568	29,791	3.141	81	6,561	9.000	531,441	4.327
32	1,024	5.657	32,768	3.175	82	6,724	9.055	551,368	4.344
33	1,089	5.745	35,937	3.208	83	6,889	9.110	571,787	4.362
34	1,156	5.831	39,304	3.240	84	7,056	9.165	592,704	4.380
35	1,225	5.916	42,875	3.271	85	7,225	9.220	614,125	4.397
36	1,296	6.000	46,656	3.302	86	7,396	9.274	636,056	4.414
37	1,369	6.083	50,653	3.332	87	7,569	9.327	658,503	4.431
38	1,444	6.164	54,872	3.362	88	7,744	9.381	681,472	4.448
39	1,521	6.245	59,319	3.391	89	7,921	9.434	704,969	4.465
40	1,600	6.325	64,000	3.420	90	8,100	9.487	729,000	4.481
41	1,681	6.403	68,921	3.448	91	8,281	9.539	753,571	4.498
42	1,764	6.481	74,088	3.476	92	8,464	9.592	778,688	4.514
43	1,849	6.557	79,507	3.503	93	8,649	9.643	804,357	4.531
44	1,936	6.633	85,184	3.530	94	8,836	9.695	830,584	4.547
45	2,025	6.708	91,125	3.557	95	9,025	9.747	857,375	4.563
46	2,116	6.782	97,336	3.583	96	9,216	9.798	884,736	4.579
47	2,209	6.856	103,823	3.609	97	9,409	9.849	912,673	4.595
48	2,304	6.928	110,592	3.634	98	9,604	9.899	941,192	4.610
49	2,401	7.000	117,649	3.659	99	9,801	9.950	970,299	4.626
50	2,500	7.071	125,000	3.684	100	10,000	10.000	1,000,000	4.642
n	n^2	$\sqrt{n}$	n^3	$\sqrt[3]{n}$	n	n^2	$\sqrt{n}$	n^3	$\sqrt[3]{n}$

Table II

Exponential Functions e^t and e^{-t} ($t = 0.00$ through 10.00)

t	e^t	e^{-t}	t	e^t	e^{-t}
0.00	1.0000	1.0000	2.50	12.182	0.0821
0.05	1.0513	0.9512	2.55	12.807	0.0781
0.10	1.1052	0.9048	2.60	13.464	0.0743
0.15	1.1618	0.8607	2.65	14.154	0.0707
0.20	1.2214	0.8187	2.70	14.880	0.0672
0.25	1.2840	0.7788	2.75	15.643	0.0639
0.30	1.3499	0.7408	2.80	16.445	0.0608
0.35	1.4191	0.7047	2.85	17.288	0.0578
0.40	1.4918	0.6703	2.90	18.174	0.0550
0.45	1.5683	0.6376	2.95	19.106	0.0523
0.50	1.6487	0.6065			
0.55	1.7333	0.5769	3.00	20.086	0.0498
0.60	1.8221	0.5488	3.05	21.115	0.0474
0.65	1.9155	0.5220	3.10	22.198	0.0450
0.70	2.0138	0.4966	3.15	23.336	0.0429
0.75	2.1170	0.4724	3.20	24.533	0.0408
0.80	2.2255	0.4493	3.25	25.790	0.0388
0.85	2.3396	0.4274	3.30	27.113	0.0369
0.90	2.4596	0.4066	3.35	28.503	0.0351
0.95	2.5857	0.3867	3.40	29.964	0.0334
			3.45	31.500	0.0317
1.00	2.7183	0.3679	3.50	33.115	0.0302
1.05	2.8577	0.3499	3.55	34.813	0.0287
1.10	3.0042	0.3329	3.60	36.598	0.0273
1.15	3.1582	0.3166	3.65	38.475	0.0260
1.20	3.3201	0.3012	3.70	40.447	0.0247
1.25	3.4903	0.2865	3.75	42.521	0.0235
1.30	3.6693	0.2725	3.80	44.701	0.0224
1.35	3.8574	0.2592	3.85	46.993	0.0213
1.40	4.0552	0.2466	3.90	49.402	0.0202
1.45	4.2631	0.2346	3.95	51.935	0.0193
1.50	4.4817	0.2231			
1.55	4.7115	0.2122	4.00	54.598	0.0183
1.60	4.9530	0.2019	4.10	60.340	0.0166
1.65	5.2070	0.1920	4.20	66.686	0.0150
1.70	5.4739	0.1827	4.30	73.700	0.0136
1.75	5.7546	0.1738	4.40	81.451	0.0123
1.80	6.0496	0.1653	4.50	90.017	0.0111
1.85	6.3598	0.1572	4.60	99.484	0.0101
1.90	6.6859	0.1496	4.70	109.95	0.0091
1.95	7.0287	0.1423	4.80	121.51	0.0082
			4.90	134.29	0.0074
2.00	7.3891	0.1353	5.00	148.41	0.0067
2.05	7.7679	0.1287	5.20	181.27	0.0055
2.10	8.1662	0.1225	5.40	221.41	0.0045
2.15	8.5849	0.1165	5.60	270.43	0.0037
2.20	9.0250	0.1108	5.80	330.30	0.0030
2.25	9.4877	0.1054	6.00	403.43	0.0025
2.30	9.9742	0.1003	7.00	1096.6	0.0009
2.35	10.486	0.0954	8.00	2981.0	0.0003
2.40	11.023	0.0907	9.00	8103.1	0.0001
2.45	11.588	0.0863	10.00	22026.0	0.00005

Table III

Natural Logarithms   ln t

t	0.00	0.01	0.02	0.03	0.04	0.05	0.06	0.07	0.08	0.09
1.0	0.0000	0.0100	0.0198	0.0296	0.0392	0.0488	0.0583	0.0677	0.0770	0.0862
1.1	0.0953	0.1044	0.1133	0.1222	0.1310	0.1398	0.1484	0.1570	0.1655	0.1740
1.2	0.1823	0.1906	0.1989	0.2070	0.2151	0.2231	0.2311	0.2390	0.2469	0.2546
1.3	0.2624	0.2700	0.2776	0.2852	0.2927	0.3001	0.3075	0.3148	0.3221	0.3293
1.4	0.3365	0.3436	0.3507	0.3577	0.3646	0.3716	0.3784	0.3853	0.3920	0.3988
1.5	0.4055	0.4121	0.4187	0.4253	0.4318	0.4383	0.4447	0.4511	0.4574	0.4637
1.6	0.4700	0.4762	0.4824	0.4886	0.4947	0.5008	0.5068	0.5128	0.5188	0.5247
1.7	0.5306	0.5365	0.5423	0.5481	0.5539	0.5596	0.5653	0.5710	0.5766	0.5822
1.8	0.5878	0.5933	0.5988	0.6043	0.6098	0.6152	0.6206	0.6259	0.6313	0.6366
1.9	0.6419	0.6471	0.6523	0.6575	0.6627	0.6678	0.6729	0.6780	0.6831	0.6881
2.0	0.6931	0.6981	0.7031	0.7080	0.7130	0.7178	0.7227	0.7275	0.7324	0.7372
2.1	0.7419	0.7467	0.7514	0.7561	0.7608	0.7655	0.7701	0.7747	0.7793	0.7839
2.2	0.7885	0.7930	0.7975	0.8020	0.8065	0.8109	0.8154	0.8198	0.8242	0.8286
2.3	0.8329	0.8372	0.8416	0.8459	0.8502	0.8544	0.8587	0.8629	0.8671	0.8713
2.4	0.8755	0.8796	0.8838	0.8879	0.8920	0.8961	0.9002	0.9042	0.9083	0.9123
2.5	0.9163	0.9203	0.9243	0.9282	0.9322	0.9361	0.9400	0.9439	0.9478	0.9517
2.6	0.9555	0.9594	0.9632	0.9670	0.9708	0.9746	0.9783	0.9821	0.9858	0.9895
2.7	0.9933	0.9969	1.0006	1.0043	1.0080	1.0116	1.0152	1.0188	1.0225	1.0260
2.8	1.0296	1.0332	1.0367	1.0403	1.0438	1.0473	1.0508	1.0543	1.0578	1.0613
2.9	1.0647	1.0682	1.0716	1.0750	1.0784	1.0818	1.0852	1.0886	1.0919	1.0953
3.0	1.0986	1.1019	1.1053	1.1086	1.1119	1.1151	1.1184	1.1217	1.1249	1.1282
3.1	1.1314	1.1346	1.1378	1.1410	1.1442	1.1474	1.1506	1.1537	1.1569	1.1600
3.2	1.1632	1.1663	1.1694	1.1725	1.1756	1.1787	1.1817	1.1848	1.1878	1.1909
3.3	1.1939	1.1970	1.2000	1.2030	1.2060	1.2090	1.2119	1.2149	1.2179	1.2208
3.4	1.2238	1.2267	1.2296	1.2326	1.2355	1.2384	1.2413	1.2442	1.2470	1.2499
3.5	1.2528	1.2556	1.2585	1.2613	1.2641	1.2669	1.2698	1.2726	1.2754	1.2782
3.6	1.2809	1.2837	1.2865	1.2892	1.2920	1.2947	1.2975	1.3002	1.3029	1.3056
3.7	1.3083	1.3110	1.3137	1.3164	1.3191	1.3218	1.3244	1.3271	1.3297	1.3324
3.8	1.3350	1.3376	1.3403	1.3429	1.3455	1.3481	1.3507	1.3533	1.3558	1.3584
3.9	1.3610	1.3635	1.3661	1.3686	1.3712	1.3737	1.3762	1.3788	1.3813	1.3838
4.0	1.3863	1.3888	1.3913	1.3938	1.3962	1.3987	1.4012	1.4036	1.4061	1.4085
4.1	1.4110	1.4134	1.4159	1.4183	1.4207	1.4231	1.4255	1.4279	1.4303	1.4327
4.2	1.4351	1.4375	1.4398	1.4422	1.4446	1.4469	1.4493	1.4516	1.4540	1.4563
4.3	1.4586	1.4609	1.4633	1.4656	1.4679	1.4702	1.4725	1.4748	1.4770	1.4793
4.4	1.4816	1.4839	1.4861	1.4884	1.4907	1.4929	1.4952	1.4974	1.4996	1.5019
4.5	1.5041	1.5063	1.5085	1.5107	1.5129	1.5151	1.5173	1.5195	1.5217	1.5239
4.6	1.5261	1.5282	1.5304	1.5326	1.5347	1.5369	1.5390	1.5412	1.5433	1.5454
4.7	1.5476	1.5497	1.5518	1.5539	1.5560	1.5581	1.5602	1.5623	1.5644	1.5665
4.8	1.5686	1.5707	1.5728	1.5748	1.5769	1.5790	1.5810	1.5831	1.5851	1.5872
4.9	1.5892	1.5913	1.5933	1.5953	1.5974	1.5994	1.6014	1.6034	1.6054	1.6074
5.0	1.6094	1.6114	1.6134	1.6154	1.6174	1.6194	1.6214	1.6233	1.6253	1.6273
5.1	1.6292	1.6312	1.6332	1.6351	1.6371	1.6390	1.6409	1.6429	1.6448	1.6467
5.2	1.6487	1.6506	1.6525	1.6544	1.6563	1.6582	1.6601	1.6620	1.6639	1.6658
5.3	1.6677	1.6696	1.6715	1.6734	1.6752	1.6771	1.6790	1.6808	1.6827	1.6845
5.4	1.6864	1.6882	1.6901	1.6919	1.6938	1.6956	1.6974	1.6993	1.7011	1.7029

Table III (*continued*)

t	0.00	0.01	0.02	0.03	0.04	0.05	0.06	0.07	0.08	0.09
5.5	1.7047	1.7066	1.7084	1.7102	1.7120	1.7138	1.7156	1.7174	1.7192	1.7210
5.6	1.7228	1.7246	1.7263	1.7281	1.7299	1.7317	1.7334	1.7352	1.7370	1.7387
5.7	1.7405	1.7422	1.7440	1.7457	1.7475	1.7492	1.7509	1.7527	1.7544	1.7561
5.8	1.7579	1.7596	1.7613	1.7630	1.7647	1.7664	1.7682	1.7699	1.7716	1.7733
5.9	1.7750	1.7766	1.7783	1.7800	1.7817	1.7834	1.7851	1.7867	1.7884	1.7901
6.0	1.7918	1.7934	1.7951	1.7967	1.7984	1.8001	1.8017	1.8034	1.8050	1.8066
6.1	1.8083	1.8099	1.8116	1.8132	1.8148	1.8165	1.8181	1.8197	1.8213	1.8229
6.2	1.8245	1.8262	1.8278	1.8294	1.8310	1.8326	1.8342	1.8358	1.8374	1.8390
6.3	1.8406	1.8421	1.8437	1.8453	1.8469	1.8485	1.8500	1.8516	1.8532	1.8547
6.4	1.8563	1.8579	1.8594	1.8610	1.8625	1.8641	1.8656	1.8672	1.8687	1.8703
6.5	1.8718	1.8733	1.8749	1.8764	1.8779	1.8795	1.8810	1.8825	1.8840	1.8856
6.6	1.8871	1.8886	1.8901	1.8916	1.8931	1.8946	1.8961	1.8976	1.8991	1.9006
6.7	1.9021	1.9036	1.9051	1.9066	1.9081	1.9095	1.9110	1.9125	1.9140	1.9155
6.8	1.9169	1.9184	1.9199	1.9213	1.9228	1.9242	1.9257	1.9272	1.9286	1.9301
6.9	1.9315	1.9330	1.9344	1.9359	1.9373	1.9387	1.9402	1.9416	1.9430	1.9445
7.0	1.9459	1.9473	1.9488	1.9502	1.9516	1.9530	1.9544	1.9559	1.9573	1.9587
7.1	1.9601	1.9615	1.9629	1.9643	1.9657	1.9671	1.9685	1.9699	1.9713	1.9727
7.2	1.9741	1.9755	1.9769	1.9782	1.9796	1.9810	1.9824	1.9838	1.9851	1.9865
7.3	1.9879	1.9892	1.9906	1.9920	1.9933	1.9947	1.9961	1.9974	1.9988	2.0001
7.4	2.0015	2.0028	2.0042	2.0055	2.0069	2.0082	2.0096	2.0109	2.0122	2.0136
7.5	2.0149	2.0162	2.0176	2.0189	2.0202	2.0215	2.0229	2.0242	2.0255	2.0268
7.6	2.0282	2.0295	2.0308	2.0321	2.0334	2.0347	2.0360	2.0373	2.0386	2.0399
7.7	2.0412	2.0425	2.0438	2.0451	2.0464	2.0477	2.0490	2.0503	2.0516	2.0528
7.8	2.0541	2.0554	2.0567	2.0580	2.0592	2.0605	2.0618	2.0631	2.0643	2.0656
7.9	2.0669	2.0681	2.0694	2.0707	2.0719	2.0732	2.0744	2.0757	2.0769	2.0782
8.0	2.0794	2.0807	2.0819	2.0832	2.0844	2.0857	2.0869	2.0882	2.0894	2.0906
8.1	2.0919	2.0931	2.0943	2.0956	2.0968	2.0980	2.0992	2.1005	2.1017	2.1029
8.2	2.1041	2.1054	2.1066	2.1078	2.1090	2.1102	2.1114	2.1126	2.1138	2.1150
8.3	2.1163	2.1175	2.1187	2.1199	2.1211	2.1223	2.1235	2.1247	2.1258	2.1270
8.4	2.1282	2.1294	2.1306	2.1318	2.1330	2.1342	2.1353	2.1365	2.1377	2.1389
8.5	2.1401	2.1412	2.1424	2.1436	2.1448	2.1459	2.1471	2.1483	2.1494	2.1506
8.6	2.1518	2.1529	2.1541	2.1552	2.1564	2.1576	2.1587	2.1599	2.1610	2.1622
8.7	2.1633	2.1645	2.1656	2.1668	2.1679	2.1691	2.1702	2.1713	2.1725	2.1736
8.8	2.1748	2.1759	2.1770	2.1782	2.1793	2.1804	2.1815	2.1827	2.1838	2.1849
8.9	2.1861	2.1872	2.1883	2.1894	2.1905	2.1917	2.1928	2.1939	2.1950	2.1961
9.0	2.1972	2.1983	2.1994	2.2006	2.2017	2.2028	2.2039	2.2050	2.2061	2.2072
9.1	2.2083	2.2094	2.2105	2.2116	2.2127	2.2138	2.2148	2.2159	2.2170	2.2181
9.2	2.2192	2.2203	2.2214	2.2225	2.2235	2.2246	2.2257	2.2268	2.2279	2.2289
9.3	2.2300	2.2311	2.2322	2.2332	2.2343	2.2354	2.2364	2.2375	2.2386	2.2396
9.4	2.2407	2.2418	2.2428	2.2439	2.2450	2.2460	2.2471	2.2481	2.2492	2.2502
9.5	2.2513	2.2523	2.2534	2.2544	2.2555	2.2565	2.2576	2.2586	2.2597	2.2607
9.6	2.2618	2.2628	2.2638	2.2649	2.2659	2.2670	2.2680	2.2690	2.2701	2.2711
9.7	2.2721	2.2732	2.2742	2.2752	2.2762	2.2773	2.2783	2.2793	2.2803	2.2814
9.8	2.2824	2.2834	2.2844	2.2854	2.2865	2.2875	2.2885	2.2895	2.2905	2.2915
9.9	2.2925	2.2935	2.2946	2.2956	2.2966	2.2976	2.2986	2.2996	2.3006	2.3016

Table IV

Common Logarithms log t

t	0	1	2	3	4	5	6	7	8	9
1.0	0.0000	0.0043	0.0086	0.0128	0.0170	0.0212	0.0253	0.0294	0.0334	0.0374
1.1	0.0414	0.0453	0.0492	0.0531	0.0569	0.0607	0.0645	0.0682	0.0719	0.0755
1.2	0.0792	0.0828	0.0864	0.0899	0.0934	0.0969	0.1004	0.1038	0.1072	0.1106
1.3	0.1139	0.1173	0.1206	0.1239	0.1271	0.1303	0.1335	0.1367	0.1399	0.1430
1.4	0.1461	0.1492	0.1523	0.1553	0.1584	0.1614	0.1644	0.1673	0.1703	0.1732
1.5	0.1761	0.1790	0.1818	0.1847	0.1875	0.1903	0.1931	0.1959	0.1987	0.2014
1.6	0.2041	0.2068	0.2095	0.2122	0.2148	0.2175	0.2201	0.2227	0.2253	0.2279
1.7	0.2304	0.2330	0.2355	0.2380	0.2405	0.2430	0.2455	0.2480	0.2504	0.2529
1.8	0.2553	0.2577	0.2601	0.2625	0.2648	0.2672	0.2695	0.2718	0.2742	0.2765
1.9	0.2788	0.2810	0.2833	0.2856	0.2878	0.2900	0.2923	0.2945	0.2967	0.2989
2.0	0.3010	0.3032	0.3054	0.3075	0.3096	0.3118	0.3139	0.3160	0.3181	0.3201
2.1	0.3222	0.3243	0.3263	0.3284	0.3304	0.3324	0.3345	0.3365	0.3385	0.3404
2.2	0.3424	0.3444	0.3464	0.3483	0.3502	0.3522	0.3541	0.3560	0.3579	0.3598
2.3	0.3617	0.3636	0.3655	0.3674	0.3692	0.3711	0.3729	0.3747	0.3766	0.3784
2.4	0.3802	0.3820	0.3838	0.3856	0.3874	0.3892	0.3909	0.3927	0.3945	0.3962
2.5	0.3979	0.3997	0.4014	0.4031	0.4048	0.4065	0.4082	0.4099	0.4116	0.4133
2.6	0.4150	0.4166	0.4183	0.4200	0.4216	0.4232	0.4249	0.4265	0.4281	0.4298
2.7	0.4314	0.4330	0.4346	0.4362	0.4378	0.4393	0.4409	0.4425	0.4440	0.4456
2.8	0.4472	0.4487	0.4502	0.4518	0.4533	0.4548	0.4564	0.4579	0.4594	0.4609
2.9	0.4624	0.4639	0.4654	0.4669	0.4683	0.4698	0.4713	0.4728	0.4742	0.4757
3.0	0.4771	0.4786	0.4800	0.4814	0.4829	0.4843	0.4857	0.4871	0.4886	0.4900
3.1	0.4914	0.4928	0.4942	0.4955	0.4969	0.4983	0.4997	0.5011	0.5024	0.5038
3.2	0.5051	0.5065	0.5079	0.5092	0.5105	0.5119	0.5132	0.5145	0.5159	0.5172
3.3	0.5185	0.5198	0.5211	0.5224	0.5237	0.5250	0.5263	0.5276	0.5289	0.5302
3.4	0.5315	0.5328	0.5340	0.5353	0.5366	0.5378	0.5391	0.5403	0.5416	0.5428
3.5	0.5441	0.5453	0.5465	0.5478	0.5490	0.5502	0.5514	0.5527	0.5539	0.5551
3.6	0.5563	0.5575	0.5587	0.5599	0.5611	0.5623	0.5635	0.5647	0.5658	0.5670
3.7	0.5682	0.5694	0.5705	0.5717	0.5729	0.5740	0.5752	0.5763	0.5775	0.5786
3.8	0.5798	0.5809	0.5821	0.5832	0.5843	0.5855	0.5866	0.5877	0.5888	0.5899
3.9	0.5911	0.5922	0.5933	0.5944	0.5955	0.5966	0.5977	0.5988	0.5999	0.6010
4.0	0.6021	0.6031	0.6042	0.6053	0.6064	0.6075	0.6085	0.6096	0.6107	0.6117
4.1	0.6128	0.6138	0.6149	0.6160	0.6170	0.6180	0.6191	0.6201	0.6212	0.6222
4.2	0.6232	0.6243	0.6253	0.6263	0.6274	0.6284	0.6294	0.6304	0.6314	0.6325
4.3	0.6335	0.6345	0.6355	0.6365	0.6375	0.6385	0.6395	0.6405	0.6415	0.6425
4.4	0.6435	0.6444	0.6454	0.6464	0.6474	0.6484	0.6493	0.6503	0.6513	0.6522
4.5	0.6532	0.6542	0.6551	0.6561	0.6571	0.6580	0.6590	0.6599	0.6609	0.6618
4.6	0.6628	0.6637	0.6646	0.6656	0.6665	0.6675	0.6684	0.6693	0.6702	0.6712
4.7	0.6721	0.6730	0.6739	0.6749	0.6758	0.6767	0.6776	0.6785	0.6794	0.6803
4.8	0.6812	0.6821	0.6830	0.6839	0.6848	0.6857	0.6866	0.6875	0.6884	0.6893
4.9	0.6902	0.6911	0.6920	0.6928	0.6937	0.6946	0.6955	0.6964	0.6972	0.6981
5.0	0.6990	0.6998	0.7007	0.7016	0.7024	0.7033	0.7042	0.7050	0.7059	0.7067
5.1	0.7076	0.7084	0.7093	0.7101	0.7110	0.7118	0.7126	0.7135	0.7143	0.7152
5.2	0.7160	0.7168	0.7177	0.7185	0.7193	0.7202	0.7210	0.7218	0.7226	0.7235
5.3	0.7243	0.7251	0.7259	0.7267	0.7275	0.7284	0.7292	0.7300	0.7308	0.7316
5.4	0.7324	0.7332	0.7340	0.7348	0.7356	0.7364	0.7372	0.7380	0.7388	0.7396
t	0	1	2	3	4	5	6	7	8	9

Table IV (*continued*)

t	0	1	2	3	4	5	6	7	8	9
5.5	0.7404	0.7412	0.7419	0.7427	0.7435	0.7443	0.7451	0.7459	0.7466	0.7474
5.6	0.7482	0.7490	0.7497	0.7505	0.7513	0.7520	0.7528	0.7536	0.7543	0.7551
5.7	0.7559	0.7566	0.7574	0.7582	0.7589	0.7597	0.7604	0.7612	0.7619	0.7627
5.8	0.7634	0.7642	0.7649	0.7657	0.7664	0.7672	0.7679	0.7686	0.7694	0.7701
5.9	0.7709	0.7716	0.7723	0.7731	0.7738	0.7745	0.7752	0.7760	0.7767	0.7774
6.0	0.7782	0.7789	0.7796	0.7803	0.7810	0.7818	0.7825	0.7832	0.7839	0.7846
6.1	0.7853	0.7860	0.7868	0.7875	0.7882	0.7889	0.7896	0.7903	0.7910	0.7917
6.2	0.7924	0.7931	0.7938	0.7945	0.7952	0.7959	0.7966	0.7973	0.7980	0.7987
6.3	0.7993	0.8000	0.8007	0.8014	0.8021	0.8028	0.8035	0.8041	0.8048	0.8055
6.4	0.8062	0.8069	0.8075	0.8082	0.8089	0.8096	0.8102	0.8109	0.8116	0.8122
6.5	0.8129	0.8136	0.8142	0.8149	0.8156	0.8162	0.8169	0.8176	0.8182	0.8189
6.6	0.8195	0.8202	0.8209	0.8215	0.8222	0.8228	0.8235	0.8241	0.8248	0.8254
6.7	0.8261	0.8267	0.8274	0.8280	0.8287	0.8293	0.8299	0.8306	0.8312	0.8319
6.8	0.8325	0.8331	0.8338	0.8344	0.8351	0.8357	0.8363	0.8370	0.8376	0.8382
6.9	0.8388	0.8395	0.8401	0.8407	0.8414	0.8420	0.8426	0.8432	0.8439	0.8445
7.0	0.8451	0.8457	0.8463	0.8470	0.8476	0.8482	0.8488	0.8494	0.8500	0.8506
7.1	0.8513	0.8519	0.8525	0.8531	0.8537	0.8543	0.8549	0.8555	0.8561	0.8567
7.2	0.8573	0.8579	0.8585	0.8591	0.8597	0.8603	0.8609	0.8615	0.8621	0.8627
7.3	0.8633	0.8639	0.8645	0.8651	0.8657	0.8663	0.8669	0.8675	0.8681	0.8686
7.4	0.8692	0.8698	0.8704	0.8710	0.8716	0.8722	0.8727	0.8733	0.8739	0.8745
7.5	0.8751	0.8756	0.8762	0.8768	0.8774	0.8779	0.8785	0.8791	0.8797	0.8802
7.6	0.8808	0.8814	0.8820	0.8825	0.8831	0.8837	0.8842	0.8848	0.8854	0.8859
7.7	0.8865	0.8871	0.8876	0.8882	0.8887	0.8893	0.8899	0.8904	0.8910	0.8915
7.8	0.8921	0.8927	0.8932	0.8938	0.8943	0.8949	0.8954	0.8960	0.8965	0.8971
7.9	0.8976	0.8982	0.8987	0.8993	0.8998	0.9004	0.9009	0.9015	0.9020	0.9025
8.0	0.9031	0.9036	0.9042	0.9047	0.9053	0.9058	0.9063	0.9069	0.9074	0.9079
8.1	0.9085	0.9090	0.9096	0.9101	0.9106	0.9112	0.9117	0.9122	0.9128	0.9133
8.2	0.9138	0.9143	0.9149	0.9154	0.9159	0.9165	0.9170	0.9175	0.9180	0.9186
8.3	0.9191	0.9196	0.9201	0.9206	0.9212	0.9217	0.9222	0.9227	0.9232	0.9238
8.4	0.9243	0.9248	0.9253	0.9258	0.9263	0.9269	0.9274	0.9279	0.9284	0.9289
8.5	0.9294	0.9299	0.9304	0.9309	0.9315	0.9320	0.9325	0.9330	0.9335	0.9340
8.6	0.9345	0.9350	0.9355	0.9360	0.9365	0.9370	0.9375	0.9380	0.9385	0.9390
8.7	0.9395	0.9400	0.9405	0.9410	0.9415	0.9420	0.9425	0.9430	0.9435	0.9440
8.8	0.9445	0.9450	0.9455	0.9460	0.9465	0.9469	0.9474	0.9479	0.9484	0.9489
8.9	0.9494	0.9499	0.9504	0.9509	0.9513	0.9518	0.9523	0.9528	0.9533	0.9538
9.0	0.9542	0.9547	0.9552	0.9557	0.9562	0.9566	0.9571	0.9576	0.9581	0.9586
9.1	0.9590	0.9595	0.9600	0.9605	0.9609	0.9614	0.9619	0.9624	0.9628	0.9633
9.2	0.9638	0.9643	0.9647	0.9652	0.9657	0.9661	0.9666	0.9671	0.9675	0.9680
9.3	0.9685	0.9689	0.9694	0.9699	0.9703	0.9708	0.9713	0.9717	0.9722	0.9727
9.4	0.9731	0.9736	0.9741	0.9745	0.9750	0.9754	0.9759	0.9763	0.9768	0.9773
9.5	0.9777	0.9782	0.9786	0.9791	0.9795	0.9800	0.9805	0.9809	0.9814	0.9818
9.6	0.9823	0.9827	0.9832	0.9836	0.9841	0.9845	0.9850	0.9854	0.9859	0.9863
9.7	0.9868	0.9872	0.9877	0.9881	0.9886	0.9890	0.9894	0.9899	0.9903	0.9908
9.8	0.9912	0.9917	0.9921	0.9926	0.9930	0.9934	0.9939	0.9943	0.9948	0.9952
9.9	0.9956	0.9961	0.9965	0.9969	0.9974	0.9978	0.9983	0.9987	0.9991	0.9996
t	0	1	2	3	4	5	6	7	8	9

Table V

Values of Trigonometric Functions

Degrees	Radians	sin	cos	tan	cot	sec	csc		
0° 00′	.0000	.0000	1.0000	.0000	——	1.000	——	1.5708	**90° 00′**
10	029	029	000	029	343.8	000	343.8	679	50
20	058	058	000	058	171.9	000	171.9	650	40
30	.0087	.0087	1.0000	.0087	114.6	1.000	114.6	1.5621	30
40	116	116	.9999	116	85.94	000	85.95	592	20
50	145	145	999	145	68.75	000	68.76	563	10
1° 00′	.0175	.0175	.9998	.0175	57.29	1.000	57.30	1.5533	**89° 00′**
10	204	204	998	204	49.10	000	49.11	504	50
20	233	233	997	233	42.96	000	42.98	475	40
30	.0262	.0262	.9997	.0262	38.19	1.000	38.20	1.5446	30
40	291	291	996	291	34.37	000	34.38	417	20
50	320	320	995	320	31.24	001	31.26	388	10
2° 00′	.0349	.0349	.9994	.0349	28.64	1.001	28.65	1.5359	**88° 00′**
10	378	378	993	378	26.43	001	26.45	330	50
20	407	407	992	407	24.54	001	24.56	301	40
30	.0436	.0436	.9990	.0437	22.90	1.001	22.93	1.5272	30
40	465	465	989	466	21.47	001	21.49	243	20
50	495	494	988	495	20.21	001	20.23	213	10
3° 00′	.0524	.0523	.9986	.0524	19.08	1.001	19.11	1.5184	**87° 00′**
10	553	552	985	553	18.07	002	18.10	155	50
20	582	581	983	582	17.17	002	17.20	126	40
30	.0611	.0610	.9981	.0612	16.35	1.002	16.38	1.5097	30
40	640	640	980	641	15.60	002	15.64	068	20
50	669	669	978	670	14.92	002	14.96	039	10
4° 00′	.0698	.0698	.9976	.0699	14.30	1.002	14.34	1.5010	**86° 00′**
10	727	727	974	729	13.73	003	13.76	981	50
20	756	756	971	758	13.20	003	13.23	952	40
30	.0785	.0785	.9969	.0787	12.71	1.003	12.75	1.4923	30
40	814	814	967	816	12.25	003	12.29	893	20
50	844	843	964	846	11.83	004	11.87	864	10
5° 00′	.0873	.0872	.9962	.0875	11.43	1.004	11.47	1.4835	**85° 00′**
10	902	901	959	904	11.06	004	11.10	806	50
20	931	929	957	934	10.71	004	10.76	777	40
30	.0960	.0958	.9954	.0963	10.39	1.005	10.43	1.4748	30
40	989	987	951	992	10.08	005	10.13	719	20
50	.1018	.1016	948	.1022	9.788	005	9.839	690	10
6° 00′	.1047	.1045	.9945	.1051	9.514	1.006	9.567	1.4661	**84° 00′**
10	076	074	942	080	9.255	006	9.309	632	50
20	105	103	939	110	9.010	006	9.065	603	40
30	.1134	.1132	.9936	.1139	8.777	1.006	8.834	1.4573	30
40	164	161	932	169	8.556	007	8.614	544	20
50	193	190	929	198	8.345	007	8.405	515	10
7° 00′	.1222	.1219	.9925	.1228	8.144	1.008	8.206	1.4486	**83° 00′**
10	251	248	922	257	7.953	008	8.016	457	50
20	280	276	918	287	7.770	008	7.834	428	40
30	.1309	.1305	.9914	.1317	7.596	1.009	7.661	1.4399	30
40	338	334	911	346	7.429	009	7.496	370	20
50	367	363	907	376	7.269	009	7.337	341	10
8° 00′	.1396	.1392	.9903	.1405	7.115	1.010	7.185	1.4312	**82° 00′**
10	425	421	899	435	6.968	010	7.040	283	50
20	454	449	894	465	6.827	011	6.900	254	40
30	.1484	.1478	.9890	.1495	6.691	1.011	6.765	1.4224	30
40	513	507	886	524	6.561	012	6.636	195	20
50	542	536	881	554	6.435	012	6.512	166	10
9° 00′	.1571	.1564	.9877	.1584	6.314	1.012	6.392	1.4137	**81° 00′**
		cos	sin	cot	tan	csc	sec	Radians	Degrees

Table V (continued)

Degrees	Radians	sin	cos	tan	cot	sec	csc		
9° 00′	.1571	.1564	.9877	.1584	6.314	1.012	6.392	1.4137	81° 00′
10	600	593	872	614	197	013	277	108	50
20	629	622	868	644	084	013	166	079	40
30	.1658	.1650	.9863	.1673	5.976	1.014	6.059	1.4050	30
40	687	679	858	703	871	014	5.955	1.4021	20
50	716	708	853	733	769	015	855	992	10
10° 00′	.1745	.1736	.9848	.1763	5.671	1.015	5.759	1.3963	80° 00′
10	774	765	843	793	576	016	665	934	50
20	804	794	838	823	485	016	575	904	40
30	.1833	.1822	.9833	.1853	5.396	1.017	5.487	1.3875	30
40	862	851	827	883	309	018	403	846	20
50	891	880	822	914	226	018	320	817	10
11° 00′	.1920	.1908	.9816	.1944	5.145	1.019	5.241	1.3788	79° 00′
10	949	937	811	974	066	019	164	759	50
20	978	965	805	.2004	4.989	020	089	730	40
30	.2007	.1994	.9799	.2035	4.915	1.020	5.016	1.3701	30
40	036	.2022	793	065	843	021	4.945	672	20
50	065	051	787	095	773	022	876	643	10
12° 00′	.2094	.2079	.9781	.2126	4.705	1.022	4.810	1.3614	78° 00′
10	123	108	775	156	638	023	745	584	50
20	153	136	769	186	574	024	682	555	40
30	.2182	.2164	.9763	.2217	4.511	1.024	4.620	1.3526	30
40	211	193	757	247	449	025	560	497	20
50	240	221	750	278	390	026	502	468	10
13° 00′	.2269	.2250	.9744	.2309	4.331	1.026	4.445	1.3439	77° 00′
10	298	278	737	339	275	027	390	410	50
20	327	306	730	370	219	028	336	381	40
30	.2356	.2334	.9724	.2401	4.165	1.028	4.284	1.3352	30
40	385	363	717	432	113	029	232	323	20
50	414	391	710	462	061	030	182	294	10
14° 00′	.2443	.2419	.9703	.2493	4.011	1.031	4.134	1.3265	76° 00′
10	473	447	696	524	3.962	031	086	235	50
20	502	476	689	555	914	032	039	206	40
30	.2531	.2504	.9681	.2586	3.867	1.033	3.994	1.3177	30
40	560	532	674	617	821	034	950	148	20
50	589	560	667	648	776	034	906	119	10
15° 00′	.2618	.2588	.9659	.2679	3.732	1.035	3.864	1.3090	75° 00′
10	647	616	652	711	689	036	822	061	50
20	676	644	644	742	647	037	782	032	40
30	.2705	.2672	.9636	.2773	3.606	1.038	3.742	1.3003	30
40	734	700	628	805	566	039	703	974	20
50	763	728	621	836	526	039	665	945	10
16° 00′	.2793	.2756	.9613	.2867	3.487	1.040	3.628	1.2915	74° 00′
10	822	784	605	899	450	041	592	886	50
20	851	812	596	931	412	042	556	857	40
30	.2880	.2840	.9588	.2962	3.376	1.043	3.521	1.2828	30
40	909	868	580	994	340	044	487	799	20
50	938	896	572	.3026	305	045	453	770	10
17° 00′	.2967	.2924	.9563	.3057	3.271	1.046	3.420	1.2741	73° 00′
10	996	952	555	089	237	047	388	712	50
20	.3025	979	546	121	204	048	356	683	40
30	.3054	.3007	.9537	.3153	3.172	1.049	3.326	1.2654	30
40	083	035	528	185	140	049	295	625	20
50	113	062	520	217	108	050	265	595	10
18° 00′	.3142	.3090	.9511	.3249	3.078	1.051	3.236	1.2566	72° 00′
		cos	sin	cot	tan	csc	sec	Radians	Degrees

Table V (*continued*)

Degrees	Radians	sin	cos	tan	cot	sec	csc		
18° 00′	.3142	.3090	.9511	.3249	3.078	1.051	3.236	1.2566	**72° 00′**
10	171	118	502	281	047	052	207	537	50
20	200	145	492	314	018	053	179	508	40
30	.3229	.3173	.9483	.3346	2.989	1.054	3.152	1.2479	30
40	258	201	474	378	960	056	124	450	20
50	287	228	465	411	932	057	098	421	10
19° 00′	.3316	.3256	.9455	.3443	2.904	1.058	3.072	1.2392	**71° 00′**
10	345	283	446	476	877	059	046	363	50
20	374	311	436	508	850	060	021	334	40
30	.3403	.3338	.9426	.3541	2.824	1.061	2.996	1.2305	30
40	432	365	417	574	798	062	971	275	20
50	462	393	407	607	773	063	947	246	10
20° 00′	.3491	.3420	.9397	.3640	2.747	1.064	2.924	1.2217	**70° 00′**
10	520	448	387	673	723	065	901	188	50
20	549	475	377	706	699	066	878	159	40
30	.3578	.3502	.9367	.3739	2.675	1.068	2.855	1.2130	30
40	607	529	356	772	651	069	833	101	20
50	636	557	346	805	628	070	812	072	10
21° 00′	.3665	.3584	.9336	.3839	2.605	1.071	2.790	1.2043	**69° 00′**
10	694	611	325	872	583	072	769	1.2014	50
20	723	638	315	906	560	074	749	985	40
30	.3752	.3665	.9304	.3939	2.539	1.075	2.729	1.1956	30
40	782	692	293	973	517	076	709	926	20
50	811	719	283	.4006	496	077	689	897	10
22° 00′	.3840	.3746	.9272	.4040	2.475	1.079	2.669	1.1868	**68° 00′**
10	869	773	261	074	455	080	650	839	50
20	898	800	250	108	434	081	632	810	40
30	.3927	.3827	.9239	.4142	2.414	1.082	2.613	1.1781	30
40	956	854	228	176	394	084	595	752	20
50	985	881	216	210	375	085	577	723	10
23° 00′	.4014	.3907	.9205	.4245	2.356	1.086	2.559	1.1694	**67° 00′**
10	043	934	194	279	337	088	542	665	50
20	072	961	182	314	318	089	525	636	40
30	.4102	.3987	.9171	.4348	2.300	1.090	2.508	1.1606	30
40	131	.4014	159	383	282	092	491	577	20
50	160	041	147	417	264	093	475	548	10
24° 00′	.4189	.4067	.9135	.4452	2.246	1.095	2.459	1.1519	**66° 00′**
10	218	094	124	487	229	096	443	490	50
20	247	120	112	522	211	097	427	461	40
30	.4276	.4147	.9100	.4557	2.194	1.099	2.411	1.1432	30
40	305	173	088	592	177	100	396	403	20
50	334	200	075	628	161	102	381	374	10
25° 00′	.4363	.4226	.9063	.4663	2.145	1.103	2.366	1.1345	**65° 00′**
10	392	253	051	699	128	105	352	316	50
20	422	279	038	734	112	106	337	286	40
30	.4451	.4305	.9026	.4770	2.097	1.108	2.323	1.1257	30
40	480	331	013	806	081	109	309	228	20
50	509	358	001	841	066	111	295	199	10
26° 00′	.4538	.4384	.8988	.4877	2.050	1.113	2.281	1.1170	**64° 00′**
10	567	410	975	913	035	114	268	141	50
20	596	436	962	950	020	116	254	112	40
30	.4625	.4462	.8949	.4986	2.006	1.117	2.241	1.1083	30
40	654	488	936	.5022	1.991	119	228	054	20
50	683	514	923	059	977	121	215	1.1025	10
27° 00′	.4712	.4540	.8910	.5095	1.963	1.122	2.203	1.0996	**63° 00′**
		cos	sin	cot	tan	csc	sec	Radians	Degrees

Table V (*continued*)

Degrees	Radians	sin	cos	tan	cot	sec	csc		
27° 00′	.4712	.4540	.8910	.5095	1.963	1.122	2.203	1.0996	**63° 00′**
10	741	566	897	132	949	124	190	966	50
20	771	592	884	169	935	126	178	937	40
30	.4800	.4617	.8870	.5206	1.921	1.127	2.166	1.0908	30
40	829	643	857	243	907	129	154	879	20
50	858	669	843	280	894	131	142	850	10
28° 00′	.4887	.4695	.8829	.5317	1.881	1.133	2.130	1.0821	**62° 00′**
10	916	720	816	354	868	134	118	792	50
20	945	746	802	392	855	136	107	763	40
30	.4974	.4772	.8788	.5430	1.842	1.138	2.096	1.0734	30
40	.5003	797	774	467	829	140	085	705	20
50	032	823	760	505	816	142	074	676	10
29° 00′	.5061	.4848	.8746	.5543	1.804	1.143	2.063	1.0647	**61° 00′**
10	091	874	732	581	792	145	052	617	50
20	120	899	718	619	780	147	041	588	40
30	.5149	.4924	.8704	.5658	1.767	1.149	2.031	1.0559	30
40	178	950	689	696	756	151	020	530	20
50	207	975	675	735	744	153	010	501	10
30° 00′	.5236	.5000	.8660	.5774	1.732	1.155	2.000	1.0472	**60° 00′**
10	265	025	646	812	720	157	1.990	443	50
20	294	050	631	851	709	159	980	414	40
30	.5323	.5075	.8616	.5890	1.698	1.161	1.970	1.0385	30
40	352	100	601	930	686	163	961	356	20
50	381	125	587	969	675	165	951	327	10
31° 00′	.5411	.5150	.8572	.6009	1.664	1.167	1.942	1.0297	**59° 00′**
10	440	175	557	048	653	169	932	268	50
20	469	200	542	088	643	171	923	239	40
30	.5498	.5225	.8526	.6128	1.632	1.173	1.914	1.0210	30
40	527	250	511	168	621	175	905	181	20
50	556	275	496	208	611	177	896	152	10
32° 00′	.5585	.5299	.8480	.6249	1.600	1.179	1.887	1.0123	**58° 00′**
10	614	324	465	289	590	181	878	094	50
20	643	348	450	330	580	184	870	065	40
30	.5672	.5373	.8434	.6371	1.570	1.186	1.861	1.0036	30
40	701	398	418	412	560	188	853	1.0007	20
50	730	422	403	453	550	190	844	977	10
33° 00′	.5760	.5446	.8387	.6494	1.540	1.192	1.836	.9948	**57° 00′**
10	789	471	371	536	530	195	828	919	50
20	818	495	355	577	520	197	820	890	40
30	.5847	.5519	.8339	.6619	1.511	1.199	1.812	.9861	30
40	876	544	323	661	501	202	804	832	20
50	905	568	307	703	1.492	204	796	803	10
34° 00′	.5934	.5592	.8290	.6745	1.483	1.206	1.788	.9774	**56° 00′**
10	963	616	274	787	473	209	781	745	50
20	992	640	258	830	464	211	773	716	40
30	.6021	.5664	.8241	.6873	1.455	1.213	1.766	.9687	30
40	050	688	225	916	446	216	758	657	20
50	080	712	208	959	437	218	751	628	10
35° 00′	.6109	.5736	.8192	.7002	1.428	1.221	1.743	.9599	**55° 00′**
10	138	760	175	046	419	223	736	570	50
20	167	783	158	089	411	226	729	541	40
30	.6196	.5807	.8141	.7133	1.402	1.228	1.722	.9512	30
40	225	831	124	177	393	231	715	483	20
50	254	854	107	221	385	233	708	454	10
36° 00′	.6283	.5878	.8090	.7265	1.376	1.236	1.701	.9425	**54° 00′**
		cos	sin	cot	tan	csc	sec	Radians	Degrees

Table V (*continued*)

Degrees	Radians	sin	cos	tan	cot	sec	csc		
36° 00'	.6283	.5878	.8090	.7265	1.376	1.236	1.701	.9425	**54° 00'**
10	312	901	073	310	368	239	695	396	50
20	341	925	056	355	360	241	688	367	40
30	.6370	.5948	.8039	.7400	1.351	1.244	1.681	.9338	30
40	400	972	021	445	343	247	675	308	20
50	429	995	004	490	335	249	668	279	10
37° 00'	.6458	.6018	.7986	.7536	1.327	1.252	1.662	.9250	**53° 00'**
10	487	041	969	581	319	255	655	221	50
20	516	065	951	627	311	258	649	192	40
30	.6545	.6088	.7934	.7673	1.303	1.260	1.643	.9163	30
40	574	111	916	720	295	263	636	134	20
50	603	134	898	766	288	266	630	105	10
38° 00'	.6632	.6157	.7880	.7813	1.280	1.269	1.624	.9076	**52° 00'**
10	661	180	862	860	272	272	618	047	50
20	690	202	844	907	265	275	612	.9018	40
30	.6720	.6225	.7826	.7954	1.257	1.278	1.606	.8988	30
40	749	248	808	.8002	250	281	601	959	20
50	778	271	790	050	242	284	595	930	10
39° 00'	.6807	.6293	.7771	.8098	1.235	1.287	1.589	.8901	**51° 00'**
10	836	316	753	146	228	290	583	872	50
20	865	338	735	195	220	293	578	843	40
30	.6894	.6361	.7716	.8243	1.213	1.296	1.572	.8814	30
40	923	383	698	292	206	299	567	785	20
50	952	406	679.	342	199	302	561	756	10
40° 00'	.6981	.6428	.7660	.8391	1.192	1.305	1.556	.8727	**50° 00'**
10	.7010	450	642	441	185	309	550	698	50
20	039	472	623	491	178	312	545	668	40
30	.7069	.6494	.7604	.8541	1.171	1.315	1.540	.8639	30
40	098	517	585	591	164	318	535	610	20
50	127	539	566	642	157	322	529	581	10
41° 00'	.7156	.6561	.7547	.8693	1.150	1.325	1.524	.8552	**49° 00'**
10	185	583	528	744	144	328	519	523	50
20	214	604	509	796	137	332	514	494	40
30	.7243	.6626	.7490	.8847	1.130	1.335	1.509	.8465	30
40	272	648	470	899	124	339	504	436	20
50	301	670	451	952	117	342	499	407	10
42° 00'	.7330	.6691	.7431	.9004	1.111	1.346	1.494	.8378	**48° 00'**
10	359	713	412	057	104	349	490	348	50
20	389	734	392	110	098	353	485	319	40
30	.7418	.6756	.7373	.9163	1.091	1.356	1.480	.8290	30
40	447	777	353	217	085	360	476	261	20
50	476	799	333	271	079	364	471	232	10
43° 00'	.7505	.6820	.7314	.9325	1.072	1.367	1.466	.8203	**47° 00'**
10	534	841	294	380	066	371	462	174	50
20	563	862	274	435	060	375	457	145	40
30	.7592	.6884	.7254	.9490	1.054	1.379	1.453	.8116	30
40	621	905	234	545	048	382	448	087	20
50	650	926	214	601	042	386	444	058	10
44° 00'	.7679	.6947	.7193	.9657	1.036	1.390	1.440	.8029	**46° 00'**
10	709	967	173	713	030	394	435	999	50
20	738	988	153	770	024	398	431	970	40
30	.7767	.7009	.7133	.9827	1.018	1.402	1.427	.7941	30
40	796	030	112	884	012	406	423	912	20
50	825	050	092	942	006	410	418	883	10
45° 00'	.7854	.7071	.7071	1.000	1.000	1.414	1.414	.7854	**45° 00'**
		cos	sin	cot	tan	csc	sec	Radians	Degrees

Table VI

Logarithms of Trigonometric Functions

Degrees	$\log_{10}$ sine	$\log_{10}$ tangent	$\log_{10}$ cotangent	$\log_{10}$ cosine	
0° 00′					**90° 00′**
10′	.4637—3	.4637—3	2.5363	0000	50′
20′	.7648—3	.7648—3	2.2352	.0000	40′
30′	.9408—3	.9409—3	2.0591	.0000	30′
40′	.0658—2	.0658—2	1.9342	.0000	20′
50′	.1627—2	.1627—2	1.8373	.0000	10′
1° 00′	.2419—2	.2419—2	1.7581	.9999—1	**89° 00′**
10′	.3088—2	.3089—2	1.6911	.9999—1	50′
20′	.3668—2	.3669—2	1.6331	.9999—1	40′
30′	.4179—2	.4181—2	1.5819	.9999—1	30′
40′	.4637—2	.4638—2	1.5362	.9998—1	20′
50′	.5050—2	.5053—2	1.4947	.9998—1	10′
2° 00′	.5428—2	.5431—2	1.4569	.9997—1	**88° 00′**
10′	.5776—2	.5779—2	1.4221	.9997—1	50′
20′	.6097—2	.6101—2	1.3899	.9996—1	40′
30′	.6397—2	.6401—2	1.3599	.9996—1	30′
40′	.6677—2	.6682—2	1.3318	.9995—1	20′
50′	.6940—2	.6945—2	1.3055	.9995—1	10′
3° 00′	.7188—2	.7194—2	1.2806	.9994—1	**87° 00′**
10′	.7423—2	.7429—2	1.2571	.9993—1	50′
20′	.7645—2	.7652—2	1.2348	.9993—1	40′
30′	.7857—2	.7865—2	1.2135	.9992—1	30′
40′	.8059—2	.8067—2	1.1933	.9991—1	20′
50′	.8251—2	.8261—2	1.1739	.9990—1	10′
4° 00′	.8436—2	.8446—2	1.1554	.9989—1	**86° 00′**
10′	.8613—2	.8624—2	1.1376	.9989—1	50′
20′	.8783—2	.8795—2	1.1205	.9988—1	40′
30′	.8946—2	.8960—2	1.1040	.9987—1	30′
40′	.9104—2	.9118—2	1.0882	.9986—1	20′
50′	.9256—2	.9272—2	1.0728	.9985—1	10′
5° 00′	.9403—2	.9420—2	1.0580	.9983—1	**85° 00′**
10′	.9545—2	.9563—2	1.0437	.9982—1	50′
20′	.9682—2	.9701—2	1.0299	.9981—1	40′
30′	.9816—2	.9836—2	1.0164	.9980—1	30′
40′	.9945—2	.9966—2	1.0034	.9979—1	20′
50′	.0070—1	.0093—1	.9907	.9977—1	10′
6° 00′	.0192—1	.0216—1	.9784	.9976—1	**84° 00′**
10′	.0311—1	.0336—1	.9664	.9975—1	50′
20′	.0426—1	.0453—1	.9547	.9973—1	40′
30′	.0539—1	.0567—1	.9433	.9972—1	30′
40′	.0648—1	.0678—1	.9322	.9971—1	20′
50′	.0755—1	.0786—1	.9214	.9969—1	10′
7° 00′	.0859—1	.0891—1	.9109	.9968—1	**83° 00′**
10′	.0961—1	.0995—1	.9005	.9966—1	50′
20′	.1060—1	.1096—1	.8904	.9964—1	40′
30′	.1157—1	.1194—1	.8806	.9963—1	30′
40′	.1252—1	.1291—1	.8709	.9961—1	20′
50′	.1345—1	.1385—1	.8615	.9959—1	10′
8° 00′	.1436—1	.1478—1	.8522	.9958—1	**82° 00′**
10′	.1525—1	.1569—1	.8431	.9956—1	50′
20′	.1612—1	.1658—1	.8342	.9954—1	40′
30′	.1697—1	.1745—1	.8255	.9952—1	30′
40′	.1781—1	.1831—1	.8169	.9950—1	20′
50′	.1863—1	.1915—1	.8085	.9948—1	10′
9° 00′	.1943—1	.1997—1	.3003	.9946—1	**81° 00′**
	$\log_{10}$ cosine	$\log_{10}$ cotangent	$\log_{10}$ tangent	$\log_{10}$ sine	Degrees

Table VI (*continued*)

Degrees	$\log_{10}$sine	$\log_{10}$tangent	$\log_{10}$cotangent	$\log_{10}$cosine	
9° 00′	.1943—1	.1997—1	.8003	.9946—1	**81° 00′**
10′	.2022—1	.2078—1	.7922	.9944—1	50′
20′	.2100—1	.2158—1	.7842	.9942—1	40′
30′	.2176—1	.2236—1	.7764	.9940—1	30′
40′	.2251—1	.2313—1	.7687	.9938—1	20′
50′	.2324—1	.2389—1	.7611	.9936—1	10′
10° 00′	.2397—1	.2463—1	.7537	.9934—1	**80° 00′**
10′	.2468—1	.2536—1	.7464	.9931—1	50′
20′	.2538—1	.2609—1	.7391	.9929—1	40′
30′	.2606—1	.2680—1	.7320	.9927—1	30′
40′	.2674—1	.2750—1	.7250	.9924—1	20′
50′	.2740—1	.2819—1	.7181	.9922—1	10′
11° 00′	.2806—1	.2887—1	.7113	.9919—1	**79° 00′**
10′	.2870—1	.2953—1	.7047	.9917—1	50′
20′	.2934—1	.3020—1	.6980	.9914—1	40′
30′	.2997—1	.3085—1	.6915	.9912—1	30′
40′	.3058—1	.3149—1	.6851	.9909—1	20′
50′	.3119—1	.3212—1	.6788	.9907—1	10′
12° 00′	.3179—1	.3275—1	.6725	.9904—1	**78° 00′**
10′	.3238—1	.3336—1	.6664	.9901—1	50′
20′	.3296—1	.3397—1	.6603	.9899—1	40′
30′	.3353—1	.3458—1	.6542	.9896—1	30′
40′	.3410—1	.3517—1	.6483	.9893—1	20′
50′	.3466—1	.3576—1	.6424	.9890—1	10′
13° 00′	.3521—1	.3634—1	.6366	.9887—1	**77° 00′**
10′	.3575—1	.3691—1	.6309	.9884—1	50′
20′	.3629—1	.3748—1	.6252	.9881—1	40′
30′	.3682—1	.3804—1	.6196	.9878—1	30′
40′	.3734—1	.3859—1	.6141	.9875—1	20′
50′	.3786—1	.3914—1	.6086	.9872—1	10′
14° 00′	.3837—1	.3968—1	.6032	.9869—1	**76° 00′**
10′	.3887—1	.4021—1	.5979	.9866—1	50′
20′	.3937—1	.4074—1	.5926	.9863—1	40′
30′	.3986—1	.4127—1	.5873	.9859—1	30′
40′	.4035—1	.4178—1	.5822	.9856—1	20′
50′	.4083—1	.4230—1	.5770	.9853—1	10′
15° 00′	.4130—1	.4281—1	.5719	.9849—1	**75° 00′**
10′	.4177—1	.4331—1	.5669	.9846—1	50′
20′	.4223—1	.4381—1	.5619	.9843—1	40′
30′	.4269—1	.4430—1	.5570	.9839—1	30′
40′	.4314—1	.4479—1	.5521	.9836—1	20′
50′	.4359—1	.4527—1	.5473	.9832—1	10′
16° 00′	.4403—1	.4575—1	.5425	.9828—1	**74° 00′**
10′	.4447—1	.4622—1	.5378	.9825—1	50′
20′	.4491—1	.4669—1	.5331	.9821—1	40′
30′	.4533—1	.4716—1	.5284	.9817—1	30′
40′	.4576—1	.4762—1	.5238	.9814—1	20′
50′	.4618—1	.4808—1	.5192	.9810—1	10′
17° 00′	.4659—1	.4853—1	.5147	.9806—1	**73° 00′**
10′	.4700—1	.4898—1	.5102	.9802—1	50′
20′	.4741—1	.4943—1	.5057	.9798—1	40′
30′	.4781—1	.4987—1	.5013	.9794—1	30′
40′	.4821—1	.5031—1	.4969	.9790—1	20′
50′	.4861—1	.5075—1	.4925	.9786—1	10′
18° 00′	.4900—1	.5118—1	.4882	.9782—1	**72° 00′**
	$\log_{10}$cosine	$\log_{10}$cotangent	$\log_{10}$tangent	$\log_{10}$sine	Degrees

Table VI (*continued*)

Degrees	$\log_{10}$sine	$\log_{10}$tangent	$\log_{10}$cotangent	$\log_{10}$cosine	
18° 00′	.4900—1	.5118—1	.4882	.9782—1	**72° 00′**
10′	.4939—1	.5161—1	.4839	.9778—1	50′
20′	.4977—1	.5203—1	.4797	.9774—1	40′
30′	.5015—1	.5245—1	.4755	.9770—1	30′
40′	.5052—1	.5287—1	.4713	.9765—1	20′
50′	.5090—1	.5329—1	.4671	.9761—1	10′
19° 00′	.5126—1	.5370—1	.4630	.9757—1	**71° 00′**
10′	.5163—1	.5411—1	.4589	.9752—1	50′
20′	.5199—1	.5451—1	.4549	.9748—1	40′
30′	.5235—1	.5491—1	.4509	.9743—1	30′
40′	.5270—1	.5531—1	.4469	.9739—1	20′
50′	.5306—1	.5571—1	.4429	.9734—1	10′
20° 00′	.5341—1	.5611—1	.4389	.9730—1	**70° 00′**
10′	.5375—1	.5650—1	.4350	.9725—1	50′
20′	.5409—1	.5689—1	.4311	.9721—1	40′
30′	.5443—1	.5727—1	.4273	.9716—1	30′
40′	.5477—1	.5766—1	.4234	.9711—1	20′
50′	.5510—1	.5804—1	.4196	.9706—1	10′
21° 00′	.5543—1	.5842—1	.4158	.9702—1	**69° 00′**
10′	.5576—1	.5879—1	.4121	.9697—1	50′
20′	.5609—1	.5917—1	.4083	.9692—1	40′
30′	.5641—1	.5954—1	.4046	.9687—1	30′
40′	.5673—1	.5991—1	.4009	.9682—1	20′
50′	.5704—1	.6028—1	.3972	.9677—1	10′
22° 00′	.5736—1	.6064—1	.3936	.9672—1	**68° 00′**
10′	.5767—1	.6100—1	.3900	.9667—1	50′
20′	.5798—1	.6136—1	.3864	.9661—1	40′
30′	.5828—1	.6172—1	.3828	.9656—1	30′
40′	.5859—1	.6208—1	.3792	.9651—1	20′
50′	.5889—1	.6243—1	.3757	.9646—1	10′
23° 00′	.5919—1	.6279—1	.3721	.9640—1	**67° 00′**
10′	.5948—1	.6314—1	.3686	.9635—1	50′
20′	.5978—1	.6348—1	.3652	.9629—1	40′
30′	.6007—1	.6383—1	.3617	.9624—1	30′
40′	.6036—1	.6417—1	.3583	.9618—1	20′
50′	.6065—1	.6452—1	.3548	.9613—1	10′
24° 00′	.6093—1	.6486—1	.3514	.9607—1	**66° 00′**
10′	.6121—1	.6520—1	.3480	.9602—1	50′
20′	.6149—1	.6553—1	.3447	.9596—1	40′
30′	.6177—1	.6587—1	.3413	.9590—1	30′
40′	.6205—1	.6620—1	.3380	.9584—1	20′
50′	.6232—1	.6654—1	.3346	.9579—1	10′
25° 00′	.6259—1	.6687—1	.3313	.9573—1	**65° 00′**
10′	.6286—1	.6720—1	.3280	.9567—1	50′
20′	.6313—1	.6752—1	.3248	.9561—1	40′
30′	.6340—1	.6785—1	.3215	.9555—1	30′
40′	.6366—1	.6817—1	.3183	.9549—1	20′
50′	.6392—1	.6850—1	.3150	.9543—1	10′
26° 00′	.6418—1	.6882—1	.3118	.9537—1	**64° 00′**
10′	.6444—1	.6914—1	.3086	.9530—1	50′
20′	.6470—1	.6946—1	.3054	.9524—1	40′
30′	.6495—1	.6977—1	.3023	.9518—1	30′
40′	.6521—1	.7009—1	.2991	.9512—1	20′
50′	.6546—1	.7040—1	.2960	.9505—1	10′
27° 00′	.6570—1	.7072—1	.2928	.9499—1	**63° 00′**
°	$\log_{10}$cosine	$\log_{10}$cotangent	$\log_{10}$tangent	$\log_{10}$sine	Degrees

Table VI (*continued*)

Degrees	$\log_{10}$sine	$\log_{10}$tangent	$\log_{10}$cotangent	$\log_{10}$cosine	
27° 00′	.6570—1	.7072—1	.2928	.9499—1	**63° 00′**
10′	.6595—1	.7103—1	.2897	.9492—1	50′
20′	.6620—1	.7134—1	.2866	.9486—1	40′
30′	.6644—1	.7165—1	.2835	.9479—1	30′
40′	.6668—1	.7196—1	.2804	.9473—1	20′
50′	.6692—1	.7226—1	.2774	.9466—1	10′
28° 00′	.6716—1	.7257—1	.2743	.9459—1	**62° 00′**
10′	.6740—1	.7287—1	.2713	.9453—1	50′
20′	.6763—1	7317—1	.2683	.9446—1	40′
30′	.6787—1	.7348—1	.2652	.9439—1	30′
40′	.6810—1	.7378—1	.2622	.9432—1	20′
50′	.6833—1	.7408—1	.2592	.9425—1	10′
29° 00′	.6856—1	.7438—1	.2562	.9418—1	**61° 00′**
10′	.6878—1	.7467—1	.2533	.9411—1	50′
20′	.6901—1	.7497—1	.2503	.9404—1	40′
30′	.6923—1	.7526—1	.2474	.9397—1	30′
40′	.6946—1	.7556—1	.2444	.9390—1	20′
50′	.6968—1	.7585—1	.2415	.9383—1	10′
30° 00′	.6990—1	.7614—1	.2386	.9375—1	**60° 00′**
10′	.7012—1	.7644—1	.2356	.9368—1	50′
20′	.7033—1	.7673—1	.2327	.9361—1	40′
30′	.7055—1	.7701—1	.2299	.9353—1	30′
40′	.7076—1	.7730—1	.2270	.9346—1	20′
50′	.7097—1	.7759—1	.2241	.9338—1	10′
31° 00′	.7118—1	.7788—1	.2212	.9331—1	**59° 00′**
10′	.7139—1	.7816—1	.2184	.9323—1	50′
20′	.7160—1	.7845—1	.2155	.9315—1	40′
30′	.7181—1	.7873—1	.2127	.9308—1	30′
40′	.7201—1	.7902—1	.2098	.9300—1	20′
50′	.7222—1	.7930—1	.2070	.9292—1	10′
32° 00′	.7242—1	.7958—1	.2042	.9284—1	**58° 00′**
10′	.7262—1	.7986—1	.2014	.9276—1	50′
20′	.7282—1	.8014—1	.1986	.9268—1	40′
30′	.7302—1	.8042—1	.1958	.9260—1	30′
40′	.7322—1	.8070—1	.1930	.9252—1	20′
50′	.7342—1	.8097—1	.1903	.9244—1	10′
33° 00′	.7361—1	.8125—1	.1875	.9236—1	**57° 00′**
10′	.7380—1	.8153—1	.1847	.9228—1	50′
20′	.7400—1	.8180—1	.1820	.9219—1	40′
30′	.7419—1	.8208—1	.1792	.9211—1	30′
40′	.7438—1	.8235—1	.1765	.9203—1	20′
50′	.7457—1	.8263—1	.1737	.9194—1	10′
34° 00′	.7476—1	.8290—1	.1710	.9186—1	**56° 00′**
10′	.7494—1	.8317—1	.1683	.9177—1	50′
20′	.7513—1	.8344—1	.1656	.9169—1	40′
30′	.7531—1	.8371—1	.1629	.9160—1	30′
40′	.7550—1	.8398—1	.1602	.9151—1	20′
50′	.7568—1	.8425—1	.1575	.9142—1	10′
35° 00′	.7586—1	.8452—1	.1548	.9134—1	**55° 00′**
10′	.7604—1	.8479—1	.1521	.9125—1	50′
20′	.7622—1	.8506—1	.1494	.9116—1	40′
30′	.7640—1	.8533—1	.1467	.9107—1	30′
40′	.7657—1	.8559—1	.1441	.9098—1	20′
50′	.7675—1	.8586—1	.1414	.9089—1	10′
36° 00′	.7692—1	.8613—1	.1387	.9080—1	**54° 00′**
	$\log_{10}$cosine	$\log_{10}$cotangent	$\log_{10}$tangent	$\log_{10}$sine	Degrees

Table VI (*continued*)

Degrees	$\log_{10}$sine	$\log_{10}$tangent	$\log_{10}$cotangent	$\log_{10}$cosine	
36° 00'	.7692—1	.8613—1	.1387	.9080—1	**54° 00'**
10'	.7710—1	.8639—1	.1361	.9070—1	50'
20'	.7727—1	.8666—1	.1334	.9061—1	40'
30'	.7744—1	.8692—1	.1308	.9052—1	30'
40'	.7761—1	.8718—1	.1282	.9042—1	20'
50'	.7778—1	.8745—1	.1255	.9033—1	10'
37° 00'	.7795—1	.8771—1	.1229	.9023—1	**53° 00'**
10'	.7811—1	.8797—1	.1203	.9014—1	50'
20'	.7828—1	.8824—1	.1176	.9004—1	40'
30'	.7844—1	.8850—1	.1150	.8995—1	30'
40'	.7861—1	.8876—1	.1124	.8985—1	20'
50'	.7877—1	.8902—1	.1098	.8975—1	10'
38° 00'	.7893—1	.8928—1	.1072	.8965—1	**52° 00'**
10'	.7910—1	.8954—1	.1046	.8955—1	50'
20'	.7926—1	.8980—1	.1020	.8945—1	40'
30'	.7941—1	.9006—1	.0994	.8935—1	30'
40'	.7957—1	.9032—1	.0968	.8925—1	20'
50'	.7973—1	.9058—1	.0942	.8915—1	10'
39° 00'	.7989—1	.9084—1	.0916	.8905—1	**51° 00'**
10'	.8004—1	.9110—1	.0890	.8895—1	50'
20'	.8020—1	.9135—1	.0865	.8884—1	40'
30'	.8035—1	.9161—1	.0839	.8874—1	30'
40'	.8050—1	.9187—1	.0813	.8864—1	20'
50'	.8066—1	.9212—1	.0788	.8853—1	10'
40° 00'	.8081—1	.9238—1	.0762	.8843—1	**50° 00'**
10'	.8096—1	.9264—1	.0736	.8832—1	50'
20'	.8111—1	.9289—1	.0711	.8821—1	40'
30'	.8125—1	.9315—1	.0685	.8810—1	30'
40'	.8140—1	.9341—1	.0659	.8800—1	20'
50'	.8155—1	.9366—1	.0634	.8789—1	10'
41° 00'	.8169—1	.9392—1	.0608	.8778—1	**49° 00'**
10'	.8184—1	.9417—1	.0583	.8767—1	50'
20'	.8198—1	.9443—1	.0557	.8756—1	40'
30'	.8213—1	.9468—1	.0532	.8745—1	30'
40'	.8227—1	.9494—1	.0506	.8733—1	20'
50'	.8241—1	.9519—1	.0481	.8722—1	10'
42° 00'	.8255—1	.9544—1	.0456	.8711—1	**48° 00'**
10'	.8269—1	.9570—1	.0430	.8699—1	50'
20'	.8283—1	.9595—1	.0405	.8688—1	40'
30'	.8297—1	.9621—1	.0379	.8676—1	30'
40'	.8311—1	.9646—1	.0354	.8665—1	20'
50'	.8324—1	.9671—1	.0329	.8653—1	10'
43° 00'	.8338—1	.9697—1	.0303	.8641—1	**47° 00'**
10'	.8351—1	.9722—1	.0278	.8629—1	50'
20'	.8365—1	.9747—1	.0253	.8618—1	40'
30'	.8378—1	.9772—1	.0228	.8606—1	30'
40'	.8391—1	.9798—1	.0202	.8594—1	20'
50'	.8405—1	.9823—1	.0177	.8582—1	10'
44° 00'	.8418—1	.9848—1	.0152	.8569—1	**46° 00'**
10'	.8431—1	.9874—1	.0126	.8557—1	50'
20'	.8444—1	.9899—1	.0101	.8545—1	40'
30'	.8457—1	.9924—1	.0076	.8532—1	30'
40'	.8469—1	.9949—1	.0051	.8520—1	20'
50'	.8482—1	.9975—1	.0025	.8507—1	10'
45° 00'	.8495—1	.0000	.0000	.8495—1	**45° 00'**
	$\log_{10}$cosine	$\log_{10}$cotangent	$\log_{10}$tangent.	$\log_{10}$sine	Degrees

Table VII

The Greek Alphabet

A	α	Alpha	N	ν	Nu
B	β	Beta	Ξ	ξ	Xi
Γ	γ	Gamma	O	o	Omicron
Δ	δ	Delta	Π	π	Pi
E	ε	Epsilon	P	ρ	Rho
Z	ζ	Zeta	Σ	σ	Sigma
H	η	Eta	T	τ	Tau
Θ	θ	Theta	Y	υ	Upsilon
I	ι	Iota	Φ	φ	Phi
K	κ	Kappa	X	χ	Chi
Λ	λ	Lambda	Ψ	ψ	Psi
M	μ	Mu	Ω	ω	Omega

ANSWERS AND SOLUTIONS

CHAPTER I

I.1.a

1. 1, 2, 3, 4, 6, 8, 12, 24; 1, 3, 9, 27, 81; 1, 2, 3, 4, 5, 6, 8, 10, 12, 15, 20, 24, 30, 40, 60, 120.

2. 496.

4. $1 \cdot 2 \cdot 3 \cdot 4 \cdot 5 \cdot 6 + 1 = 720 + 1 = 7 \cdot 103$;
$10! + 1 = 3,628,801 = 11 \cdot 329,891.$

5. For example, $a = 3$ and $p = 5$ gives $3^5 - 3 = 5 \cdot 48.$

6. 3, 4, 5; 5, 12, 13; 7, 24, 25.

7. $1729 = 12^3 + 1^3 = 10^3 + 9^3.$

8. (a) $(a + b) + c = a + (b + c) = a + (c + b) = (c + b) + a.$
(b) $(a + b) + (c + d) = a + (b + (c + d)) = a + ((b + c) + d) = a + (d + (b + c)) = (a + d) + (b + c).$

9. (a) If $a = 2c$, $b = 2d$, then $a + b = 2(c + d).$

11. Possible values for a are 1, 2, 3. For these, $b + c = 6, 3, 2$. This determines b and c; e.g., $a = 2$, $b + c = 3$ implies $b = 1, 2$, $c = 2, 1.$

19. Write $x \in A$ to denote "x belongs to A." Then if $x \in A \cup B$, either $x \in A$ or $x \in B$ (or both). Thus $x \in B \cup A$. Hence $A \cup B \subset B \cup A$. (This is the definition of "$\subset$".) Show now that $B \cup A \subset A \cup B$. This then shows that $A \cup B = B \cup A$. (By definition, $C = D$ in case $C \subset D$ and $D \subset C$.)

20.   If $x \in (A \cap B) \cap C$, then $x \in A \cap B$ and $x \in C$. Since $x \in A \cap B$, $x \in A$ and $x \in B$. Hence $x \in B \cap C$ and finally $x \in A \cap (B \cap C)$. Thus $(A \cap B) \cap C \subset A \cap (B \cap C)$. Now show that $A \cap (B \cap C) \subset (A \cap B) \cap C$ and this gives $A \cap (B \cap C) = (A \cap B) \cap C$.

21.   If $x \in A \cap (B \cup C)$, $x \in A$ and (either $x \in B$ or $x \in C$). Suppose $x \in B$. Then $x \in A \cap B$ hence $x \in (A \cap B) \cup (A \cap C)$. Thus $A \cap (B \cup C) \subset (A \cap B) \cup (A \cap C)$. (The case $x \in C$ is similar).

If $x \in (A \cap B) \cup (A \cap C)$, then $x \in A \cap B$ or $x \in A \cap C$. The first gives $x \in A$ and $x \in B$. The second gives $x \in A$ and $x \in C$. So in any case $x \in A$. Also $x \in B \cup C$. Thus $(A \cap B) \cup (A \cap C) \subset A \cap (B \cup C)$. Thus $A \cap (B \cup C) = (A \cap B) \cup (A \cap C)$.

I.1.b

1. (a) $27 = 4 \cdot 6 + 3$;
   (c) $641 = 32 \cdot 20 + 1$;
   (e) $1 = 101 \cdot 0 + 1$;
   (g) $96 = 24 \cdot 4 + 0$.
2. (a) $30 = 2 \cdot 3 \cdot 5$;
   (c) $64 = 2 \cdot 2 \cdot 2 \cdot 2 \cdot 2 \cdot 2$;
   (e) 101 is prime;
   (g) $2077 = 31 \cdot 67$.
3. (a) If in the factorization of a into primes the prime 3 occurs m times, then it occurs $2m$ times in the factorization of a^2. If in the factorization of b, the prime 3 enters n times then in the factorization of $3b^2$ it enters $2n + 1$ times. If $a^2 = 3b^2$ then $2m = 2n + 1$, an impossibility.
4. $c = 4, 9, 16$.
5. $x + (x + 1) + (x + 2) = 3x + 3 = 3(x + 1)$.
6.   Write $n = 2m + 1$. Then $n^2 = 4(m^2 + m) + 1$.
7.   Either $n = 4m + 1$ or $n = 4m + 3$. Now $(4m + 1)^2 = 8(2m^2 + m) + 1$ and $(4m + 3)^2 = 8(2m^2 + 3m + 1) + 1$.
10. $(2a + 1) + (2b + 1) = 2(a + b + 1)$; $(2a + 1)(2b + 1) = 2(2ab + a + b) + 1$.
11. (a) $12, 18, 24$;
    (b) $3, 45, 87$;
    (c) $4, 9, 16$;
    (d) $8, 27, 64$;
    (e) $64, 729, 4096$, that is, $2^6, 3^6, 4^6$.
13.   There are sets of natural numbers for which the statement is false, e.g. the set of all natural numbers. For, if n is a natural number, $n + 1$ is a natural number. Also $n + 1 > n$.

I.2.a

1. (a) 3, 4, 5; **(b)** 2, 3, 4;
(c) 2, 3, 4, 5, -2, -3, -4, -5;
(d) 4, 5, 6;
(e) 4, 5, 6, 7, 0, -1, -2, -3;
(f) $n + 1$, $n + 2, \cdots, 2n$.

2. (a) (0, 0), (0, 1), (0, 2), (0, 3), (1, 0), (1, 1), (1, 2), (2, 0), (2, 1), (2, 2), (3, 0) with all possible variations in sign;
(c) (0, 0), (0, ± 1), (± 1, 0);
(e) (0, 5), (3, 4), (4, 3), (5, 0) with all possible variations in sign.

I.2.b

1. (a) -3, -2, -1, 0, 1, 2, 3;
(b) -1, 0, 1;
(c) 4, 5, 6;
(d) -5;
(e) 3;
(f) no solutions;
(g) -11, -10, -9, -8.

2. (a) 0; **(b)** -2, -3, $-4, \cdots$; **(c)** -2, 1;
(d) none; **(e)** none.

3. If $x < y$, then $x + x < x + y$ and $x + y < y + y$. Hence
$$x < \frac{x + y}{2} < y.$$

4. (a) $|b - a| = |(-1)(a - b)| = |-1||a - b| = |a - b|$;
(c) $|a| = |(a + b) + (-b)| \le |a + b| + |b|$, hence $|a + b| \ge |a| - |b|$.

5. (a) $|(a + b) + c| \le |a + b| + |c| \le |a| + |b| + |c|$.

6. (0, ± 4), (± 4, 0), (± 1, ± 3), (± 3, ± 1), (± 2, ± 2).

7. Either a and b have the same sign or $a \cdot b = 0$.

8. (a) $y = x \pm 1$ where x is arbitrary;
(b) $y = \pm x$.

I.3.a

1. (a) $\frac{1}{5}$; **(c)** $-\frac{7}{2}$; **(e)** -16; **(g)** $\dfrac{2^2 \cdot 5^3 \cdot 7}{11^2 \cdot 13}$; **(i)** $\frac{533}{391}$.

2. (a) $\frac{41}{35}$; **(b)** 2; **(c)** $\frac{58}{21}$; **(d)** $\frac{65}{24}$.

4. (a) $\dfrac{a}{b^2}$; **(b)** $\dfrac{a^2}{c^2}$; **(c)** $\dfrac{r}{4s}$; **(d)** $\dfrac{2^2 \cdot 3^2 \cdot ab^5}{5^2 c^4}$.

5. (a) $\dfrac{a^3 + 2b^2}{a^2 b^2}$; **(c)** $\dfrac{4b^4}{ac}$; **(e)** $\dfrac{b^2 x^2 - a^2 y^2}{a^2 b^2}$;

(g) $\dfrac{bc + ac + ab}{abc}$;   **(i)** $\dfrac{(x + y)^3}{6}$;   **(k)** $\dfrac{2ab}{a + b}$.

8. Try $n > \frac{45}{4}$; 12; $n > 10^6$; $n \geq 1$.

10. (a) One has $pq > 0$ and $rs > 0$. Hence $(ps + rq)qs = pqs^2 + rsq^2 > 0$

(b) $\dfrac{p}{q} \cdot \dfrac{r}{s} = \dfrac{pr}{qs}$ and $(pr)(qs) = (pq)(rs) > 0$.

11. $2qr \cdot a = 2qr \cdot \dfrac{p}{q} = 2pr > \dfrac{r}{s} = b$; $n = qr$ does not satisfy $na > b$
when $p = s = 1$.

12.   If $\dfrac{p}{q} < \dfrac{r}{s}$ then $\dfrac{p}{q} < \dfrac{1}{2}\left(\dfrac{p}{q} + \dfrac{r}{s}\right) < \dfrac{r}{s}$.

13. $\dfrac{2 + n}{1 + n}$, $n = 1, 2, \cdots, 100$.

14. $\dfrac{1}{n}$, $n = 1, 2, \cdots, 100$.

15. (a) $0.3 = \dfrac{3}{10}$; $0.33 = \dfrac{33}{100}$; $\cdots$.

(b) $3 = \dfrac{3}{1}$; $3.1 = \dfrac{31}{10}$; $3.14 = \dfrac{314}{100}$; $\cdots$.

I.4.a

2. (a) 0, 0.7, 0.70, 0.707, $\cdots$.
   (c) 3, 3.1, 3.14, 3.141, $\cdots$.
   (e) 4, 4, 4, $\cdots$.
   (g) 0.2, 0.28, 0.285, 0.2857, 0.28571, 0.28571428, $\cdots$.
5. (a) 1, 1.5, 1.57, 1.573, $\cdots$.
   (c) 3, 3.1, 3.14, 3.145, $\cdots$.
6. (a) The square of 1.4, 1.41, 1.414, $\cdots$ is 1.96, 1.9881, 1.999396, $\cdots$.
8. (a) 0.5000 $\cdots$;   **(b)** 0.111 $\cdots$;   **(c)** 6.666 $\cdots$;   **(d)** 0.142850714 $\cdots$;
   (e) 4.999 $\cdots$ or 5.000 $\cdots$;   **(f)** 0.07692307 $\cdots$.
9. (a) $\frac{1}{3}$;   **(b)** $\frac{27}{100}$;   **(c)** $\frac{5}{9}$;   **(d)** $\frac{7}{3}$;   **(e)** 1.

I.4.b

1.   Find n such that $nx > 1$. Then $x > \dfrac{1}{n}$.

3. (a) Lower bounds: $-\pi$, -1, 0; g.l.b.: 0.
   Upper bounds: 1, $\sqrt{2}$, 10^{10}; l.u.b.: 1.
   (c) No lower bounds; l.u.b.: 1.
   (e) G.l.b.: $-\sqrt{5}$; l.u.b.: $\sqrt{5}$.
   (g) Same as (e).
4. (a) G.l.b.: -1; l.u.b.: 3.
   (c) Same as (a).
   (e) G.l.b.: $-\sqrt{6}$; l.u.b.: $\sqrt{6}$.
   (g) No bounds.

6. If c were rational, then $\dfrac{c-a}{b-a} = \dfrac{\sqrt{2}}{2}$ would also be rational. Clearly

   $c > a$ since $(b-a)\dfrac{\sqrt{2}}{2} > 0$. Since $\dfrac{\sqrt{2}}{2} < 1$, $c = a + (b-a)\dfrac{\sqrt{2}}{2} <$

   $a + (b-a) = b$.

7. If $a + r$ is rational, then $a = (a+r) - r$ is also rational. If $b = \dfrac{1}{a}$

   is rational, then $\dfrac{1}{b} = a$ is rational. $a = m + \sqrt{2}$. $b = \dfrac{1}{m+\sqrt{2}}$.

I-Appendix

1. $(a + b\sqrt{2}) + (a' + b'\sqrt{2}) = (a + a') + (b + b')\sqrt{2}$. Note that $a + a'$ and $b + b'$ are rational. Next, $(a + b\sqrt{2})(a' + b'\sqrt{2}) = (aa' + 2bb') + (ab' + a'b)\sqrt{2}$.

2. Note that the product of two odd numbers is odd. Also the product of an odd number by an even number is even. Thus in the factorization of an odd number into primes, only odd primes can occur. By the unique factorization theorem for the natural numbers, factorization in this system is unique.

3. $1296 = 6 \cdot 6 \cdot 6 \cdot 6 = 16 \cdot 81$ and 6, 16, 81 are primes in the multiplicative system. The factorizations are distinct and the number of primes in the two factorizations is not the same.

4. Proof of ring property similar to that in exercise 1.

5. Note that $(a + b\sqrt{-5})(a' + b'\sqrt{-5}) = (aa' - 5bb') + (ab' + a'b)\sqrt{-5}$.

CHAPTER II

II.1.a

1. (a) **R**; (b) **R**;
   (c) **R**; (d) **R** $- \{2, -2\}$;

(e) $\mathbf{R} - \{-2\}$;   (f) $\mathbf{R}$;

(g) $\mathbf{M}$ is set of x such that $x \geq 0$ and $x \neq 2$.

(h) $\mathbf{M}$ is set of x such that $|x| \geq 2$;

(i) $\mathbf{M}$ is set of x such that $x \neq 0$, $x \neq -1$;

(j) $\mathbf{M}$ is set of t such that $t \geq 3$;

(k) $\mathbf{M}$ is set of t such that $t \geq 3$;

(l) $\mathbf{M}$ is set of t such that $t \leq 0$ or $t \geq 3$.

2. (a) $1, 0, \frac{93}{8}, 22$;

   (c) $1, \sqrt{2}, \sqrt{\frac{7}{2}}, 2$;

   (e) $0, 1, \frac{5}{2}, 3$;

   (g) c, c, c, c.

3. $f(a) = a^2 + 3$, $f(2a) = 4a^2 + 3$, $f(\sqrt{a}) = a + 3$, $f(a + b) = (a + b)^2 + 3$, $f(a) + f(b) = a^2 + b^2 + 6$, $f(0) + f(1) = 3 + 4 = 4 + 3 = f(2)$, $f(2) + f(3) = 7 + 12 = 19 \neq 28 = f(2 + 3)$.

4. If $\sqrt{a} = \sqrt{b}$ then by squaring $a = b$.

5. 1.25; 3.50; 3.50.

6. Let f be defined over $\mathbf{R}$ by $f(x) = 5$ if x is of the form $x = a + b\sqrt{2}$ where a and b are integers and $f(x) = 0$ in the contrary case.

7. $f(x) = 7$ for $x = 0, 4$; $f(x) = 3$ for $x = 2$; $f(x) = 2$ for no real value of x; $f(x) = a$ for those values of x, if any such that $x^2 - 4x + 7 - a = 0$. It follows that a must ≥ 3 in order to have real solutions.

8. $f(x) = 4x, f(x) = x^3, f(x) = \frac{1}{4}x^5, f(x) = 2x + \frac{1}{2}x^3$.

9. Find the value of each of the thirty-one functions for $x = \pi$ ($x = 100$ if you prefer). This will give a certain number of real numbers (not more than 31). Let c be different from any of these. Define f by $f(x) = c$.

10. $f(a + b) = c(a + b) = c \cdot a + c \cdot b = f(a) + f(b)$.

II.2.a

1. (a) $f + g$ and $f \cdot g$ are defined for those x such that $x \geq 0$; $\dfrac{f}{g}$ is defined for $x \geq 0$ and $x \neq 1$.

   (c) $f + g, f \cdot g, \dfrac{f}{g}$ are defined for $\mathbf{R}$.

   (e) $f + g, f \cdot g, \dfrac{f}{g}$ are defined for $x \neq 0$, $x \neq 2$;

   (g) $f + g$ and $f \cdot g$ are defined for all x; $\dfrac{f}{g}$ are defined for those x such that $b_0 + b_1 x + b_2 x^2 \neq 0$.

2. (a) $(f \circ g)(x) = \sqrt{x^2 - 1}$, defined for $|x| \geq 1$;

   $(g \circ f)(x) = x - 1$, defined for $x \geq 0$.

(c) $(f \circ g)(x) = x^4 + 4x^2 + 4$, defined for **R**;
$(g \circ f)(x) = x^4 - 8x^3 + 24x^2 - 32x + 12$, defined for **R**.

(f) $(f \circ g)(x) = (g \circ f)(x) = x$, defined for **R**.

3. (a) $(f + g)(3) = f(3) + g(3) = \sqrt{3} + 8; (f \cdot g)(3) = f(3) \cdot g(3) = 8\sqrt{3}$;

$\left(\dfrac{f}{g}\right)(3) = \dfrac{\sqrt{3}}{8}; (3f + 2g)(1) = 3f(1) + 2g(1) = 3 + 0 = 3$;

$(2f \cdot g)(1) = 2f(1) \cdot g(1) = 2 \cdot 0 = 0; \dfrac{f + g}{g}(3) = \dfrac{\sqrt{3} + 8}{8}$.

4. (e) $(2x)^2 - 1$, $(x + 2)^2 - 1$, $\left(\dfrac{2}{x}\right)^2 - 1$, $(x^2)^2 - 1$, $2(x^2 - 1)$, $2[(3x^2 + 4)^2 - 1]$, $(x^2 - 1)^2$, $[(x^2)^2 - 1]^3$, $(x^2 - 1)^2 - 1$.

5. $f(x) = 3x$, $g(x) = x^2$, $g(x) = x^3$, $g(x) = x + 1$.

6. $(f \circ g)(x) = x^6 - 4x^4 + 2x^3 + 4x^2 - 4x + 3; (g \circ f)(x) = x^6 + 6x^4 + 10x^2 + 5$.

7. If $f(x) = x$, then $(f \circ g)(x) = g(x)$.
If $f(x) = x^2$, then $(f \circ g)(x) = [g(x)]^2$ which is a polynomial.
If $f(x) = a_0 + a_1 x + a_2 x^2$, then $(f \circ g)(x) = a_0 + a_1 g(x) + a_2 [g(x)]^2$ which is a polynomial.

11. If $f(x) = \dfrac{p(x)}{q(x)}$ and $g(x) = \dfrac{r(x)}{s(x)}$, where p, q, r, s are polynomials then

$(f \cdot g)(x) = \dfrac{p(x) \cdot r(x)}{q(x) \cdot s(x)}$ and by exercise 9, this function is rational.

II.3.a

1. (a)

$f(x) = x$

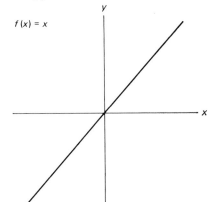

(c)

$f(x) = \dfrac{1}{x + 1}$

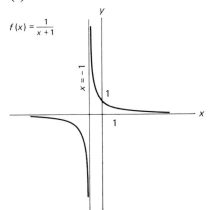

(e)

$f(x) = \dfrac{1}{x} + 1$

$y = 1$

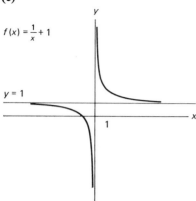

(f)

$f(x) = \sqrt{x} - 1$

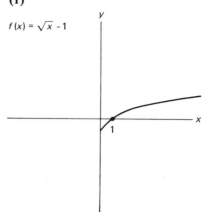

(h)

$f(x) = |x| + x$

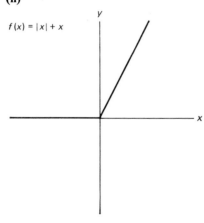

(j)

$f(x) = [x]$

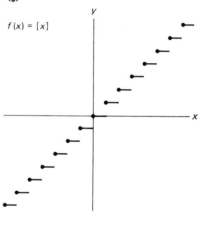

2. (a)

$f(x) = x^2 - 4$

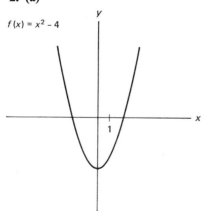

(c)

$h(u) = \dfrac{1}{u^2 - 4}$

$u = -2$ v $u = 2$

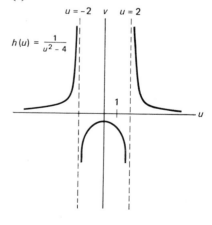

(e)

$g(u) = \sqrt{u^2} - 4$

$\quad\quad = |u| - 4$

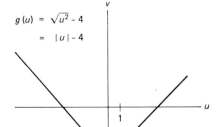

3. (a)

$f(x) = \sqrt{4 - x^2}$

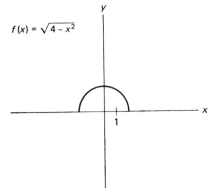

(c)

$f(x) = \frac{2}{3} \sqrt{4 - x^2}$

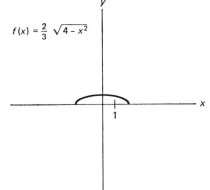

4. (a)

$f(x) = x^3$

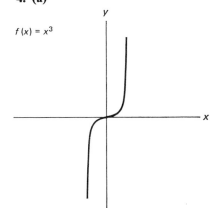

(b)

$f(x) = \frac{1}{x^3}$

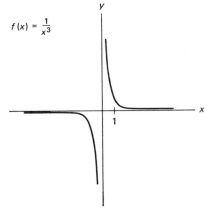

(c)

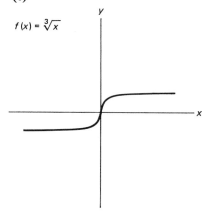

$f(x) = \sqrt[3]{x}$

5.

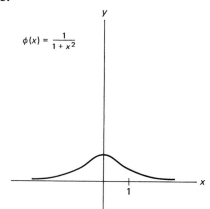

$\phi(x) = \dfrac{1}{1 + x^2}$

7.

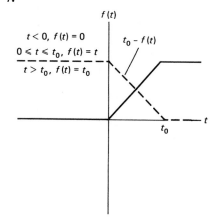

$t < 0, \; f(t) = 0$

$0 \leqslant t \leqslant t_0, \; f(t) = t$

$t > t_0, \; f(t) = t_0$

II.4.a

1. (a) $3x - 2y = 0$;   (c) $2x + 7y = 0$;
   (e) $4x - 3y = 0$;   (g) $y_0 x - x_0 y = 0$.
2. (a) $y + 1 = 0$;   (c) $x - y = 0$;
   (e) $x + 2y - 2 = 0$;   (g) $dx - cy = 0$.
3.

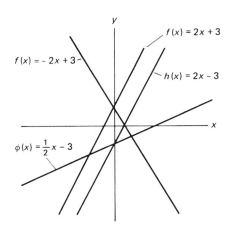

4. $f = 4.9d$; $d = 0.204f$ (1968).
      $f = 5.1d$; $d = 0.196f$ (1971).

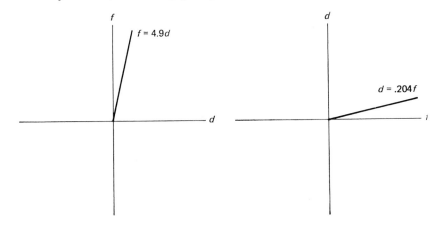

5. Man was ill with temperature of F $= 104$.

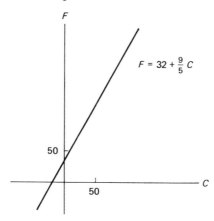

$$F = 32 + \frac{9}{5} C$$

6. $w_M = \frac{1}{6}w_E$; 300 lbs.

8. $c = 0$ for $0 \le w \le 44$; $c = 2(w - 44)$ for $w \ge 44$.

10.

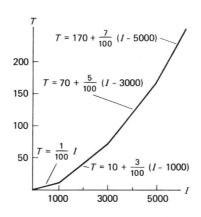

$$T = 170 + \frac{7}{100} (I - 5000)$$

$$T = 70 + \frac{5}{100} (I - 3000)$$

$$T = \frac{1}{100} I$$

$$T = 10 + \frac{3}{100} (I - 1000)$$

II.5.a

2. 175.3 feet.

3. 3.26 feet $\approx$ 3 feet 3 inches; 102.23 feet.

4. 26 feet.

5. $x_0 = \dfrac{m}{k}$.

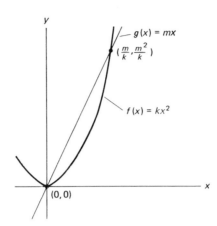

$g(x) = mx$

$(\frac{m}{k}, \frac{m^2}{k})$

$f(x) = kx^2$

$(0, 0)$

6.   The equation is presumably $s = f(v) = cv^2$ where c is a constant.
$\dfrac{f(50)}{f(20)} = \dfrac{25}{4}$.

II.5.b

1. (a) -16;   (c) 16;   (e) -24.
2. (a) $f(x) = (x - 2)^2$; $\Delta = 0$; min at $x = 2$, no max.
   (c) $\psi(x) = 2(x + \tfrac{1}{2})^2 + \tfrac{1}{2}$; $\Delta = -4$.
   (h) $\varphi(t) = \left(t + \dfrac{1}{\sqrt{2}}\right)^2 - \dfrac{7}{2}$; $\Delta = 14$.
3. $\Delta = 4c^2 - 4$. $\Delta = 0$ for $c = \pm 1$; $\Delta > 0$ if $|c| > 1$; $\Delta < 0$ if $|c| < 1$.
4. $f(x) = 3.2 - 0.2x + 0.7x^2$.
5. $c = 2$ and $h = 3$; $c = \tfrac{2}{9}$ and $h = -1$.

II.6.a

1.   Maximum height 64 feet reached in 2 seconds.
2.   A square. Maximum area is 64.

A square of side $\dfrac{p}{4}$. Maximum area is $\dfrac{p^2}{16}$.

4.   Let n be the point of nausea (hence where pleasure becomes negative). Since $p(0) = 0$ and $p(n) = 0$ while intermediate values of x give $p(x) > 0$, we have $\Delta > 0$, $a < 0$ (refer to table of quadratic functions). Obviously $p(0) = c = 0$. Thus $p(x) = a\left(x + \dfrac{b}{2a}\right)^2 - \dfrac{b^2}{4a}$.

Maximum pleasure is obtained for $x = -\dfrac{b}{2a}$ (remember that $a < 0$)

and since $0 = p(n) = an^2 + bn$, $n = -\dfrac{b}{a}$.

5. $n = -10t^2 + 80t$. Maximum of career for $t = 4$. Forgotten for $t = 8$.

II.7.a

2. (a) $c = 0$; none.
   (b) $c = 0$; none.
3.   The left-hand side is 0 if $i \neq j$; it is 1 if $i = j$. The right-hand side is 1 in all cases.

II.7.b

1. (a) $m_a = \frac{25}{2}$; $m_g = 12$.
   (c) $m_a = \frac{31}{3}$; $m_g = 6$.
2.   A was first with $6480^{1/4}$. B was second with $6300^{1/4}$. C was third with $6000^{1/4}$.
5.   Assume that $\dfrac{x_1 + \cdots + x_m}{m} \geq (x_1 \cdots x_m)^{1/m}$. Now

$$\frac{y_1 + \cdots + y_{2m}}{2m} = \frac{\dfrac{y_1 + \cdots + y_m}{m} + \dfrac{y_{m+1} + \cdots + y_{2m}}{m}}{2} = \frac{a + b}{2}$$

$$\geq (a \cdot b)^{1/2}$$
$$\geq [(y_1 \cdots y_m)^{1/m}(y_{m+1} \cdots y_{2m})^{1/m}]^{1/2}$$
$$= (y_1 \cdots y_{2m})^{1/2m}.$$

Here $a = \dfrac{y_1 + \cdots + y_m}{m}$ and $b = \dfrac{y_{m+1} + \cdots + y_{2m}}{m}$.

II.8.a

1. $f(x_1) = f(x_2); f(x_1 + x_2) = f(x_1 \cdot x_2); 2f(x_1 + x_2) = f(x_1) + f(x_2)$.
2.   Since $f(0 + 0) = 2f(0) + f(0)$, we have $f(0) = 0$. Next $f(x) = f(x + 0) = 2f(x) + f(0) = 2f(x)$. Hence $f(x) = 0$.
3. $f(\sqrt{f(x)}) = f(\sqrt{x^2}) = f(|x|) = |x|^2 = x^2 = f(x)$.

4. First $f(x) = f(x + 0 + 0) = f(x) + f(0) + f(0)$; hence $f(0) = 0$. Next, $f(x_1 + x_2) = f(x_1 + x_2 + 0) = f(x_1) + f(x_2) + f(0) = f(x_1) + f(x_2)$.

5. (a) even; (b) odd;
   (d) even and odd; (g) if $c \neq 0$, neither even nor odd; if $c = 0$, even.

6. $g(-x) = \dfrac{f(-x) + f(x)}{2} = g(x)$ hence g is even.

   $h(-x) = \dfrac{f(-x) - f(x)}{2} = -h(x)$ hence h is odd.

7. (a) $g(x) = x^2 - 3, h(x) = 2x$;
   (c) $g(x) = |x|, h(x) = 0$;
   (d) $g(x) = 0, h(x) = 0$.

8. If φ and ψ are even, then $(\varphi + \psi)(-x) = \varphi(-x) + \psi(-x) = \varphi(x) + \psi(x) = (\varphi + \psi)(x)$ hence $\varphi + \psi$ is even. If f is even, then $(g \circ f)(-x) = g[f(-x)] = g[f(x)] = (g \circ f)(x)$; hence $g \circ f$ is even.

11. If $f(-x) = f(x)$ and $f(-x) = -f(x)$, then $f(x) = -f(x)$ and $f(x) = 0$.

II.9.a

1. If f admits all real numbers as periods, then for any two real numbers x_1 and x_2, $f(x_2) = f[x_1 + (x_2 - x_1)] = f(x_1)$ since $x_2 - x_1$ is a period.

2. Since p is a period, $f(x + 2p) = f[(x + p) + p] = f(x + p) = f(x)$; hence $2p$ is a period. The proof that np is a period for any natural number is now easy. If n is a negative integer, write $n = -m$ where m is natural number. Then

$$f(x + np) = f(x - mp) = f[(x - mp) + mp] = f(x).$$

5. 24 hours.

7. If f and g have period p, so do $f + g$ and $f \cdot g$. If $g(x + p) = g(x)$, then for any f $(f \circ g)(x + p) = f[g(x + p)] = f[g(x)] = (f \circ g)(x)$, hence $f \circ g$ is periodic with period p.

8. Suppose f is a polynomial function which is periodic of period p. Let c be any constant. Then the polynomial $g(x) = f(x) - f(c)$ has the property that $g(c) = 0$, $g(c + p) = f(c + p) - f(c) = f(c) - f(c) = 0$ and in general, for any integer s, $g(c + sp) = 0$. This contradicts the information given in the problem.

10. If $f(x) = f(-x)$ and $f(x + p) = f(x)$, then $f(p - x) = f(x - p) = f(x)$ (since $-p$ is a period).

II.10.a

1. (c)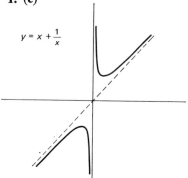

$y = x + \dfrac{1}{x}$

(f)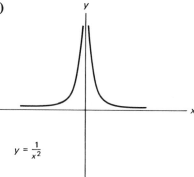

$y = \dfrac{1}{x^2}$

2. (a)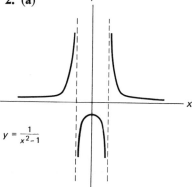

$y = \dfrac{1}{x^2-1}$

(b)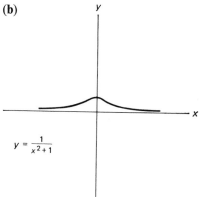

$y = \dfrac{1}{x^2+1}$

(c)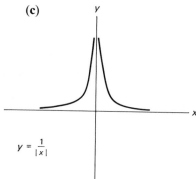

$y = \dfrac{1}{|x|}$

(f)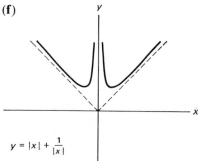

$y = |x| + \dfrac{1}{|x|}$

3. (b)

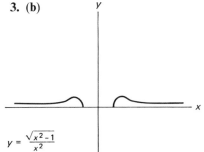

$$y = \frac{\sqrt{x^2 - 1}}{x^2}$$

(c)

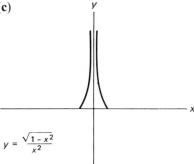

$$y = \frac{\sqrt{1 - x^2}}{x^2}$$

4.   It must be shown that if (a, b) is on the graph, (b, a) is also on the graph.

(a) If $b = \dfrac{1}{a}$, then $a = \dfrac{1}{b}$.

(c) If $b = \sqrt{1 - a^2}$ with $0 \le a \le 1$, then $0 \le b \le 1$ and since $b^2 = 1 - a^2$, $a = \sqrt{1 - b^2}$.

II.11.a

1. (a)

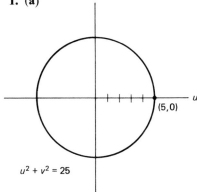

$u^2 + v^2 = 25$

(c)

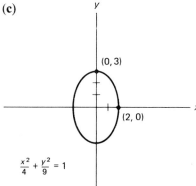

$$\frac{x^2}{4} + \frac{y^2}{9} = 1$$

(e)

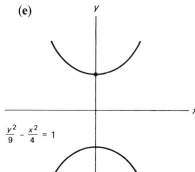

$$\frac{y^2}{9} - \frac{x^2}{4} = 1$$

(f)

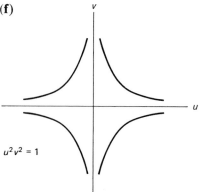

$u^2 v^2 = 1$

2. (b)

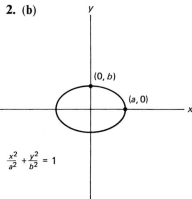

$(0, b)$

$(a, 0)$

$$\frac{x^2}{a^2} + \frac{y^2}{b^2} = 1$$

(d)

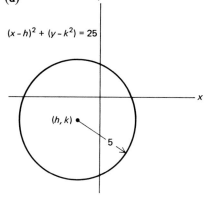

$(x - h)^2 + (y - k^2) = 25$

(h, k)

5

3. (a)

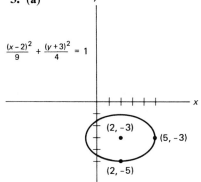

$$\frac{(x-2)^2}{9} + \frac{(y+3)^2}{4} = 1$$

$(2, -3)$

$(5, -3)$

$(2, -5)$

(d)

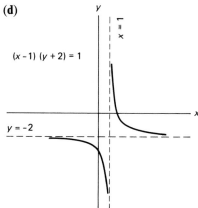

$(x - 1)(y + 2) = 1$

$x = 1$

$y = -2$

5. (a)

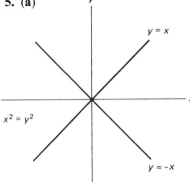

$y = x$

$x^2 = y^2$

$y = -x$

(d)

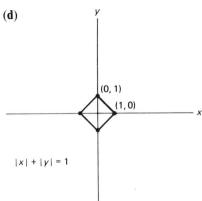

$(0, 1)$

$(1, 0)$

$|x| + |y| = 1$

(e)

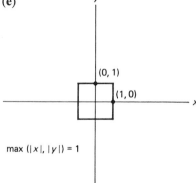

$(0, 1)$

$(1, 0)$

$\max(|x|, |y|) = 1$

6. (a)

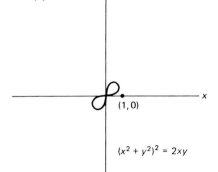

$(1, 0)$

$(x^2 + y^2)^2 = 2xy$

(b)

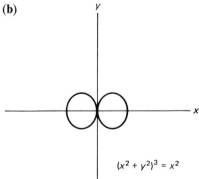

$(x^2 + y^2)^3 = x^2$

10. If $y = mx$, $\dfrac{x^2}{9} - \dfrac{m^2 x^2}{16} = 1$ hence $x = \pm \dfrac{1}{\sqrt{\dfrac{1}{9} - \dfrac{m^2}{16}}}$. Thus

$-\frac{4}{3} \le m \le \frac{4}{3}$. Giving m appropriate values, one obtains values of x and subsequently of y giving a point (x, y) on the curve.

11. Using a diagram similar to Figure 50 one obtains $1100^2 + x^2 = (1100 + \frac{1}{1980})^2$, where x is the number of miles per second. Thus $x^2 = \frac{2200}{1980} \approx 1.11$ and $x = 1.05$.

CHAPTER III

III.1.a

1. (a) $L = 10$; (b) $L = 10$;
   (c) $L = 3$; (d) $L = 100$.

2. (a) Add 1 to $-\frac{1}{2} < -x < \frac{1}{2}$.
   (b) Since $0 < x^2 < \frac{1}{4}, 0 > -3x^2 > -\frac{3}{4}$, hence $1 > 1 - 3x^2 > \frac{1}{4}$.

3. (a) If $|x| > 2$, $\dfrac{1}{|x|} < \dfrac{1}{2}$, $\left|1 - \dfrac{1}{x}\right| \ge 1 - \dfrac{1}{|x|} > 1 - \frac{1}{2} = \frac{1}{2}$. Hence

$|x^3 - x^2| = |x^3|\left|1 - \dfrac{1}{x}\right| > 8 \cdot \frac{1}{2} = 4.$

(b) $|x^5 - x^3 + x| = |x^5|\left|1 - \dfrac{1}{x^2} + \dfrac{1}{x^4}\right| \ge |x^5|\left(1 - \dfrac{1}{|x|^2} - \dfrac{1}{|x|^4}\right)$
$> 32(1 - \frac{1}{4} - \frac{1}{16}) > 32 \cdot \frac{1}{2} = 16.$

4. $|10^{-5}x^5 - 10^8 x| = |x|(10^{-5}|x|^4 - 10^8) > 10^4(10^{-5} \cdot 10^{16} - 10^8) = 10^{15} - 10^{12} > 10^{14}.$

5. (a) $|f(x)| \le \dfrac{1}{|x|} + \dfrac{1}{|x|^2}$. If $|x| > 4$, $\dfrac{1}{|x|} + \dfrac{1}{|x|^2} < \dfrac{1}{4} + \dfrac{1}{16} < \dfrac{1}{2}$.

(b) $|f(x)| \le \dfrac{1}{|x|} + \dfrac{2}{|x|^2} + \dfrac{3}{|x|^3} < \dfrac{1}{2}$ if $|x| > 6$.

7. $|x^7 - 10x^2 + 30x - 14| \ge |x|^7\left(1 - \dfrac{10}{|x|^5} - \dfrac{30}{|x|^6} - \dfrac{14}{|x|^7}\right) >$
$|x|^7 \cdot \frac{1}{2}$ if $|x| > 10$. If $|x| > 10^{15}$, $\frac{1}{2}|x|^7 > \frac{1}{2}10^{105} > 10^{100}$. Thus $k = 15$.

III.2.a

1. (c) $(f + g)(x) = x^3 + 2x^2 + 1$; $(f \cdot g)(x) = x^5 - x$.
   (e) $(f + g)(x) = 2x^3$; $(f \cdot g)(x) = x^6 - 1$.
   (f) $(f + g)(x) = x^4 + x^3 - 2x^2 - x + 1$; $(f \cdot g)(x) = x^7 - 3x^5 + 3x^3 - x$.

2. (a) $18, -8, 0;$ **(c)** $2, 3, 1;$
  (e) $0, 0, 0.$
3. (a) $1 + 5x + 10x^2 + 10x^3 + 5x^4 + x^5;$
  $1 + 5 + 10 + 10 + 5 + 1 = 32$ (set $x = 1$ in the above);
  $(1 + 1)^5 = 32$ (set $x = 1$ in $(x + 1)^5$).
4. Let $f \neq 0$ and $g \neq 0$ be defined as in (6) and (7). Then $f \cdot g$ has
  degree $n + m$ since $c_{n+m} = a_n \cdot b_m \neq 0$. Thus the product is not 0.
  Hence if $f \cdot g = 0$, either $f = 0$ or $g = 0$.
5. (a) $s = 1, 2;$ **(b)** $s = 1;$
  (c) no value of $s;$ **(e)** $s = 0.$

III.3.a

1. (a) $x^3 + x^2 + x + 1 = (x - 1)(x^2 + 2x + 3) + 4;$
  (b) $x^5 - 1 = (x - 1)(x^4 + x^3 + x^2 + x + 1) + 0;$
  (d) $x^3 + 3x^2 + 3x + 1 = (x + 1)(x^2 + 2x + 1);$
  (f) $x^4 - 3x^2 + x - 2 = (2x^2 + x - 4)(\frac{1}{2}x^2 - \frac{1}{4}x - \frac{3}{8}) + (\frac{3}{8}x - \frac{7}{2}).$
2. (b) $x^4 - 1 = (x + 1)(x^3 - x^2 + x - 1);$
  (d) $q = 0, r = f;$
  (f) $q(x) = x^4 + x^3 + x + 1, r = 0.$
4. The ideal of all polynomials of the form $x^n \cdot f(x)$ where f is an
  arbitrary polynomial. In case $n = 0$, this gives the ideal of all
  polynomials.

III.4.a

3. If $g(x) = f(x) - f(c)$, then $g(c) = 0$. Hence the remainder after
  dividing $g(x)$ by $x - c$ is 0.
4. (a) $f(-5) = 4; f(-9) = 4.$
  $f(x) = (x + 5)(x + 9) + 4$ so $q(x) = x + 9$ and $q(-9) = 0.$
  (c) $f(3) = 21; f(-1) = 21$
  $f(x) = (x - 3)q(x) + 21$ with $q(x) = x^3 - x^2 + 3x + 5; q(-1) = 0.$
5. $f(x) = (x - c)q(x) + f(c)$ implies $f(d) = (d - c)q(d) + f(c).$ If
  $q(d) = 0, f(c) = f(d).$

III.4.b

2. $f(x) = (x - 4)^2(x - 5)$ or $g(x) = (x - 4)(x - 5)^2.$ Except for
  constant factors these are the only ones.
4. $x^n - a^n = (x - a)(x^{n-1} + ax^{n-2} + a^2x^{n-2} + \cdots + a^{n-2}x + a^{n-1}).$

5. (a) Since $x^4 - 3x^2 + 2 = (x + 1)(x - 1)(x + \sqrt{2})(x - \sqrt{2})$, distinct zeros are $1, -1, \sqrt{2}, -\sqrt{2}$.

(c) 1;

(d) $1, -1$;

(f) $0, \frac{5}{4}, \frac{1}{3}$.

6. $x^5 + 6x^4 + 13x^3 + 14x^2 + 12x + 8 = (x + 2)^3(x^2 + 1)$.

7. (a) $f(2) = 4 - 2s + 2 = 6 - 2s$. Since $f(2) = 0$, $s = 3$.

(c) $f(2) = (2s)^3 - 4s + s = 8s^3 - 3s$. Since $f(2) = 0$, $s = 0$, $\dfrac{\sqrt{6}}{4}$, $-\dfrac{\sqrt{6}}{4}$.

8. (a) $f(-1) = 4s - 4$. Since $f(-1) = 0$, $s = 1$;

(c) $f(-1) = s$. Since $f(-1) = 0$, $s = 0$.

9. $(x - \sqrt{2})(x - \sqrt{3}) = x^2 - (\sqrt{2} + \sqrt{3})x + \sqrt{6}$;
$(x - \sqrt{2})(x + \sqrt{2})(x - \sqrt{3})(x + \sqrt{3}) = (x^2 - 2)(x^2 - 3) = x^4 - 5x^2 + 6$.

10. $0 = f(c) = c^n + a_{n-1}c^{n-1} + \cdots + a_1c + a_0$
$$= c(c^{n-1} + a_{n-1}c^{n-2} + \cdots + a_1) + a_0.$$
Thus $a_0 = -c \cdot A$ where A is the integer in the parenthesis.

III.5.a

1. (a) $x^2 - 5x + 6 = (x - 2)(x - 3)$; zeros are 2 and 3, each of multiplicity 1.

(b) $0, \sqrt{17}, -\sqrt{17}$ each of multiplicity 1.

(c) $-a$, of multiplicity 15.

(e) 0 of multiplicity 2 and $\dfrac{5}{2} + \dfrac{\sqrt{21}}{2}, \dfrac{5}{2} - \dfrac{\sqrt{21}}{2}$ each of multiplicity 1.

2. $x^2 + 1; x^2 + 5; (x^2 + 1)(x^2 + 5)$.

3. $(x^2 + 1)(x^2 - 1)$.

III.6.a

1. (a) If $|x|$ is large, $x > 0$, then $\dfrac{1}{x} > 0$ and is small.

If $|x|$ is large, $x < 0$, then $\dfrac{1}{x} < 0$ and is small.

If $|x|$ is small, $x > 0$, then $\dfrac{1}{x} > 0$ and $\dfrac{1}{x}$ is large.

If $|x|$ is small, $x < 0$, then $\dfrac{1}{x} < 0$ and $\left|\dfrac{1}{x}\right|$ is large.

(c) If $|x|$ is large, $|f(x)|$ is large; for $|x|$ large, $f(x)$ has the same sign as x. If x is small, $f(x)$ is close to 117.

2. (b) See II.10.a., 2(b).
   (c) See II.10.a., 2(a). (The answer is the reflection about the x-axis given there.)

(d)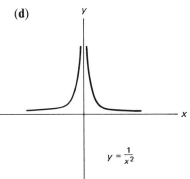

$$y = \frac{1}{x^2}$$

(e)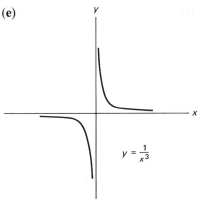

$$y = \frac{1}{x^3}$$

3. (a)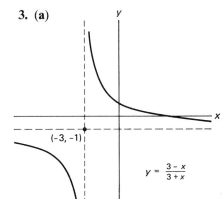

$(-3, -1)$

$$y = \frac{3 - x}{3 + x}$$

(d)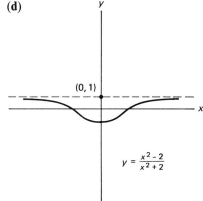

$(0, 1)$

$$y = \frac{x^2 - 2}{x^2 + 2}$$

7.   If $r = \dfrac{p}{q}$, let p be of degree n and q be of degree m. There are three cases: (a) $m > n$; (b) $m = n$; (c) $m < n$. In case (a) $|r(x)|$ is large when $|x|$ is large. In case (c), $|r(x)|$ is small when $|x|$ is large. In case (b) $|r(x)|$ is close to a constant $(\neq 0)$ when $|x|$ is large. The sketch of the proof for case (a) follows. Write

$$r(x) = \frac{a_n x^n + \cdots + a_0}{b_m x^m + \cdots + b_0} \qquad \text{with } a_n \neq 0 \text{ and } b_m \neq 0.$$

We have $n > m$. Dividing through by x^n, we obtain

$$r(x) = \frac{a_n + \dfrac{a_{n-1}}{x} + \cdots + \dfrac{a_0}{x^n}}{\dfrac{b_m}{x^{n-m}} + \cdots + \dfrac{b_0}{x^n}}.$$

Since $n - m > 0$, for $|x|$ large the denominator is close to 0. The numerator is close to a_n ($\neq 0$), hence the quotient is large in absolute value.

III-Appendix

2. Since $|f(x)|$ is large where $|x|$ is large, we see that for $|x| > L$ (where L is appropriately chosen) $|f(x)| > 1$. Thus all real zeros of f lie in the interval $-L \leq x \leq L$.

3. See III.6.a. exercise 7.

4. Suppose f is periodic of period $p > 0$. Let $a > 0$ be any real number. If f is a polynomial, it has a degree ≥ 1 (f is non-constant) and hence there is a number L such that if $|x| > L$, $|f(x)| > |f(a)|$. Choose an integer n such that $np > L$ (Archimedean property). Then $a + np > L$ and $|f(a + np)| > |f(a)|$. However, by periodicity $f(a + np) = f(a)$. This gives a contradiction.

5. If $f(x) = |x|$ is a polynomial, it is of degree ≥ 2 since f is even. Suppose this polynomial is $g(x) = a_n x^n + \cdots + a_0$ where $a_n \neq 0$.

    Now $\dfrac{|x|}{x^n}$ is small when $|x|$ is large, $x > 0$. On the other hand $\dfrac{g(x)}{x^n}$ is close to a_n when $|x|$ is large, $x > 0$. This is a contradiction.

CHAPTER IV

IV.1.a

2. (a) $\sqrt{7} = 2.646$; (b) $\sqrt{13} = 3.606$; (d) $\sqrt[3]{2} = 1.260$;
    (f) $29^2 = 841$; (g) $33^3 = 35{,}937$.

3. (a) $1^2 = 1$, $2^2 = 4$, $3^2 = 9$. Hence $2 < \sqrt{5} < 3$. $2.1^2 = 4.41$, $2.2^2 = 4.84$, $2.3^2 = 5.29$. Hence correct to one decimal place, $\sqrt{5} = 2.2$.

    (e) $2^3 = 8$, $3^3 = 27$. Hence $2 < \sqrt[3]{25} < 3$. Since 25 is close to 27, we start with the calculation of 2.8^3. $2.8^3 = 21.952$; $2.9^3 = 24.389$. Thus $2.9 < \sqrt[3]{25} < 3.0$.

4. Let $0 < x < 1$. $\dfrac{\sqrt{x}}{x} = \dfrac{1}{\sqrt{x}}$. Since $x < 1$, $\sqrt{x} < 1$ and $\dfrac{1}{\sqrt{x}} > 1$.

    Suppose k is such that if $0 < x \leq k$, then $\dfrac{1}{\sqrt{x}} > 100$. Thus $\dfrac{1}{\sqrt{k}} > 100$ and $\sqrt{k} < \dfrac{1}{100}$, that is, $k < \dfrac{1}{10{,}000}$. It remains to check that when $k < \dfrac{1}{10{,}000}$, we have $\dfrac{1}{\sqrt{x}} > 100$. This is easy since the inequalities that we wrote can be read in reverse order.

6. $\sqrt{x^2} = \pm x$ where the sign is that which makes the quantity positive. Also $|x| = \pm x$ where the sign is that which makes the quantity positive. Hence $\sqrt{x^2} = |x|$.

7. Let $n < m$. If $0 < x < 1$, then $x^m < x^n$ and by the monotonicity of the function "$m \cdot n$th root of" $(x^m)^{1/mn} < (x^n)^{1/mn}$. Thus $x^{1/n} < x^{1/m}$.

IV.2.a

1. (a) 5; **(b)** 13; **(c)** $\sqrt{85}$; **(e)** 0; **(f)** $\sqrt{2(a^2 + b^2)}$;
 (g) $|c|\sqrt{x^2 + y^2}$; **(h)** $\sqrt{x^2 + y^2}$.

4. (a) 5; **(e)** $\sqrt{(x - 3)^2 + (y - 6)^2}$; **(f)** $\sqrt{(c - a)^2 + (d - b)^2}$;
 (j) $\sqrt{(a + c)^2 + (b + d)^2}$.

6. The lengths of the sides are $\sqrt{45}, \sqrt{20}, \sqrt{65}$. Since $(\sqrt{65})^2 = (\sqrt{45})^2 + (\sqrt{20})^2$, the triangle is a right triangle.

7. The lengths if the sides are $\sqrt{18}, \sqrt{29}, \sqrt{29}$, hence the triangle is isosceles.

8. $a = 1 \pm \sqrt{3}$.

9. We have by a straight-forward calculation
$$\overline{OA}^2 + \overline{AC}^2 + \overline{CB}^2 + \overline{BO}^2$$
$$= (\sqrt{x_1^2 + y_1^2})^2 + (\sqrt{x_2^2 + y_2^2})^2 + (\sqrt{x_1^2 + y_1^2})^2 + (\sqrt{x_2^2 + y_2^2})^2$$
$$= 2(x_1^2 + x_2^2 + y_1^2 + y_2^2).$$
On the other hand,
$$\overline{OC}^2 + \overline{BA}^2$$
$$= (\sqrt{(x_1 + x_2)^2 + (y_1 + y_2)^2})^2 + (\sqrt{(x_2 - x_1)^2 + (y_2 - y_1)^2})^2$$
$$= (x_1^2 + 2x_1x_2 + x_2^2 + y_1^2 + 2y_1y_2 + y_2^2)$$
$$\qquad\qquad + (x_2^2 - 2x_1x_2 + x_1^2 + y_2^2 - 2y_1y_2 + y_1^2)$$
$$= 2(x_1^2 + x_2^2 + y_1^2 + y_2^2).$$

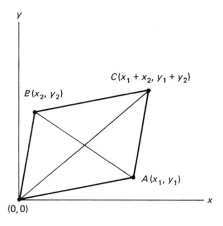

10.   In the first place, $D(A, B) \geq 0$ since $|x_2 - x_1| \geq 0$ and $|y_2 - y_1| \geq 0$. Next $D(A, B) = D(B, A)$ since $|x_2 - x_1| = |x_1 - x_2|$ and $|y_2 - y_1| = |y_1 - y_2|$. Finally, for any point $C(x_3, y_3)$, we have

$$\begin{aligned} D(AC) &= |x_3 - x_1| + |y_3 - y_1| \\ &= |(x_3 - x_2) + (x_2 - x_1)| + |(y_3 - y_2) + (y_2 - y_1)| \\ &\leq |x_3 - x_2| + |x_2 - x_1| + |y_3 - y_2| + |y_2 - y_1| \\ &= D(A, B) + D(B, C). \end{aligned}$$

Note that $D(A, B) = 0$ if and only if $A = B$.

12. (a) $(x - 4)^2 + (y - 3)^2 = 4$;

(b) $(x + 4)^2 + (y - 3)^2 = 2$;

(e) $x^2 + y^2 - ax - by = 0$ or $\left(x - \dfrac{a}{2}\right)^2 + \left(y - \dfrac{b}{2}\right)^2 = \left[\dfrac{a^2 + b^2}{4}\right]$.

IV.2.b

1. (a) $x^2 + y^2 - 6x - 8y = 0$;

(c) $x^2 + y^2 - 2ax - 2(3a - 2)y + a^2 + (3a - 2)^2 - 4c^4 = 0$;

(h) $x^2 + y^2 - 2hx - 2ky = 0$.

2. (a) $(2, 3)$, 1;   (c) $(\tfrac{3}{2}, -\tfrac{5}{2})$, $\dfrac{\sqrt{34}}{2}$;

(e) $(a, a - 1)$, a.

3. (d)

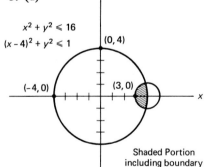

$x^2 + y^2 \leqslant 16$
$(x - 4)^2 + y^2 \leqslant 1$

(0, 4)

(−4, 0)   (3, 0)

Shaded Portion
including boundary

(e)

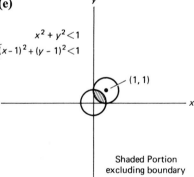

$x^2 + y^2 < 1$
$(x - 1)^2 + (y - 1)^2 < 1$

(1, 1)

Shaded Portion
excluding boundary

4. (a) 0;   (b) 3;   (c) 4.

5. (a) -1;   (b) 0 or -6.

IV.3.a

1. $\overline{PF_1} + \overline{PF_2} = 2a$.

$$\sqrt{(x - 0)^2 + (y - c)^2} + \sqrt{(x - 0)^2 + (y + c)^2} = 2a.$$

$$\sqrt{x^2 + (y - c)^2} = 2a - \sqrt{x^2 + (y + c)^2}.$$

$$x^2 + y^2 - 2cy + c^2$$
$$= 4a^2 - 4a\sqrt{x^2 + (y + c)^2} + x^2 + y^2 + 2cy + c^2.$$
$$cy + a^2 = a\sqrt{x^2 + (y + c)^2}.$$
$$c^2y^2 + 2a^2cy + a^4 = a^2x^2 + a^2y^2 + 2a^2cy + a^2c^2.$$
$$a^2x^2 + (a^2 - c^2)y^2 = a^2(a^2 - c^2).$$
$$\frac{x^2}{a^2 - c^2} + \frac{y^2}{a^2} = 1.$$

Since $a > c$, $a^2 - c^2 > 0$. Write $a^2 - c^2 = b^2$. Then equation reads $\dfrac{x^2}{b^2} + \dfrac{y^2}{a^2} = 1$. Note that $b^2 \leq a^2$ hence $b \leq a$.

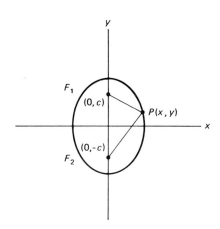

2. (a) $(0, 0)$, 3, 2, $(\pm\sqrt{5}, 0)$, $\dfrac{\sqrt{5}}{3}$, 6π.

  (b) Same as (a) with roles of x and y interchanged.

  (c) $\sqrt{6}$, $\dfrac{\sqrt{24}}{3}$, $(1, -1)$, $\left(\pm\dfrac{\sqrt{30}}{3} + 1, -1\right)$, $\dfrac{\sqrt{5}}{3}$, 4π.

4. $3x^2 - 2xy + 3y^2 - 8 = 0.$

6.   Given that (x, y) satisfies $(a^2 - c^2)x^2 + a^2y^2 = a^2(a^2 - c^2)$. Then $(a^2 - cx)^2 = a^2((x - c)^2 + y^2)$.

  Now clearly $x^2 \leq a^2$ $\left(\text{since } \dfrac{x^2}{a^2} + \dfrac{y^2}{a^2 - c^2} = 1\right)$ and hence $-a \leq x \leq a$. Thus $-a^2 \leq -ca \leq cx \leq ca \leq a^2$. Hence $a^2 - cx \geq 0$. This means that when taking square roots above, we obtain
$$a^2 - cx = a\sqrt{(x - c)^2 + y^2}.$$
It is now easy to obtain equation (5).

9.   Just below $9.2 \cdot 10^7$.

IV.4.a

1. $\overline{PF_1} - \overline{PF_2} = \pm 2a \qquad c > a.$

$\sqrt{x^2 + (y + c)^2} - \sqrt{x^2 + (y - c)^2} = \pm 2a.$

$\sqrt{x^2 + (y + c)^2} = \pm 2a + \sqrt{x^2 + (y - c)^2}.$

$x^2 + y^2 + 2cy + c^2$
$\qquad\qquad = 4a^2 \pm 4a\sqrt{x^2 + (y - c)^2} + x^2 + y^2 - 2cy + c^2.$

$cy - a^2 = \pm a\sqrt{x^2 + (y - c)^2}.$

$c^2y^2 - 2a^2cy + a^4 = a^2x^2 + a^2y^2 - 2a^2cy + a^2c^2.$

$(c^2 - a^2)y^2 - a^2x^2 = a^2(c^2 - a^2).$

Since $c > a$, $c^2 > a^2$. Set $c^2 - a^2 = b^2$. Then

$$b^2y^2 - a^2x^2 = a^2b^2 \qquad \text{and} \qquad \frac{y^2}{a^2} - \frac{x^2}{b^2} = 1.$$

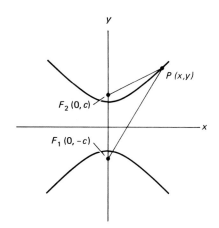

2. (a)

(b)

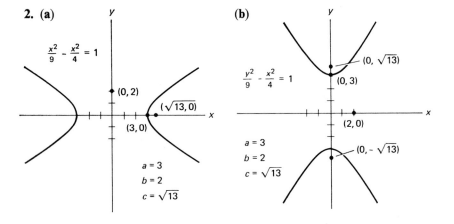

(e) Center $(2, -3)$, $a = 3$, $b = 2$, $c = \sqrt{13}$, foci at $(2 \pm \sqrt{13}, -3)$.

(h) Center $(-1, 2)$, $a = \sqrt{30}$, $b = \sqrt{20}$, $c = \sqrt{50}$, foci at $(-1, 2 \pm \sqrt{50})$.

3. (a)

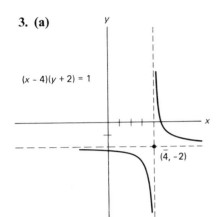

$(x - 4)(y + 2) = 1$

$(4, -2)$

(d)

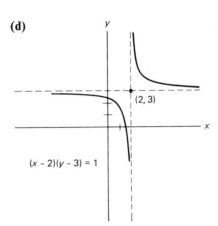

$(2, 3)$

$(x - 2)(y - 3) = 1$

4.
$$\sqrt{(x - 1)^2 + (y - 1)^2} - \sqrt{(x + 1)^2 + (y + 1)^2} = \pm 2.$$
$$\sqrt{(x - 1)^2 + (y - 1)^2} = \pm 2 + \sqrt{(x + 1)^2 + (y + 1)^2}.$$
$$x^2 - 2x + 1 + y^2 - 2y + 1$$
$$= 4 \pm 4\sqrt{(x + 1)^2 + (y + 1)^2} + x^2 + 2x + 1 + y^2 + 2y + 1.$$
$$x + y + 1 = \mp\sqrt{(x + 1)^2 + (y + 1)^2}.$$
$$x^2 + y^2 + 1 + 2xy + 2x + 2y = x^2 + 2x + 1 + y^2 + 2y + 1.$$
$$2xy = 1.$$

5.
$$3x^2 - 8xy + 3y^2 - 7 = 0.$$

9.
$$\frac{x^2}{a^2} - \frac{y^2}{b^2} = 1 \quad \text{or} \quad y = \pm \frac{b}{a}\sqrt{x^2 - a^2}$$

Consider $x > 0$ and $y > 0$. The point H on the hyperbola has coordinates $\left(x, \frac{b}{a}\sqrt{x^2 - a^2}\right)$. The coordinates of the point L on the line $y = \frac{b}{a}x$ are $\left(x, \frac{b}{a}x\right)$. For the distance $\overline{HL}$ we have

$$\overline{HL} = \frac{b}{a}x - \frac{b}{a}\sqrt{x^2 - a^2} = \frac{b}{a}(x - \sqrt{x^2 - a^2})$$

$$= \frac{b}{a}(x - \sqrt{x^2 - a^2})\frac{x + \sqrt{x^2 - a^2}}{x + \sqrt{x^2 - a^2}} = \frac{b}{a}\frac{x^2 - (x^2 - a^2)}{x + \sqrt{x^2 - a^2}}$$

$$= \frac{b}{a}\frac{a^2}{x + \sqrt{x^2 - a^2}} = \frac{ab}{x + \sqrt{x^2 - a^2}}.$$

Now, if x is very large, then $x + \sqrt{x^2 - a^2}$ is even larger and ab divided by $(x + \sqrt{x^2 - a^2})$ is small (close to 0). This shows that the line $y = \dfrac{b}{a} x$ is an asymptote to the hyperbola. The argument for $x < 0$ is similar. In the same way one can prove that the line $y = -\dfrac{b}{a} x$ is an asymptote to the curve.

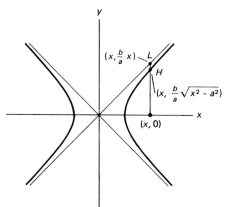

10. (a)

$y^2 = 4x$

(b)

$x^2 = 4y$

(f)

$y = 1$

$(y-1)^2 = 2x$

(h)

$(y - k)^2 = 2p(x - h)$

$\overline{PF} = \overline{AP}$

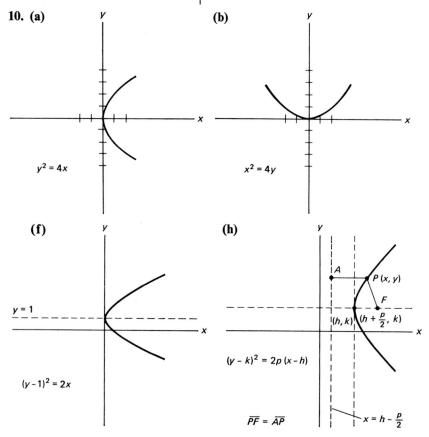

IV.5.a

1. (a)

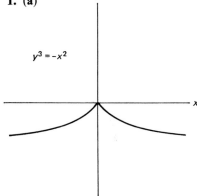

$y^3 = -x^2$

(b)

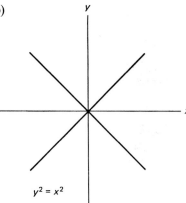

$y^2 = x^2$

(d)

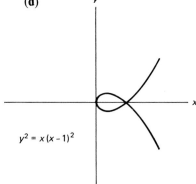

$y^2 = x(x-1)^2$

(h)

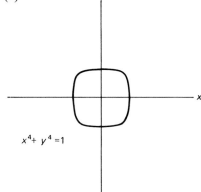

$x^4 + y^4 = 1$

3. $p^2 = ka^3$ hence $k = \dfrac{p^2}{a^2}$. The values obtained for k using the data for Mercury, Venus, Earth, Mars, Jupiter, Saturn, Uranus, Neptune are 1.25, 1.24, 1.24, 1.28, 1.26, 1.23, 1.25, 1.24, each multiplied by 10^{-6}.

CHAPTER V

V.1.a

1. (a) 3^{12};   (b) 6^{-5};   (e) x^{-12};   (g) 1;   (h) -8^3;   (i) $2^5 \cdot 3^4$.
2. (a) 3^4;   (b) $3^{-20} \cdot 7^{16}$;   (d) a^{12};   (f) $a^{40}b^{30}$;
   (g) $2^{-7} \cdot 3^{-2}x^{-1}y^{-2}z^{-3}$.
3. (a) $1.86 \cdot 10^5$;   (b) $3 \cdot 10^8$;   (c) $2.25 \cdot 10^{11}$;   (d) $1 \cdot 10^{-5}$.
4. (a) $1.5 \cdot 10^{-5}$;   (b) $1.5 \cdot 10^5$;   (e) $1.2 \cdot 10^{-8}$;   (f) 4.
5. (a) $4.8 \cdot 10^2$;   (b) $1.6875 \cdot 10^{58}$;   (c) $1.505 \cdot 10^{29}$;   (d) $3.21 \cdot 10^{17}$.

6. (a) $8 \cdot 10^{12}$;   **(b)** $1.5 \cdot 10^6$;   **(c)** $3 \cdot 10^{-5}$;   **(d)** 4;   **(e)** $3 \cdot 10^2$;
  (f) $1.2 \cdot 10^7$.

7.   Proof of $(a^n)^m = a^{nm}$.
    Case 1. $n > 0, m > 0$.
$$(a^n)^m = (a \cdots a)(a \cdots a) \cdots (a \cdots a)$$
    where there are m parentheses and each one contains n a's. By the
    associative law for multiplication the result is $a^{n \cdot m}$.
    Case 2. $n > 0, m = 0$.
      $(a^n)^m = (a^n)^0 = 1$. On the other hand $a^{n \cdot m} = a^{n \cdot 0} = a^0 = 1$.
    Hence $(a^n)^m = a^{nm}$.
    Case 3. $n > 0, m < 0$. Write $m = -r$ where $r > 0$.
$$(a^n)^m = (a^n)^{-r} = \frac{1}{(a^n)^r} = \frac{1}{a^{nr}} = a^{-nr} = a^{nm}.$$
    where the third equality is valid by case 1.
    Case 4. $n < 0, m < 0$.
$$(a^n)^m = \frac{1}{(a^n)^{-m}} = \frac{1}{a^{-nm}} = a^{nm}$$
    where the second equality is valid by case 3.

9.   360.

V.2.a

1. (a) 8;   **(b)** 512;
  (c) 81;   **(d)** $\frac{1}{5}$;
  (e) 0.001;   **(g)** $\frac{1}{8}$;
  (i) 243;   **(j)** 32;
  (k) 6;   **(l)** $\frac{1}{64}$.

2. (a) a^{10};   **(h)** $a^{-1/3}$;
  (c) $a^{3/2}b^{-1}c^{2/3}$;   **(d)** a^{-1};
  (e) $a^{11}b^6c^2$;   **(f)** $2^7x^6y^2$;
  (h) $6^{3/5}a^{12/5}b^3$;   **(i)** $2 \cdot 3^{-2}a^2b^{-2}$.

3. (a) $x = \frac{22}{3}$;   **(b)** $x = 2$;
  (c) $x = 5^{2/3}$;   **(d)** $y = 3^{3/2} \cdot 2^{1/6}$;
  (e) $x = \frac{8}{3}$;   **(f)** $x = 10^{1/2}$.

4. (a) $\sqrt{7} = 2.646$; $\sqrt{20} = 4.472$; $\sqrt{41} = 6.403$.

  (b) $\sqrt[3]{7} = 1.913$; $\sqrt[3]{20} = 2.714$; $\sqrt[3]{41} = 3.448$.

  (c) $7\sqrt{7} + \sqrt[3]{7} = 7 \cdot 2.646 + 1.913 = 20.435$.

  (d) $\dfrac{\sqrt{7}}{\sqrt[3]{7}} = \dfrac{2.646}{1.913} = 1.385$.

5.   14,140.

V.3.a

2. (a) $e^5 = 148.41$;   **(b)** $e^{1.55} = 4.7115$;

   (c) $e^{-4.15} = 0.0158$;   **(d)** $e^{2.30} = 9.9742$;

   (e) $10^{\sqrt{3}} = e^{2.30 \cdot \sqrt{3}} = e^{3.98}$ and $51.935 < e^{3.98} < 54.598$;

   (f) $2 = e^{0.70}$ hence $2^{\sqrt{2}} = e^{0.70 \cdot \sqrt{2}} = e^{0.99}$ (≈ 2.69).

3. (a) $2e^2 = 2 \cdot (7.3891) = 14.7782$;   **(b)** $2^2 e^2 = 29.5564$

   (c) $2 + e^2 = 2 + 7.3891 = 9.3891$;   **(d)** $2 \cdot e^{-4} = 0.0366$.

5.   If $e^u = 2$, $u \approx 0.70$. Hence

$$1 + 2 + 2^2 + 2^3 + 2^4 = 1 + e^{0.70} + e^{2 \cdot 0.70} + e^{3 \cdot 0.70} + e^{4 \cdot 0.70}.$$

V.4.a

1. (a)

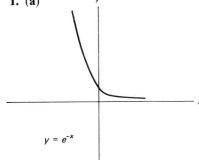

$y = e^{-x}$

(b)

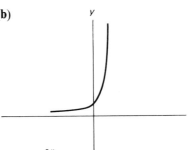

$y = e^{2x}$

(c)

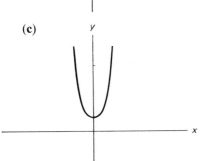

$y = e^{x^2}$

(d)

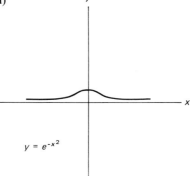

$y = e^{-x^2}$

3. $\left(\dfrac{e^x + e^{-x}}{2} \right)^2 - \left(\dfrac{e^x - e^{-x}}{2} \right)^2$

$$= \tfrac{1}{4}(e^{2x} + 2 + e^{-2x}) - \tfrac{1}{4}(e^{2x} - 2 + e^{-2x}) = 1.$$

5.   Since $-x_1 > 0$, $\exp(-x_1) > 1$. Thus $\exp(x_1) = \dfrac{1}{\exp(-x_1)} < 1$.

Also $\exp(x_2) > 1$ since $x_2 > 0$. Thus $\exp(x_2) > \exp(x_1)$.

V.5.a

1.   If $N(t)$ represents the number of deer in the herd after t years, $N(t) = N(0)e^{ct}$. Here $N(0) = 200$. Since $400 = 200 \cdot e^{7c}$, $7c = 0.70$ and $c = 0.10$. Thus $N(25) = 200 \cdot e^{2.5} = 200 \cdot 12.18 = 2436$. If $1000 = 200e^{0.10t}$, then $0.10t \approx 1.60$ or $t = 16$.

2.   9.7.

3.   12.9.

4.   10.

7.   3.5.

V.6.a

1. (a) $\ln 1 = 0$;   **(b)** $\ln e = 1$;
   (d) $\ln 10 = 2.302$;   **(e)** $s = \ln 3$;
   (f) $t = \ln u > 0$;   **(g)** $\ln e^{3x+2} = \ln e^{3x} + \ln e^2$;
   (h) $\ln e^{tx} = t \ln e^x$;   **(i)** $\ln 2 = 0.70$;
   (j) $t = \ln u$ takes on all values;
   (k) $t = \ln u$ is defined only for $u > 0$.

2. (a) $e^{2.302} = 10$;
   (b) The equation $\ln 10 = \ln 2 + \ln 5$, that is, $2.3025 = 0.6931 + 1.6094$ gives $e^{2.3025} = e^{0.6931} \cdot e^{1.6094}$, that is, $10 = 2 \cdot 5$.
   (c) $\exp(1) = e$;   **(d)** $\exp(0) = 1$;
   (e) $\exp(t) > 0$;   **(f)** $\exp(t)$ is defined for all t;
   (g) $\exp(u) > 1$ where $u = \ln t$;   **(h)** $\exp(w) > e^2$ where $w = \ln v$.

3. (a) $\ln 6 = \ln 2 + \ln 3 = 0.6931 + 1.0986 = 1.7917$;
   (c) $\ln \frac{1}{3} = \ln 1 - \ln 3 = -1.0986$;
   (d) $\ln 125 = 3 \ln 5 = 3 \cdot 1.6094 = 4.8282$;
   (g) $\ln 100 = 2 \ln 2 + 2 \ln 5$ etc.

4. (a) 7;   **(b)** -3;   **(d)** e^2;   **(e)** $3e$;   **(f)** 2.

V.6.b

2. (a) 0.7642;   **(b)** 1.4997;
   (d) 6.2695;   **(e)** Between 0.4330 and 0.4346;
   (g) 0.0449;   **(i)** $0.3336 - 2$.

3. (a) $0.7782 = 0.3010 + 0.4771$;
   (d) $1.3802 = 1.8573 - 0.4771$.

4. (a) 4;   **(b)** 18;   **(d)** $\frac{3}{2}$;   **(f)** $\frac{1}{4}$.

5. (a) Write $\log_7 6 = x$. Then $7^x = 6$. Since $10^{0.8451} = 7$, $7^x = 10^{0.8451x} = 6 = 10^{0.7782}$. Hence $0.8451x = 0.7782$ and $x \approx 0.92$.

6. (a) Let $\ln 2 = x$. Then $e^x = 2$. Since $e^{2.302} = 10$ and $10^{0.3010} = 2$, one obtains $e^{2.302 \cdot 0.3010} = 2$. Hence $x = 2.302 \cdot 0.3010 = 0.6929$. Table III gives $\ln 2 = 0.6931$.

7. (a) Let $\log_3 8 = x$. Then $3^x = 8$. Now, $10^{0.4771} = 3$, hence $10^{0.4771x} = 3^x = 8 = 10^{0.9031}$. Thus $0.4771x = 0.9031$ and $x = \dfrac{0.9031}{0.4771}$.

(d) $\log_\pi 10 = \dfrac{1}{0.4969}$.

9. $\log_{10} \sqrt{10} = 0.5000$; $\log_{10} \pi = 0.4969$. Since $10^{0.5000} > 10^{0.4969}$, we have $\sqrt{10} > \pi$. Also $1.00 < \dfrac{\sqrt{10}}{\pi} = 10^{0.5000 - 0.4968} = 10^{0.0032} < 1.01$. Hence the error is less than 1 percent.

V.7.a

1. (a) 0.5391;   **(b)** 2.7570;
   (d) 0.4221 − 3;   **(e)** 1.1576.

2. (a) 6.02;   **(b)** 0.0901;
   (c) 4.56 × 10⁵;   **(d)** 2.076;
   (g) 95.72;   **(h)** 1.27.

3. (a) 0.2983 with interpolation and 0.299 without.
   (b) 1.837 × 10¹⁹ with interpolation and 1.84 × 10¹⁹ without.
   (d) 10.0 with or without interpolation.
   (e) 39.45 with interpolation and 39.4 without.

4. For the first bank, the amount after t years is $a(t) = 100(1 + 0.06)^t$. For $t = 10$, this gives $a(10) = 179.00$. For the second bank $b(t) = 100(1 + 0.015)^{4t}$. Hence $b(10) = 180.30$.

5. 6.

CHAPTER VI

VI.1.a

1. (a)

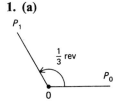

(b)

2 right angles

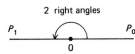

(c)

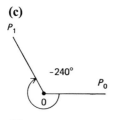

(d)

(h)

(k)

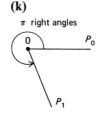

2. The circumference of the spool in inches is $2\pi r = 2\pi$. The length of the thread is 300×36 (in inches). Thus the angle of rotation is $\dfrac{300 \times 36}{2\pi}$ revolutions $= 300 \times 36$ radians $= \dfrac{300 \times 36}{2\pi} \cdot 360°$.

3. $2\pi \cdot 450 \approx 2820$.

5. 12.8 revolutions or 80 radians. $\frac{80}{132} = 0.605$ radians.

6. New York to Chicago: 447,000 revolutions approximately.
Paris to Marseille: 255,000 revolutions approximately.

7. 2.29 inches.

9. The degree measure of α is $\dfrac{180}{\pi} x$. Since α and β have the same terminal side one has $\dfrac{180}{\pi} x = x + n \cdot 360$ where n is some integer.

Hence $x = n \left(\dfrac{1}{2\pi} - \dfrac{1}{360} \right)^{-1} \approx 6.41n$. $n = 0, 1\, 2, 3, \cdots$ give $x = 0$, 6.41, 12.81, 19.23, $\cdots$.

VI.2.a

1. (a) $\dfrac{\sqrt{3}}{2}$; (b) $\frac{1}{2}$; (c) 1;

(e) -1; (f) $0 + (-1) = -1$; (h) $\dfrac{0}{-1} = 0$;

(i) $\frac{1}{4} - \frac{3}{4} = -\frac{1}{2}$; (j) $\dfrac{\sqrt{3}}{2} \cdot (-\frac{1}{2}) = \dfrac{-\sqrt{3}}{4}$.

2. (a) $\sin 0.2443 = 0.2419$; (b) $\cos 1.2915 = 0.2756$;
(c) $\sin 1 = 0.8414$; (d) $\cos \frac{1}{2} = \cos 0.500 = 0.8774$.

3. (a) $x = \dfrac{\pi}{6}, \dfrac{5\pi}{6}$;   **(b)** $x = \dfrac{\pi}{6}, 2\pi - \dfrac{\pi}{6}$;

   (d) $x = \dfrac{\pi}{4}, \dfrac{5\pi}{4}$;   **(e)** $x = \dfrac{2\pi}{3}$;

   (f) $x = \dfrac{\pi}{2}, \dfrac{3\pi}{2}$;   **(i)** $x = 0, \dfrac{\pi}{2}, \pi$.

4. (a)   **(e)**

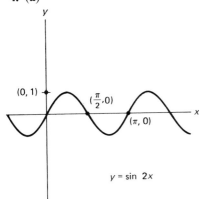

$y = \sin\ 2x$

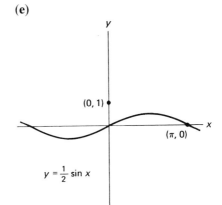

$y = \dfrac{1}{2} \sin x$

(i)

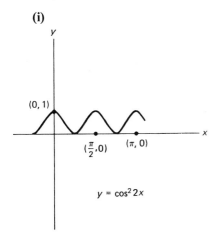

$y = \cos^2 2x$

VI.2.b

1. (a) $\tan 0.2094 = 0.2126$;   **(b)** $\cot 0.4043 = 2.337$;
   (c) $\tan 1.2915 = 3.495$;   **(f)** $\cot 1.0472 = 0.5774$.
2. (a) $\sin(-0.6632) = -0.6157$;   **(b)** $\cos(-0.7359) = 0.7412$;
   (c) $\sin(\pi + 0.6632) = -0.6157$;   **(d)** $\cos(\pi + 0.7359) = -0.7412$;
   (g) $\sin 4 = \sin(\pi + 4 - \pi) = -\sin(4 - \pi) = -\sin(0.8584) = -0.7568$.

3. $x - \sin x \geq 0.0001$ if $x \geq 0.0495$;
           $x - \sin x \geq 0.0010$ if $x \geq 0.1804$.

This seems to suggest that $\dfrac{\sin x}{x}$ is very close to 1 if x is close to 0.

The conclusion is correct. Its proof cannot be given here.

5. (a)   **(b)**

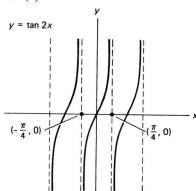

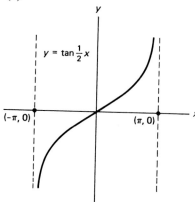

(c)   **(g)**

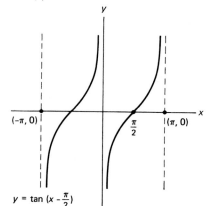

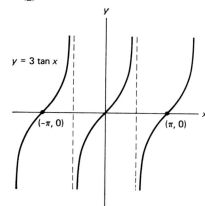

VI.3.a

1. $y = \frac{31}{2} \sin(2\pi \cdot 29^{-1}t)$. Here y is in minutes (angle measure) and t is in days. As written down $t = 0$ corresponds to a half-moon. As stated, the quantity y should be added to $\frac{31}{2}$ to obtain the angle which the moon subtends at the earth.

2. $y = 2 \sin(2\pi \cdot \frac{1}{3}t)$ where t is in seconds and y is in feet. Note that the function has period 3.

4.   167,200 feet or 31.9 miles.

5.   Let the girl's pulse rate be ω. Then the equation describing her foot's motion is $y = \frac{1}{8}\sin(2\pi\omega t)$. Here y is in inches and t is in minutes. Thus in one minute, her foot moves up and down a total distance of

$4 \cdot \frac{1}{8} \cdot \omega = \dfrac{\omega}{2}$ (in inches). In 30 minutes this gives a total displace-

ment of 90 feet. Thus $90 \cdot 12 = \dfrac{\omega}{2} \cdot 30$; $\omega = 72$.

The hypothesis of simple harmonic motion is unnecessary. On the other hand simple periodicity is not sufficient. It is necessary that during a half cycle starting with the foot at the bottom, the motion upward be monotone (and similarly on the way down). For example the curve describing the foot's motion might be similar to the Sisyphus curve. (See Figure II.40.)

7. $c = 0.10$, $\omega = \frac{1}{4}$.
8.   For the radius r, $r = 20 + \frac{5}{4}\sin 2\pi(5.366)^{-1}t$.

VI.4.a

1. (a) $(\sin t + \cos t)^2 = \sin^2 t + 2\sin t \cos t + \cos^2 t = 1 + 2\sin t \cos t.$

(c) $\dfrac{1 + \tan^2 x}{\tan^2 x} = \dfrac{\sec^2 x}{\tan^2 x} = \dfrac{1}{\cos^2 x} \cdot \dfrac{\cos^2 x}{\sin^2 x} = \dfrac{1}{\sin^2 x} = \csc^2 x.$

(e) $(1 - \sin x)(1 + \sin x) = 1 - \sin^2 x = \cos^2 x = \dfrac{1}{\sec^2 x}$

$$= \dfrac{1}{1 + \tan^2 x}.$$

(g) $\dfrac{1 - \tan^2 x}{1 + \tan^2 x} = \dfrac{1 - \dfrac{\sin^2 x}{\cos^2 x}}{1 + \dfrac{\sin^2 x}{\cos^2 x}} = \dfrac{\cos^2 x - \sin^2 x}{\cos^2 x + \sin^2 x} = \cos^2 x - \sin^2 x$

$$= (\cos x - \sin x)(\cos x + \sin x).$$

(h) $1 - 2\sin^2 y = 1 - 2(1 - \cos^2 y) = 1 - 2 + 2\cos^2 y = 2\cos^2 y - 1.$

(k) $\dfrac{1 - \tan u}{1 + \tan u} = \dfrac{\tan u\left(\dfrac{1}{\tan u} - 1\right)}{\tan u\left(\dfrac{1}{\tan u} + 1\right)} = \dfrac{\cot u - 1}{\cot u + 1}.$

(m) $\dfrac{\tan x}{1 - \cot x} + \dfrac{\cot x}{1 - \tan x}$

$$= \dfrac{\tan x}{\tan x - 1} + \dfrac{\cot x}{1 - \tan x} = \dfrac{\tan^2 x - \cot x}{\tan x - 1}$$

$$= \dfrac{\tan x}{\dfrac{1}{\tan x}} \cdot \dfrac{\tan^3 x - 1}{\tan x - 1} = \dfrac{1}{\tan x}(\tan^2 x + \tan x + 1)$$

$$= \tan x + 1 + \cot x.$$

2. (a) $\pm \dfrac{\pi}{3} + 2n\pi$; **(b)** $\dfrac{\pi}{2} \cdot n$; **(c)** $\dfrac{\pi}{12} + \pi n$;

(e) $\frac{1}{2} + 2n$; **(g)** $\pm \dfrac{\pi}{3} + \pi n$.

3. (a) The graph gives an idea of the solution. The tables give as a fairly accurate solution $x \approx \pm 1.8966$ since $\sin(1.8966) = \sin(\pi - 1.8966) = \sin 1.2450 = 0.9474 = \frac{1}{2}(1.8948)$.

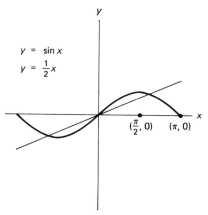

(c) $\sin x > x^2$ is valid for $0 < x < 0.875$ since $\sin(0.875) \approx 0.768$ and $(0.875)^2 \approx 0.765$.

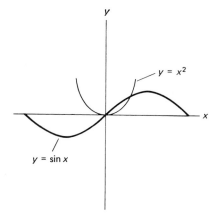

(e) $2 \cos x = e^x$ and $x > 0$ imply $x \approx 0.538$ since $\cos(0.538) \approx 0.859$, $e^{0.538} \approx 1.71 \approx 2(0.859)$.

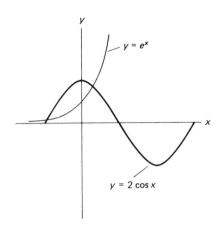

VI.5.a

1. (a) $\cos(x - y) = \cos[x + (-y)] = \cos x \cos(-y) - \sin x \sin(-y)$
$$= \cos x \cos y - \sin x(-\sin y)$$
$$= \cos x \cos y + \sin x \sin y.$$

(c) $\cot(x + y) = \dfrac{\cos(x + y)}{\sin(x + y)} = \dfrac{\cos x \cos y - \sin x \sin y}{\sin x \cos y + \cos x \sin y}$

$$= \dfrac{\dfrac{\cos x \cos y}{\sin x \sin y} - \dfrac{\sin x \sin y}{\sin x \sin y}}{\dfrac{\sin x \cos y}{\sin x \sin y} + \dfrac{\cos x \sin y}{\sin x \sin y}} = \dfrac{\cot x \cot y - 1}{\cot y + \cot x}.$$

(e) $\sin\left(\dfrac{\pi}{2} - x\right) = \sin\dfrac{\pi}{2} \cos x - \cos\dfrac{\pi}{2} \sin x$
$$= 1 \cdot \cos x - 0 \cdot \sin x = \cos x.$$

(g) $\sin(\pi - x) = \sin \pi \cos x - \cos \pi \sin x$
$$= 0 \cdot \cos x - (-1) \sin x = \sin x.$$

2. (a) $\sin(x + y) + \sin(x - y)$
$$= (\sin x \cos y + \cos x \sin y) + (\sin x \cos y - \cos x \sin y)$$
$$= 2 \sin x \cos y.$$

(c) $\cos(x + y) + \cos(x - y)$
$$= (\cos x \cos y - \sin x \sin y) + (\cos x \cos y + \sin x \sin y)$$
$$= 2 \cos x \cos y.$$

3. (a) $\sin u + \sin v = \sin(x + y) + \sin(x - y)$
$$= 2 \sin x \cos y = 2 \sin\dfrac{u + v}{2} \cos\dfrac{u - v}{2}.$$

Here $u = x + y$, $v = x - y$, $x = \dfrac{u + v}{2}$, $y = \dfrac{u - v}{2}$.

(d) $\cos u - \cos v = \cos(x + y) - \cos(x - y)$

$$= -2 \sin x \sin y = -2 \sin \frac{u + v}{2} \sin \frac{u - v}{2}.$$

5. (a) $\sin(x + y) \sin(x - y)$

$$= (\sin x \cos y + \cos x \sin y)(\sin x \cos y - \cos x \sin y)$$
$$= \sin^2 x \cos^2 y - \cos^2 x \sin^2 y$$
$$= \sin^2 x(1 - \sin^2 y) - (1 - \sin^2 x) \sin^2 y$$
$$= \sin^2 x - \sin^2 x \sin^2 y - \sin^2 y + \sin^2 x \sin^2 y$$
$$= \sin^2 x - \sin^2 y.$$

(c) $\cos(x + y) \cos y + \sin(x + y) \sin y = \cos[(x + y) - y] = \cos x.$

VI.6.a

1. (a) $\cos^2 2x = \cos 2x \cdot \cos 2x = (2 \cos^2 x - 1)(1 - 2 \sin^2 x)$

$$= 2 \cos^2 x + 2 \sin^2 x - 1 - 4 \sin^2 x \cos^2 x$$
$$= 1 - 4 \sin^2 x \cos^2 x.$$

(c) $\dfrac{1 - \cos 2x}{\sin 2x} = \dfrac{1 - (1 - 2 \sin^2 x)}{2 \sin x \cos x} = \dfrac{2 \sin^2 x}{2 \sin x \cos x} = \tan x.$

(d) $\dfrac{2 \tan x}{1 + \tan^2 x} = \dfrac{2 \dfrac{\sin x}{\cos x}}{1 + \dfrac{\sin^2 x}{\cos^2 x}} = \dfrac{2 \dfrac{\sin x}{\cos x}}{\dfrac{\cos^2 x + \sin^2 x}{\cos^2 x}}$

$$= 2 \sin x \cos x = \sin 2x.$$

(f) $\tan^2 \dfrac{x}{2} = \dfrac{\sin^2 \dfrac{x}{2}}{\cos^2 \dfrac{x}{2}} = \dfrac{\dfrac{1 - \cos x}{2}}{\dfrac{1 + \cos x}{2}} = \dfrac{(1 - \cos x)(1 + \cos x)}{(1 + \cos x)(1 + \cos x)}$

$$= \dfrac{1 - \cos^2 x}{(1 + \cos x)^2} = \left(\dfrac{\sin x}{1 + \cos x}\right)^2.$$

This gives the result $\tan \dfrac{x}{2} = \pm \dfrac{\sin x}{1 + \cos x}$ where the sign is still to be determined. Note that $\tan \dfrac{x}{2}$ has period 2π $\Big($since

$\tan \dfrac{x + 2\pi}{2} = \tan \left(\dfrac{x}{2} + \pi\right) = \tan \dfrac{x}{2}\Big)$ and $\dfrac{\sin x}{1 + \cos x}$ has period 2π.

We show that for $0 \le x < 2\pi$, the proper sign to choose is "$+$."

Note that $1 + \cos x \geq 0$ for all x. Thus the sign of $\dfrac{\sin x}{1 + \cos x}$ is the same as the sign of $\sin x$.

Now, $\sin x \geq 0$ for $0 \leq x < \pi$ and $\sin x \leq 0$ for $\pi < x \leq 2\pi$.

Also $\tan \dfrac{x}{2} \geq 0$ for $0 \leq x < \pi$ and $\tan \dfrac{x}{2} \leq 0$ for $\pi < x \leq 2\pi$.

Hence for all x $\tan \dfrac{x}{2} = \dfrac{\sin x}{1 + \cos x}$.

(j) $\begin{aligned}[t] \sin 3x &= \sin(2x + x) = \sin 2x \cos x + \cos 2x \sin x \\ &= 2 \sin x \cos x \cdot \cos x + (1 - 2 \sin^2 x) \sin x \\ &= 2 \sin x(1 - \sin^2 x) + \sin x - 2 \sin^3 x \\ &= 3 \sin x - 4 \sin^3 x. \end{aligned}$

2. (a) $\frac{1}{4}(\sqrt{2} - \sqrt{6})$;   (b) $\frac{1}{4}(\sqrt{2} - \sqrt{6})$.

3. $\cos \dfrac{\pi}{16} = \frac{1}{2}(2 + (2 + 2^{1/2})^{1/2})^{1/2}$.

4. (a) $\frac{24}{25}$;   (b) $\frac{7}{25}$;   (d) $\frac{1}{10}\sqrt{10}$;   (f) $\frac{1}{3}$(use 1.(g));   (g) $\frac{117}{125}$.

5. $\begin{aligned}[t] \cos 4x &= \cos[2(2x)] = 2 \cos^2 2x - 1 = 2(2 \cos^2 x - 1)^2 - 1 \\ &= 2(4 \cos^4 x - 4 \cos^2 x + 1) - 1 = 8 \cos^4 x - 8 \cos^2 x + 1. \end{aligned}$

$\begin{aligned}[t] \cos 5x &= \cos(3x + 2x) = \cos 3x \cos 2x - \sin 3x \sin 2x \\ &= (4 \cos^3 x - 3 \cos x)(2 \cos^2 x - 1) \\ &\qquad\qquad - (3 \sin x - 4 \sin^3 x)(2 \sin x \cos x) \\ &= 8 \cos^5 x - 10 \cos^3 x + 3 \cos x \\ &\qquad\qquad - 2 \sin^2 x(3 - 4 \sin^2 x) \cos x \end{aligned}$

where we used equation (9) and exercise 1(j). Now

$\begin{aligned}[t] 2 \sin^2 x(3 - 4 \sin^2 x) &= 2(1 - \cos^2 x)[3 - 4(1 - \cos^2 x)] \\ &= 2(1 - \cos^2 x)(-1 + 4 \cos^2 x) \\ &= -2 + 10 \cos^2 x - 8 \cos^4 x. \end{aligned}$

Hence

$\begin{aligned}[t] \cos 5x &= 8 \cos^5 x - 10 \cos^3 x + 3 \cos x + 8 \cos^5 x \\ &\qquad\qquad - 10 \cos^3 x + 2 \cos x \\ &= 16 \cos^5 x - 20 \cos^3 x + 5 \cos x. \end{aligned}$

6. $\cos \dfrac{\pi}{10} = \frac{1}{4}\sqrt{10 + 2\sqrt{5}}$.

7. $\dfrac{\sin x - \sin y}{\cos x + \cos y} = \dfrac{2 \cos \dfrac{x + y}{2} \sin \dfrac{x - y}{2}}{2 \cos \dfrac{x + y}{2} \cos \dfrac{x - y}{2}} = \dfrac{\sin \dfrac{x - y}{2}}{\cos \dfrac{x - y}{2}}$

$= \tan \dfrac{x - y}{2}.$

Use is made of exercise 3(b) and (c) in VI.5.a. Setting $y = 0$ above

$\tan \dfrac{x}{2} = \dfrac{\sin x - \sin 0}{\cos x + \cos 0} = \dfrac{\sin x}{1 + \cos x}.$

VI.7.a

1. (a) $\arcsin \dfrac{1}{\sqrt{2}} = \dfrac{\pi}{4}$; **(b)** $\tan^{-1} 0 = 0$;

(c) $\cos^{-1} 1 = 0$; **(d)** $\arctan 1 = \dfrac{\pi}{4}$;

(f) $\arccos 0 = \dfrac{\pi}{2}$; **(i)** $\sec^{-1} 2 = \dfrac{\pi}{3}$.

2. (a) $\sin^{-1} 0.2250 = 0.2269$; **(b)** $\arctan 0.6745 = 0.5934$;

(d) $\cos^{-1} 0.9511 = 0.3142$; **(e)** $\arcsin 0.7071 = \dfrac{\pi}{4}$.

3. (a) $\sin(\sin^{-1} \frac{3}{5}) = \frac{3}{5}$; **(b)** $\cos(\sin^{-1} \frac{3}{5}) = \frac{4}{5}$;

(c) Write $\cos^{-1} \frac{12}{13} = \alpha$. Then $\cos \alpha = \frac{12}{13}$ and $\sin \alpha = \frac{5}{13}$. Therefore

$$\tan(\cos^{-1} \tfrac{12}{13}) = \tan \alpha = \frac{\sin \alpha}{\cos \alpha} = \frac{\frac{5}{13}}{\frac{12}{13}} = \frac{5}{12}.$$

(d) Let $\sin^{-1} \frac{3}{5} = \beta$. Then $\sin \beta = \frac{3}{5}$ and $\cos \beta = \frac{4}{5}$. $\sin(2 \sin^{-1} \frac{3}{5}) = \sin 2\beta = 2 \sin \beta \cos \beta = 2 \cdot \frac{3}{5} \cdot \frac{4}{5} = \frac{24}{25}$.

(g) $\sin(\sin^{-1} \frac{3}{5} + \cos^{-1} \frac{12}{13}) = \sin(\beta + \alpha) = \sin \beta \cos \alpha + \cos \beta \sin \alpha$
$$= \frac{3}{5} \cdot \frac{12}{13} + \frac{4}{5} \cdot \frac{5}{13} = \frac{56}{65}.$$

4. (a) $\sqrt{1 - x^2}$; **(b)** $\dfrac{x\sqrt{1 - x^2}}{1 - x^2}$; **(c)** $2x\sqrt{1 - x^2}$;

(d) $\sqrt{\dfrac{1 - \sqrt{1 - x^2}}{2}}$; **(e)** $1 - 2x^2$; **(g)** $\dfrac{x}{\sqrt{1 + x^2}}$;

(h) $\dfrac{1 - x^2}{1 + x^2}$.

5. (a) $\frac{3}{4}$; **(b)** $\frac{1}{2}$; **(d)** $\frac{4}{7}$; **(f)** $\frac{1}{5}$; **(j)** $\dfrac{\pi}{4}$; **(l)** $\dfrac{\pi}{3}$.

CHAPTER VII

VII.1.a

1.   The verification for $n = 1$ will not be set down. In each case the formula is assumed for $n = a$ and the case $n = a + 1$ is treated.

(a) $1 + 3 + 5 + \cdots + (2a - 1) + [2(a + 1) - 1]$
$$= a^2 + [2(a + 1) - 1]$$
$$= a^2 + 2a + 1 = (a + 1)^2.$$

(b) $2 + 4 + \cdots + 2a + 2(a + 1)$
$$= a(a + 1) + 2(a + 1) = (a + 1)(a + 2).$$

(g) $[1 + 2 + \cdots + a + (a + 1)]^2$

$\qquad = (1 + 2 + \cdots + a)^2 + 2(a + 1)(1 + 2 + \cdots + a) + (a + 1)^2$

$\qquad = (1 + 2 + \cdots + a)^2 + 2(a + 1)\dfrac{a(a + 1)}{2} + (a + 1)^2$

$\qquad = (1 + 2 + \cdots + a)^2 + (a + 1)^2(a + 1)$

$\qquad = (1 + 2 + \cdots + a)^2 + (a + 1)^3$

$\qquad = 1^3 + 2^3 + \cdots + a^3 + (a + 1)^3.$

The last step uses the induction hypothesis. Use is also made of the formula $1 + 2 + \cdots + n = \dfrac{n(n + 1)}{2}$.

2.   Verification for $n = 1$ will not be set down.

(a) Suppose $a(a + 1)(a + 2) = 6k$. Then $(a + 1)(a + 2)(a + 3) = a(a + 1)(a + 2) + 3(a + 1)(a + 2) = 6k + 3(a + 1)(a + 2)$. Since one of $a + 1$, $a + 2$ is even, $(a + 1)(a + 2) = 2m$. Thus $(a + 1) \cdot (a + 2)(a + 3) = 6(k + m)$.

(c) $2^{a-1} \leq 1 \cdot 2 \cdots a$ gives

$$2^a = 2^{a-1} \cdot 2 \leq 2(1 \cdot 2 \cdots a) \leq 1 \cdot 2 \cdots a(a + 1)$$

since $2 \leq a + 1$.

3. $2^0 + 2^1 + 2^2 + \cdots + 2^n = 1 + 3 \sin n.$

4. $1 + 2 + \cdots + n = 17 + \dfrac{n(n + 1)}{2}.$

5.   The set **N**. The set of even natural numbers. The

$$\mathbf{M} = \{0, 2, 4, 5, 6, 7, \cdots\}.$$

And so on. An infinite number.

7.   Smallest set: $\{0, 1, 5, 5^2, 5^3, \cdots\}.$

Largest set: **N**.

8.   Assume $2^n > n$. Then $2^{n+1} = 2 \cdot 2^n > 2 \cdot n = n + n \geq n + 1$ if $n \geq 1$.

10. $p(n) = n(n - 1)(n - 2) \cdots (n - k)$ has exactly the numbers $n = 0, 1, \cdots, k$ for its zeros. Thus the formula $p(n) = 0$ can be established for $n = 0, 1, \cdots, k$ but is false for $n = k + 1$. That is, one can write formulas which are not valid for all n but are valid for any finite collection of natural numbers.

VII.2.a

1. (a) $(x + y)^8$

$\qquad = x^8 + 8x^7y + \dfrac{8 \cdot 7}{1 \cdot 2}x^6y^2 + \dfrac{8 \cdot 7 \cdot 6}{1 \cdot 2 \cdot 3}x^5y^3 + \dfrac{8 \cdot 7 \cdot 6 \cdot 5}{1 \cdot 2 \cdot 3 \cdot 4}x^4y^4 + \cdots$

$\qquad = x^8 + 8x^7y + 28x^6y^2 + 56x^5y^3 + 70x^4y^4 + 56x^3y^5$

$\qquad + 28x^2y^4 + 8xy^7 + y^8.$

(b) $(1 + x)^6 = 1 + 6x + 15x^2 + 20x^3 + 15x^4 + 6x^5 + x^6.$

(d) $\left(\dfrac{x}{y} + \dfrac{y}{x}\right)^4 = \left(\dfrac{x}{y}\right)^4 + 4\left(\dfrac{x}{y}\right)^2 + 6 + 4\left(\dfrac{y}{x}\right)^2 + \left(\dfrac{y}{x}\right)^4.$

(h) $\left(x - \dfrac{1}{x}\right)^6 = x^6 - 6x^4 + 15x^2 - 20 + 15\,\dfrac{1}{x^2} - 6\,\dfrac{1}{x^4} + \dfrac{1}{x^6}.$

2. $n = 1, 2, 3$ give $\left(1 + \dfrac{1}{n}\right)^n = 2,\ 2.25,\ 2.3703.$

3. (a) $(0.97)^{10} = (1 - 0.03)^{10} = 1 - 0.3 + 0.0405 - 0.00324$
$\approx 0.73726.$

(c) $(51)^7 = (\tfrac{102}{2})^7 = 2^{-7} \cdot 100^7(1 + 0.02)^7,$ etc.

(d) Write $\cos 0.0349 = 1 - \varepsilon$ and proceed as in (a). Use the tables to find the value of ε.

4. For $n = 4$, $p = q = \tfrac{1}{2}$ gives
$$(p + q)^n = (\tfrac{1}{2} + \tfrac{1}{2})^4 = \tfrac{1}{16}(1 + 4 + 6 + 4 + 1) = 1.$$
The case $n = 3$, $p = \tfrac{1}{6}$, $q = \tfrac{5}{6}$ gives
$$(p + q)^n = (\tfrac{1}{6} + \tfrac{5}{6})^3 = \dfrac{1}{6^3}(1 + 3 \cdot 5 + 3 \cdot 5^2 + 5^3) = \dfrac{216}{6^3} = 1.$$

5. (a) $(e^x - e^{-x})^4 = e^{4x} - 4e^{2x} + 6 - 4e^{-2x} + e^{-4x}.$

(b) $(a + b + c)^2 = [a + (b + c)]^2 = a^2 + 2a(b + c) + (b + c)^2$
$= a^2 + b^2 + c^2 + 2ab + 2ac + 2bc.$

6. (b) $0 = (1 - 1)^n = 1 - n + \dfrac{n(n - 1)}{2!} - \dfrac{n(n - 1)(n - 2)}{3!} + \cdots$
$$+ (-1)^n \cdot 1.$$
If n is odd the terms at the same distances from the two ends of the formula cancel. If n is even, this is not so. For example, $n = 4$ gives
$$0 = (1 - 1)^4 = 1 - 4 + 6 - 4 + 1.$$

VII.3.a

1. $\left(1 + \dfrac{1}{n}\right)^n = 1 + n\,\dfrac{1}{n} + \dfrac{n(n - 1)}{2!}\,\dfrac{1}{n^2} + \dfrac{n(n - 1)(n - 2)}{3!}\,\dfrac{1}{n^3} + \cdots$

$= 1 + 1 + \dfrac{1}{2!}\,\dfrac{n - 1}{n} + \dfrac{1}{3!}\,\dfrac{n - 1}{n} \cdot \dfrac{n - 2}{n} = \cdots$

If n is large,

$\dfrac{n - 1}{n} = 1 - \dfrac{1}{n} \approx 1,\quad \dfrac{n - 1}{n} \cdot \dfrac{n - 2}{n} = \left(1 - \dfrac{1}{n}\right)\left(1 - \dfrac{2}{n}\right) \approx 1, \cdots$

Hence for n large, the expansion above starts off approximately with

$1 + 1 + \dfrac{1}{2!} + \dfrac{1}{3!} + \cdots$. This is the beginning of the infinite series

for e. The conclusion is that $\left(1 + \dfrac{1}{n}\right)^n$ seems to be very close to e

when n is large. The conclusion is correct. To verify it requires quite an arsenal of knowledge and techniques.

2. $\left(1 + \dfrac{1}{n}\right)^{nx}$

$$= 1 + nx \cdot \frac{1}{n} + \frac{nx(nx - 1)}{2!} \frac{1}{n^2} + \frac{nx(nx - 1)(nx - 2)}{3!} \frac{1}{n^3} + \cdots$$

$$= 1 + x + \frac{1}{2!} \frac{nx}{n} \frac{nx - 1}{n} + \frac{1}{3!} \frac{nx}{n} \cdot \frac{nx - 1}{n} \cdot \frac{nx - 2}{n} + \cdots$$

$$= 1 + x + \frac{1}{2!} x \left(x - \frac{1}{n}\right) + \frac{1}{3!} x \left(x - \frac{1}{n}\right)\left(x - \frac{2}{n}\right) + \cdots$$

If n is large, then

$$x\left(x - \frac{1}{n}\right) \approx x^2, \qquad x\left(x - \frac{1}{n}\right)\left(x \cdot \frac{2}{n}\right) \approx x^3, \cdots.$$

3. $\left(1 + \dfrac{x}{m}\right)^m$

$$= 1 + x + \frac{1}{2!} m(m - 1) \frac{x^2}{m^2} + \frac{1}{3!} m(m - 1)(m - 2) \frac{x^3}{m^3} + \cdots.$$

For m large, the expansion starts off approximately with $1 + x + \dfrac{1}{2!} x^2 + \dfrac{1}{3!} x^3 + \cdots$. This is the beginning of the infinite series for e^x. The conclusion is that probably $\left(1 + \dfrac{x}{m}\right)^m$ is close to e^x when m is large. The conclusion is correct. Its verification is difficult.

CHAPTER VIII

VIII.1.a

2. (a) $\beta = \gamma = 30°$, $c = 3$, $a = 3\sqrt{3}$.
(c) $\gamma = 60°$, $a = 7$, $c = 7$.

(e) $\beta = 75°$, $b = \cos 15° = \sqrt{\dfrac{1 + \cos 30°}{2}} = \frac{1}{2}\sqrt{2 + \sqrt{3}}$,

$a = \sin 15° = \frac{1}{2}\sqrt{2 - \sqrt{3}}$.

3. $5\sqrt{2}$; 25.

4. $\dfrac{3\sqrt{3}}{2\pi} \approx 0.83$.

5. Length of side is $8 \sin 22\frac{1}{2}° = 8\sqrt{\dfrac{1 - \cos 45°}{2}} = 4\sqrt{2 - \sqrt{2}}$. Radius of inscribed circle is $4 \cos 22\frac{1}{2}° = 2\sqrt{2 + \sqrt{2}}$.

6. Side of regular pentagon is $2r \sin 36°$.

Let $5x = 90°$. Then $3x = 90° - 2x$ and $\sin 3x = \cos 2x$. Thus $3 \sin x - 4 \sin^3 x = 1 - 2 \sin^2 x$. Hence $4 \sin^3 x - 2 \sin^2 x - 3 \sin x + 1 = 0$. Therefore $(\sin x - 1)(4 \sin^2 x + 2 \sin x - 1) = 0$.

Since $\sin x \neq 1$ and $\sin x > 0$, we obtain $\sin x = \frac{1}{4}(\sqrt{5} - 1)$.
Also $\cos x = \frac{1}{4}\sqrt{10 + 2\sqrt{5}}$. Finally $\sin 36° = \sin 2x = 2 \sin x \cos x = \frac{1}{4}\sqrt{10 - 2\sqrt{5}}$.

VIII.2.a

1. (a) $c = 13$, $\alpha = 22° 40'$, $\beta = 67° 20'$.
   (e) $\alpha = 55°$, $a = 16.384$, $b = 11.472$.
2. (a) $b = 34.98$, $\alpha = 42° 10'$, $\beta = 47° 50'$.
   (c) $\beta = 52° 18'$, $c = 9430$.
   (e) $\beta = 21° 45'$, $a = 0.1525$.
3. If α is the angle of depression $\cos \alpha = 0.999996$. The four place
    tables give $0° 0' < \alpha < 0° 40'$. The approximation $\cos x \approx 1 - \dfrac{x^2}{2}$
    valid for small x gives $x \approx 0.003$ radians. This turns out to be about
    10'. (The approximation is discussed in Chapter IX.)
4. Distance is 196,000 miles.
5. Deed is incorrect. Side a is in error.
7. The perimeter is 6.264. Setting this equal to the circumference of the
    circle gives $2\pi \approx 6.264$ hence $\pi \approx 3.132$. The use of 4 place tables
    seems to give reasonable results for π to 3 places. If one wished to
    calculate π more accurately by using a regular polygon of, say,
    360×60 sides, four place tables would be quite inadequate.

VIII.3.a

1. (a) $\alpha = 78° 28'$, $\beta = 44° 20'$, $\gamma = 57° 12'$.
   (c) $a = 7.38$, $\beta = 107° 07'$, $\gamma = 27° 53'$.
   (e) $\beta = 35° 40'$, $\gamma = 84° 20'$, $c = 34.6$.
   (g) $\alpha = 91° 06'$, $\beta = 55° 11'$, $\gamma = 33° 43'$.
   (i) $\alpha = 57° 10'$, $\beta = 77° 50'$, $c = 8.42$.
   (k) no solution.
2. 5.45 miles.
3. From the sine law we see that $a = \dfrac{c \sin \alpha}{\sin \gamma} = \dfrac{1.8 \cdot 10^8 \sin 85°}{\sin 1''}$.

    Since 1'' (1 second) is $\frac{1}{3600}°$, the radian measure of 1'' is $\dfrac{\pi}{3600 \cdot 180} = $
    4.8×10^{-6}. The formula for a gives
    $$a = \frac{1.8 \times 10^8 \times 0.996}{4.8 \times 10^{-6}} = 3.73 \times 10^{13} \text{ (in miles)}.$$

In one year light travels $186,000 \times 365 \times 24 \times 3600 = 5.85 \times 10^{12}$ miles. Thus the light from the star reaches us after $\dfrac{3.73 \times 10^{13}}{5.85 \times 10^{12}} = 6.36$ years.

4.   *Hint:* The lengths of the sides of the triangle are $4 + 5 = 9$, $5 + 6 = 11$, $6 + 4 = 10$.

6.   If such a triangle exists, according to the sine law, $\dfrac{\sin \alpha}{a} = \dfrac{\sin \beta}{b}$,

hence $\dfrac{\sin 2\beta}{2b} = \dfrac{\sin \beta}{b}$.

This gives $2 \sin \beta = \sin 2\beta = 2 \sin \beta \cos \beta$. Hence $\sin \beta = 0$ or $\cos \beta = 1$. Both of these lead to the conclusion $\beta = 0$ and $\alpha = 0$, and the triangle is degenerate. Thus Lavinia's intuition was correct.

CHAPTER IX

IX.1.a

1. (a) $g_0(x) = 3$; $g_1(x) = 3 - 6x$; $g_2(x) = 3 - 6x + x^2$.
  (c) $g_0(x) = 2$; $g_1(x) = 2$; $g_2(x) = 2 + x^2$.
  (d) $f(x) = (x^2 + 2x + 1)(x - 1) = x^3 + x^2 - x - 1$ and $g_0(x) = -1$;
    $g_1(x) = -1 - x$; $g_2(x) = -1 - x + x^2$.
  (f) $g_0(x) = 8$; $g_1(x) = 8$; $g_2(x) = 8$.
  (h) $g_0(x) = 1$; $g_1(x) = 1 + 3x$; $g_2(x) = 1 + 3x + 3x^2$.
2. (a) $f(x) = 3 - 6x + x^2$. $f(0) = 3$; $f(\tfrac{1}{2}) = \tfrac{1}{4}$; $f(\tfrac{1}{10}) = 2.41$; $f(1) = -2$.
    $g_0(0) = 3$; $g_1(0) = 3$; $g_2(0) = 3$. $g_0(\tfrac{1}{10}) = 3$; $g_1(\tfrac{1}{10}) = 2.4$;
    $g_2(\tfrac{1}{10}) = 2.41$. $g_0(1) = 3$; $g_1(1) = -3$; $g_2(1) = -2$.
3. (a) $(1 + 0.02)^{10}$

$$= 1 + 10 \cdot (0.02) + \frac{10 \cdot 9}{1 \cdot 2}(0.02)^2 + \frac{10 \cdot 9 \cdot 8}{1 \cdot 2 \cdot 3}(0.02)^2 + \cdots$$

$$= 1 + 0.2 + 45(0.0004) + 120(0.000008) + \cdots$$

  (b) $(0.97)^{13} = (1 - 0.03)^{13} = 1 - 13(0.03) + \dfrac{13 \cdot 12}{1 \cdot 2}(0.0009) - \cdots$

  (c) $(0.101)^5 = \left(\dfrac{1.01}{10}\right)^5 = 10^{-5}(1 + 0.01)^5$.

  (d) $(\tfrac{5}{4})^8 = (1 + 0.25)^8$.

4.   For $f(x) = 1 + x + \dfrac{x^2}{2}$, $f(1) = 2.5$, $f(\tfrac{1}{2}) = 1.625$, $f(-0.1) = 0.9005$. The tables for e^x give $e^1 = 2.718$, $e^{1/2} = 1.6487$, $e^{-0.1} = 0.9048$.

5. (a) If $|x| \le 5$, $|2x| \le 10$.

If $|x| \le \frac{1}{20}$, $|2x| \le \frac{1}{10}$.

If $|x| < \dfrac{1}{10^7}$, $|2x| < \dfrac{1}{10^6}$.

(d) $|f(x)| = |x + 2x^2 + 16x^3| \le |x| + 2|x|^2 + 16|x|^3 = g(x)$.

If $|x| \le \frac{1}{10}$, $g(x) \le \frac{1}{10} + \frac{2}{100} + \frac{16}{1000} \le 10$.

If $|x| \le \dfrac{1}{10^2}$, $g(x) \le \dfrac{1}{10^2} + \dfrac{2}{10^4} + \dfrac{16}{10^6} < \dfrac{3}{10^2} < \dfrac{1}{10}$.

If $|x| \le \dfrac{1}{10^7}$, $g(x) \le \dfrac{1}{10^7} + \dfrac{2}{10^{14}} + \dfrac{16}{10^{21}} < \dfrac{1}{10^6}$.

(g) $f(x) = x^n$, $n \ge 1$. If $|x| \le k$ and $k < 1$, then $|x^2| = |x|^2 \le k^2 < k$ and in general $|x^n| \le k^n \le k$. Thus, $|f(x)| \le 10^{-1}$ or 10^{-6} when $|x| \le 10^{-1}$ or 10^{-6}.

(h) $f(x) = ax^2$, $a > 0$. If $a \le 1$, then $|ax^2| \le |x^2|$ and the solution is given in 5(g). If $a > 1$, then $|ax^2| \le 10^{-1}$ or 10^{-6} whenever $|x| \le 10^{-1} \cdot a^{-1}$ or $10^{-6} \cdot a^{-1}$ since $|ax^2| \le |ax|^2$. In this exercise, as in the others of this type, there is an embarrassing choice of solutions.

IX.2.a

1. (a) $f(x) = 5 + 5(x - 1) + (x - 1)^2$;

(c) $f(x) = 5 - 5(x + 1) + 2(x + 1)^2$;

(d) $f(x) = 3 + 2(x - 0) - (x - 0)^4$;

(f) $f(x) = 1 + 0(x - 3) + 0(x - 3)^2 + 0(x - 3)^3$
$$+ 0(x - 3)^4 + (x - 3)^5;$$

(h) $f(x) = -2(x + 1)^2 + (x + 1)^3$;

(i) $f(x) = 3 + 2(x - 1) + (x - 1)^2$.

2. (a) $f(x) = 2 - x + x^2 = 4 + 3(x - 2) + (x - 2)^2$;

(b) $f(x) = 3 + 4x = -13 + 4(x + 4)$;

(c) $f(x) = 5$;

(d) $f(x) = (1 - x)^3 = 8 - 12(x + 1) + 6(x + 1)^2 - (x + 1)^3$;

(e) $f(x) = (x + 1)(x - 2)^2 = (x - 2 + 3)(x - 2)^2$
$$= (x - 2)^3 + 3(x - 2)^2;$$

(g) $f(x) = 2x^2 + 3x - 4 = 1 + 7(x - 1) + 2(x - 1)^2$.

3. $f(x) = (2 - 3c + c^2) + (-3 + 2c)(x - c) + (x - c)^2$.
For $c = \frac{3}{2}$, $f(x) = -\frac{1}{4} + (x - \frac{3}{2})^2$.

4. $1 \pm \dfrac{\sqrt{3}}{3}$.

5. Write $g_2(x) = (x - 1) - \dfrac{(x - 1)^2}{2}$ and

$$g_3(x) = (x - 1) - \frac{(x - 1)^2}{2} + \frac{(x - 1)^3}{3}.$$

Then
$$g_2(\tfrac{3}{2}) = \tfrac{1}{2} - \tfrac{1}{8} = \tfrac{3}{8} = 0.375$$
$$g_3(\tfrac{3}{2}) = \tfrac{1}{2} - \tfrac{1}{8} + \tfrac{1}{24} = 0.416$$
$$\ln(\tfrac{3}{2}) = 0.4055$$
$$g_2(\tfrac{5}{4}) = \tfrac{1}{4} - \tfrac{1}{32} = 0.25000 - 0.03125 = 0.21875$$
$$g_3(\tfrac{5}{4}) = g_2(\tfrac{5}{4}) + \frac{(\tfrac{1}{4})^3}{3} \approx 0.22396$$
$$\ln(\tfrac{5}{4}) = 0.2231.$$

IX.3.a

1. (a)

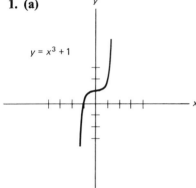

$y = x^3 + 1$

(b)

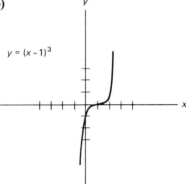

$y = (x - 1)^3$

(c)

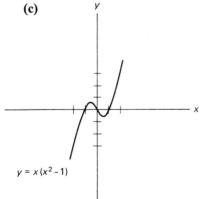

$y = x(x^2 - 1)$

(e)

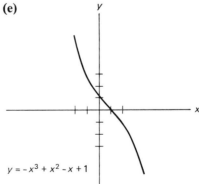

$y = -x^3 + x^2 - x + 1$

2. (a)

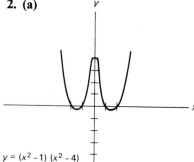

$y = (x^2 - 1)(x^2 - 4)$

(c)

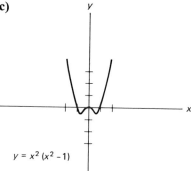

$y = x^2 (x^2 - 1)$

(f)

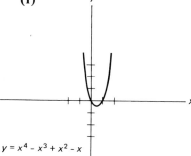

$y = x^4 - x^3 + x^2 - x$

3. (a)

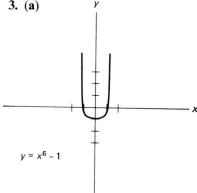

$y = x^6 - 1$

(c)

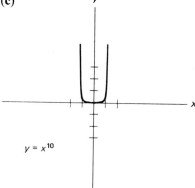

$y = x^{10}$

4. If $f(x) = a_0 + a_2x^2 + a_4x^4 + \cdots$, then
$$f(-x)$$
$$= a_0 + a_2(-x)^2 + a_4(-x)^4 + \cdots = a_0 + a_2x^2 + a_4x^4 + \cdots$$
$$= f(x).$$

5. If $f(x) = -f(-x)$, then

$$
\begin{aligned}
f(-x) &= a_0 + a_1(-x) + a_2(-x)^2 + \cdots \\
&= a_0 - a_1 x + a_2 x^2 - a_3 x^3 + \cdots \\
&= -[a_0 + a_1 x + a_2 x^2 + \cdots] \\
&= -a_0 - a_1 x - a_2 x^2 - a_3 x^3 - \cdots
\end{aligned}
$$

and, equating coefficients, $a_0 = -a_0$, $-a_1 = -a_1$, $a_2 = -a_2$, $-a_3 = -a_3$, $\cdots$. Thus $a_0 = 0$, $a_2 = 0$, $a_4 = 0$, $\cdots$.

Conversely if $a_0 = 0$, $a_2 = 0$, $a_4 = 0$, $\cdots$ then $f(x) = a_1 x + a_3 x^3 + a_5 x^5 + \cdots$ and $f(-x) = a_1(-x) + a_3(-x)^3 + \cdots = -a_1 x - a_3 x^3 - \cdots = -f(x)$.

IX.4.a

2. $(1, 3, 6, 10, 15, \cdots)$.

3. $(a_0, a_1, a_2, \cdots) * (b_0, b_1, b_2, \cdots)$
$$= (a_0 b_0, a_0 b_1 + a_1 b_0, a_0 b_2 + a_1 b_1 + a_2 b_0, \cdots)$$
$(b_0, b_1, b_2, \cdots) * (a_0, a_1, a_2, \cdots)$
$$= (b_0 a_0, b_0 a_1 + b_1 a_0, b_0 a_2 + b_1 a_1 + b_2 a_0, \cdots).$$
Since $a_0 b_0 = b_0 a_0$, $a_0 b_1 + a_1 b_0 = b_0 a_1 + b_1 a_0$, $a_0 b_2 + a_1 b_1 + a_2 b_0 = b_0 a_2 + b_1 a_1 + b_2 a_0, \cdots$ we conclude that convolution is commutative.

5. $(a_0, a_1, a_2, \cdots) * (0, 1, 0, 0, \cdots)$
$$
\begin{aligned}
&= (a_0 \cdot 0,\ a_0 \cdot 1 + a_1 \cdot 0,\ a_0 \cdot 0 + a_1 \cdot 1 + a_2 \cdot 0, \cdots) \\
&= (0, a_0, a_1, a_2, \cdots).
\end{aligned}
$$
The operation of multiplication by $(0, 1, 0, 0, \cdots)$ is called: shift to the right by one place. If you wish to shift by two places, multiply by $(0, 0, 1, 0, 0, \cdots)$.

6. Here is one approach. $A_n = (A_1)^n$ where of course $(A_1)^n = A_1 * A_1 * \cdots * A_1$ (n factors). Then, obviously, $A_n * A_m = (A_1)^n * (A_1)^m = (A_1)^{n+m} = A_{n+m}$.

7. If the indicated product is $(c_0, c_1, c_2, \cdots)$, then for the first few coefficients an easy calculation gives $c_0 = 1 \cdot 1$, $c_1 = 1 \cdot (-1) + 1 \cdot 1 = 0$, $c_2 = 1 \cdot \frac{1}{2} + 1 \cdot (-1) + \frac{1}{2} \cdot 1 = 0$. The formula for c_n, $n \ge 1$, is:

$$
\begin{aligned}
c_n &= 1 \cdot (-1)^n \frac{1}{n!} + 1 \cdot (-1)^{n-1} \frac{1}{(n-1)!} \\
&\quad + \frac{1}{2!} (-1)^{n-2} \frac{1}{(n-2)!} + \cdots + \frac{1}{n!} \\
&= \frac{1}{n!} (-1)^n \left[1 - n + \frac{n(n-1)}{2} - \cdots + (-1)^n \right] \\
&= \frac{(-1)^n}{n!} (1 - 1)^n = 0.
\end{aligned}
$$

Note: In infinite series language the problem states: Show that $e^x \cdot e^{-x} = 1$.

10. Try it coefficient by coefficient. That is, calculate $s(x) * s(x)$, $c(x) * c(x)$ and add. It takes a little time. To get a real proof, it is necessary to give an induction argument for the nth coefficient, showing that it is 0. This is a bit like riding a bronco. Take courage and go!

INDEX

Abscissa, 56
Absolute value, 19
Abstract power series, 298
Acute angle. *See* Angle, acute
Addition, 6
   of functions, 49
   of polynomials, 120
Addition formulas
   circular functions, 234
   exponential function, 181
Additive identity, 7
Algebraic functions, 167
Algorithm, 13
   division, 13
Amplitude, 225
Analysis, 37
Analytic geometry, 56
Angle, 209, 263
   acute, 273
   of depression, 270
   of elevation, 270
   negative, 208
   obtuse, 273
   positive, 208
   right, 209
Angle measure
   degree, 210
   radian, 210

   revolution, 210
   right angle, 210
Approximation
   of cos x, 287
   of exp x, 282
   of ln x, 291
   of polynomials, 282
   of sin x, 282
Arccosine, 246
Archimedean property, 25
Archimedes, 28
Arcsine, 245
Arctangent, 246
Area of a circle, 153
Arithmetic mean, 89
Associative law, 6
Astronautics, 110
Asymptote
   horizontal, 101
   of a hyperbola, 167
   vertical, 101
Axis, 54

Base of logarithms, 198
Behavior at infinity, 100, 139
Binomial theorem, 256
Bolzano, 38
Bound

greatest lower, 37
least upper, 35
lower, 37
upper, 36
Bounded
on the left, 35
on the right, 35

Cantor, 38
Cauchy, 38
Cauchy inequality, 86
Circle, 149
area, 153
circumference, 153
Circular function, 213
Coefficient, 112
leading, 119
Collection, 4
Common logarithm, 199
Commutative laws, 6
Completeness of **R**, 35
Completing the square, 75
Complex numbers, 133
Composite number, 8
Composition of functions, 51
Constant function, 46
Convolution, 121
Coordinate axes, 55
Coordinatized plane, 56
Cosecant, 220
Cosine, 213
Cotangent, 220
Cubic polynomial, 120
Cycle, 225

Damped harmonic motion, 228
Decay, 193
Decreasing function, 144
Dedekind, 38, 127
Degree of a polynomial, 112, 119
Dense, 29
Dependent variable, 45
Descartes, 56
Discriminant, 79
Distance, 21, 147, 151
Distance formula, 148
Distributive law, 6
Division algorithm, 13, 123
Domain of a function, 45
Duplicating the cube, 240

e, 182, 189
transcendency of, 190
Element, 3
Ellipse, 155
center, 159
definition of, 155
eccentricity of, 160

major and minor axes of, 159
Equal functions, 46
Equal sets, 10
Even function, 96
Exponent
integral, 173
laws of, 175
rational, 177
real, 183
Exponential function, 187
existence of, 181
Exponential growth and decay, 193

Factor theorem, 130
Factorial, 186
Factorial zero, 257
Factorization into primes, 13, 39
Fermat, 11
Fermat's little theorem, 9
Field, 24
Focus, 159
Fourier, 230
Frequency, 225
Function, 43
algebraic, 167
circular, 213
constant, 46
equal, 46
even, 96
identity, 47
implicit, 103
increasing, 144
inverse, 196
linear, 62
odd, 96
periodic, 97
polynomial, 52
quadratic, 63
rational, 52
Functional equations, 93
Fundamental theorem of algebra, 134

Gauss, 135
Geometric mean, 89
Graph, 54
Greater than, 11
Greatest common divisor, 39
Greatest lower bound, 37
principle of, 37
Greek alphabet, 321
Gregory, 291
Growth, 193

Half-life, 193
Harmonic analysis, 218
Heine, 38
Hermite, 190
Horizontal asymptote, 101

Hyperbola, 161
    asymptotes of, 167
    definition of, 161
    focal distance, 162
Hypotenuse, 269

Ideal, 19
Identities, 7, 217
Identity function, 47
Implicit functions, 103
Increasing function, 144
Independent variable, 45
Induction, mathematical, 5, 250
Inequality, 11
    Cauchy, 86
    geometric and arithmetic means, 89
    triangle, 22
Infinite decimal, 30
Infinite set, 4
Infinity, behavior at, 100
Integer, 16
Interpolation, 202
Intersection of sets, 10
Inverse function, 196, 243
Irrational number, 30

Kummer, 127

Law, 6
    associative, 6
    commutative, 6
    of cosines, 275
    distributive, 6
    of exponents, 95, 175
    of sines, 274
Least upper bound, 35
    principle of, 36
Less than, 10
Limit, 30
Lindemann, 190
Line, 29
    equation of, 64
    slope of, 68
Linear equation, 62
Linear polynomial, 62
Logarithm, 196
Lower bound, 35

Maclaurin, 291
Major axis, 159
Mathematical induction, 251
Maximum, 71, 292
Maximum-minimum problems, 82
Minimum, 71, 292
Minor axis, 159
Monotone decreasing, 144
Monotone increasing, 144
Multiple angle formulas, 238

Multiple zero, 134
Multiplication, 6
    of functions, 49
Multiplicative identity, 7
Multiplicative system, 41

Natural number. *See* Number, natural
Negative integer, 17
Neutral element, 7
Number, 3
    complex, 133
    integral, 16
    natural, 3, 4
    rational, 23
    real, 29

Odd function, 96
Odd number, 8
Ordinate, 56
Origin O, 54

Parabola, 165
Pentagon, 267
Period, 97
Periodic function, 97
Pi (π), transcendency of, 190
Piecewise linear function, 70
Polynomial, 52
    degree of, 112, 119
    zero of, 129
Polynomial function, 52
Positive integer, 17
Prime, 9
Prime factorization theorem, 14
Prime number, 8
Principal Ideal, 19
    Theorem, 125
Principle of mathematical induction, 5, 250
Pythagoras, 92
Pythagorean theorem, 89, 269

Quadratic polynomial, 63
Quartic polynomial, 120
Quotient, 12
    of two functions, 50

Radians, 210
Radioactive decay, 193
Ramanujan, 11
Rational function, 135
Rational number, 23
Real function, 43
Real number, 29
Rectangular coordinates, 56
Remainder, 12
Remainder theorem, 127
Riemann, 249

Right triangle, 266
Ring of integers, 17
    of polynomials, 121, 122
Root, 129
Ruler and compass constructions, 240

Scientific notation, 174
Secant, 220
Sequence, 30, 298
Sets, 3
    equal, 10
    union of, 10
    intersection of, 10
Side
    initial, 209
    terminal, 209
    of a triangle, 264
Simple harmonic motion, 228
Simple zero, 134
Sine, 213
Slide rule, 203
Slope, 68
Solution of a triangle, 264
Square root, 143
Square root of 2, 26
Squaring the circle, 240
Symmetry, 100

Tangent, 220
Taylor, 291
Taylor expansion, 289
Tchebycheff, 240
Transcendental number, 190

Triangle inequality, 22
Trigonometric functions, 213
Trigonometry, 265
Trisection of angles, 240

Union of sets, 10
Unique representation property, 111
Uniqueness of factorization, 39
Unit of angle measure, 210
Unit circle, 213
Upper bound, 35

Variable, 43
    dependent, 45
    independent, 45
    real, 43
Vertical asymptote, 101

Weierstrass, 38
Well-ordering property, 12
Wilson's theorem, 9
Winding number, 207

x-axis, 54

y-axis, 54

Zero, 4
Zero exponent, 174
Zero factorial, 257
Zero of a function, 129
Zero of multiplicity k, 134
Zero polynomial, 119